basic skills in science

David E. Newton

J. Weston Walch, Publisher
Portland, ME 04104

Copyright 1982
J. Weston Walch, Publisher
Portland, Maine 04104

Cover and book design: Wladislaw Finne

Contents

TEACHER INTRODUCTION ... v

SECTION **one** VERBAL SKILLS ... 1

Activity Page 1: Recognizing Prefixes, Suffixes, and Roots ... 7
2: Defining Words in Sentences ... 8
3: Matching Definitions ... 10
4: Recognizing Topic Sentences ... 13
5: Reading for Understanding–I ... 28
6: Reading for Understanding–II ... 30

SECTION **two** LIBRARY SKILLS ... 33

Activity Page 7: Using the Card Catalog ... 36
8: Using Reference Books ... 39
9: Using the *Readers' Guide* ... 44
10: Checking False References ... 46

SECTION **three** WRITING REPORTS ... 47

Activity Page 11: Writing a Formal Laboratory Report –I ... 50
12: Writing a Formal Laboratory Report–II ... 51

SECTION **four** MATH SKILLS WITH HAND CALCULATORS ... 53

Activity Page 13: Working with a Hand Calculator–I ... 57
14: Working with a Hand Calculator–II ... 58

SECTION **five** MATH SKILLS WITH MEASUREMENT   59

    Activity Page 15: Measuring Length   66
                      16: Measuring Weight   68
                      17: Measuring Volume   74
                      18: Measuring Temperature   76
                      19: Finding Density   78

SECTION **six** MATH SKILLS WITH GRAPHS   79

    Activity Page 20: Making Histograms   89
                      21: Interpreting Histograms   93
                      22: Writing Formulas from Data   97
                      23: Making Data Tables from Formulas   98
                      24: Setting Up Graphs and Plotting Points   101
                      25: Plotting Points   104
                      26: Drawing Curves   109
                      27: Extrapolating from Graphs   116

SECTION **seven** EXPERIMENTING AND RELATED SKILLS   119

    Activity Page 28: Interpreting Optical Illusions   125
                      29: The Skill of Observing   129
                      30: The Skill of Inferring   135
                      31: The Skill of Classifying   141
                      32: The Skill of Generalizing–I   146
                      33: The Skill of Generalizing–II   148
                      34: Controls   152
                      35: Designing Experiments   155
                      36: Planning a Field Trip   158

SECTION **eight** DECISION-MAKING SKILLS   159

    Activity Page 37: Analyzing Case Study #1   164
                      38: Analyzing Case Study #2   166
                      39: Analyzing Case Study #3   168
                      40: Analyzing Case Study #4   170
                      41: Analyzing Case Study #5   172

SECTION nine SPECIAL SCIENTIFIC SKILLS 173

Activity Page		
42:	Writing Chemical Formulas	178
43:	Balancing Chemical Equations	183
44:	Using a Leaf Key	206
45:	Using a Mineral Key	212
46:	Drawing Schematics for Electrical Circuits—I	219
47:	Drawing Schematics for Electrical Circuits—II	220
48:	Drawing Schematics for Electrical Circuits—III	221
49:	Drawing Schematics for Electrical Circuits—IV	222
50:	Understanding Topographic Maps	231
51:	Understanding Weather Maps	244
52:	Writing Flow Charts—I	251
53:	Writing Flow Charts—II	252
54:	Writing Flow Charts—III	253
55:	Developing Safe Laboratory Procedures	255

ANSWER SECTION FOR ACTIVITY PAGES 258

ANSWER SECTION FOR TEXTUAL QUESTIONS 273

Teacher Introduction

The great science educator Philip Johnson used to point out that good science teaching involved three important factors: **A**ttitudes, **S**kills, and **K**nowledges. A sound ASK program, he believed, was essential to a sound science education program. How does a science teacher incorporate all of these factors in his or her own science classroom?

The last of the three—the Knowledges aspect—is probably the easiest to take care of. Textbooks and other written materials usually do a good job of providing students with the factual information they need in science. The first of the list—the development of Attitudes—is perhaps the most difficult and the one for which we have the least concrete teaching materials. It is in the area of Skills that we probably have the greatest potential . . . and about which we actually may do the least.

The significance of helping students develop scientific skills has been recognized at least since the post-Sputnik "revolution" in science education in the late 1950's. A major emphasis of the NSF-funded "alphabet" courses (PSSC, CBA, BSCS, ESCP, etc.) was on the "processes" of science. These included skills such as observation, inference, comparison and contrast, experimental skills, and the like. The scientists and science educators involved in the development of those programs recognized the absolutely fundamental nature of skills such as these for scientists and for those who would understand and use the problem-solving approaches of science.

Unfortunately, the long-term impact of this part of the NSF-funded curricula has been problematic. In the three decades since reform of the science curriculum began, textbooks, school systems, and individual teachers appear to have shifted back once more to an emphasis on **product**, rather than **process**. It is infinitely easier to teach for a command of factual information than for an understanding of conceptual ideas . . . and either is probably simpler than promoting the development of useful intellectual and scientific skills.

Many roadblocks prevent classroom teachers from doing all they could with skill development. Not the least of these is the lack of materials with which to work. Most textbooks and textbook programs seem to treat skill development in an off-handed way that makes it peripheral to the teaching of facts and concepts. It is in response to that situation that this text is written.

Basic Skills in Science is not a textbook in the traditional sense. Its primary function is not to provide a vast amount of factual information or even an extensive amount of instruction in scientific skills. It is primarily a workbook that provides opportunity for students to review the basic ideas behind these skills and then to practice on them. The book is not designed with any one science specifically in mind. The skills included here are fundamental to most, if not all, fields of science. Every biologist, chemist, physicist, and earth or space scientist is expected to be proficient at reading and writing the English language, making and interpreting graphs, measuring objects, using the library, and so forth. It is this basic skills background which the text hopes to help students develop.

The *Basic Skills* program consists of two parts: 1) The text provides brief introductions to a variety of skills. The introductions are written in a "workbook" style—that is, with the expectation that students will solve problems, write answers, and be otherwise actively involved in the explanation as they read along. 2) At the conclusion of certain sections in the text, students are referred to additional exercises contained on activity pages. These can be assigned by the teacher, worked on individually or in groups, and discussed or exchanged for corrections and comment.

Please note that the activity pages provide spaces for answers. If the text is intended to be used by other students—or if the teacher wishes to correct the activity pages—be sure to provide paper on which to write answers and instruct students not to write in the book.

In many instances an "answer sheet" for questions or exercises in the text or activity pages is inappropriate. Students' responses will be based on specific assignments made by the teacher or on individual choices made by the students themselves. In some cases, however, we have suggested a range of answers that students might suggest or that might otherwise be acceptable. For those cases in which specific answers are possible, please see the two answer sections, one for activity pages (page 258) and one for textual questions (page 273). These answer sections also contain some specific comments about ways in which the text or activity pages can be used by the teacher.

The nine sections in the text are arranged in a somewhat arbitrary order. The sections have all been written so as to be independent of each other. It should be possible, that is, to do Section Nine (Special Scientific Skills) before Section One (Verbal Skills). There is, however, a certain logic about the order indicated in the Contents. It may be useful, for example, to be sure that students know something about Measurement Skills before going on to Graphing Skills. A good deal will depend, however, on the specific background of students in your own class. You may well choose a quite different sequence of topics to use in your own course.

Our hope is that *Basic Skills in Science* will be useful to students of many levels in many scientific courses. The reading level is fairly low, which means that the text and activity pages should be well within reach of most students in grades 7-9. Students in upper level courses with reading problems may be especially happy to find materials they can read and understand. Given the nature of the materials, even average students in biology, chemistry, and physics should find the content of the materials—if not specifically at their reading level—suitable to their needs and interesting to do.

The author is eager to hear from you about your successes and failures in using this book. What can we do in future revisions of the publication that will make it more helpful to you? Please use the form on the following page to let us know your reactions to *Basic Skills in Science*. We appreciate any response you can give us.

TO: Dr. David E. Newton
c/o J. Weston Walch, Publisher
P.O. Box 658
Portland, ME 04104-0658

The thing(s) I like best about *Basic Skills in Science* is (are):

The thing(s) I like least about the book is (are):

The change(s) I think you should consider for revision is (are):

My Name (optional): _____

School Address: _____
_____

Section one
Verbal Skills

The term **verbal skills** means knowing how to use words correctly and effectively. It means knowing how to read and write. "What is a skill like that doing in a book on **science**?" you may ask. The answer is easy. People communicate with each other most often **with words**. That is as true in science as it is in any other field. Of course, scientists use other ways of communicating, but being able to read and write is still absolutely essential.

You're learning many of the things you need to know in your English courses right now. We can't very well repeat everything you're learning there, but we will review a few of the most important skills with words that you should be good at. These include

1. Vocabulary skills: knowing the meaning of words
2. Sentence skills: being able to recognize key sentences
3. Understanding skills: being able to read a selection and understand what it means

1. Vocabulary Skills

Intramolecular dehydration is a common type of chemical reaction. What on earth does the term mean? For many students, the most difficult part of studying science is just learning vocabulary. There seem to be a half dozen new words on every page of a science text. How can a person ever learn the meaning of all those terms?!? Answering that question is important because one never masters a science until the language of that science is familiar.

One way to solve this problem is simply to memorize every new term you meet. For some people, that method works just fine—but many of us don't memorize that well. It would help if there were a simpler system for learning terms. Fortunately, there is. The system still requires some memorization, but not nearly as much as the "brute force" method of learning each separate term. Here's how the system works:

Many words in science consist of three parts: a prefix, a stem (or root), and a suffix. Let's look at an example:

We can figure out the meaning of this word if we know the meaning of each of the three parts. As you'll soon learn, each of the above parts has these meanings:

de-	a prefix:	means "take away"
hydrogen	a stem:	the name of a gas
-ase	a suffix:	means "an enzyme"

So the term **dehydrogenase** refers to an enzyme that takes away hydrogen from a compound.

At first, it would seem that our task has become more difficult rather than simpler. We now have three things to memorize—a prefix, a stem, and a suffix—instead of a single word. The thing that makes this system easier is that certain prefixes, stems, and suffixes are used over and over again. Once you learn them, you can almost always analyze any new term.

The next five pages list a number of prefixes, stems, and suffixes that occur often in scientific terms. You should memorize the ones your instructor requires or as many as you can. Then complete Activity Pages 1 through 3, pages 7-10. The first of these asks you to define certain words by using the meanings of prefixes, suffixes, and roots. In the second activity page, you must do the same thing for words that are used in sentences. Finally, Activity Page 3 consists of some matching questions that will test your skill of word analysis.

TABLE 1:
Some Common Prefixes

PREFIX	MEANING	PREFIX	MEANING
ab-	from	meta-	between, beyond
ad-	to	multi-	many
amphi-	both, around	neo-	new
an-	without	non-	not
ante-	before	omni-	all
anti-	against	ortho-	straight, correct
circum-	around	paleo-	old, ancient
com- (also occurs as co-, col-, con-, cor-)*	with	para-	beside, near, beyond
		per-	through, greater than
de-	from	peri-	around
dia-, dis-	across, through apart	poly-	many
epi-	on, outside, to	post-	after
ex-	out of	pre-	before (time)
extra-	outside of, beyond	pro-	before (place)
fore-	before	re-	again
hyper-	over, excessive	retro-	backward, behind
hypo-	under, less than	sub-	under, below
in-	in, not	super-	over, above, better than
inter-	between	sym-, syn-	with, together
intra-	within, among	trans-	across, through,
iso-	equal, same	ultra-	more than
		un-	not

---

*The exact form of many prefixes changes slightly from word to word. The reason is simply to make a word easier to pronounce. An especially good example of this is the prefix "ad-," which means "to" or "toward." This prefix may occur within a word as ac-, ag-, al-, an-, ap-, ar-, as-, and at-.

TABLE 2:
Prefixes that Stand for Numbers

PREFIX	MEANING	PREFIX	MEANING
semi-, hemi-	half	octa-	eight
uni-, mono-	one	nona-	nine
di-, bi-	two	deca-	ten
tri-	three	centi-, hecto-	hundred
quadra-, tetra-	four	milli-	thousand
quinqu-, penta-	five	mega-	million (also means simply "very large")
sex-, hexa-	six		
sept-, hepta-	seven		

TABLE 3:
Roots*

ROOT	MEANING	ROOT	MEANING
-aero-	air, oxygen	-dent-	tooth
-anthrop-	human	-derm-	skin
-aqua-	water	-dic-	spoken, said
-astra-, -aster-, -astro-	star	-dynam-	force
		-meter-	measure
-aud-, -audio-	hear	-micro-	small
-auto-	self, same	-mis-, -mit-	send
-avi-	bird	-morph-	form, shape
-bar-, -baro-	pressure	-mort-	death
-bibli-	book	-osteo-	bone
-bio-	life	-ovi-	egg
-cardio-	heart	-pan-	all
-centro-	center	-patho-	disease
-cephalo-	head	-ped-, -pod-	foot
-chloro-	green	-pel-, -puls-	drive
-chrom-	color	-pend-, -pens-	hang
-cosmo-	universe	-petro-	rock
-cryo-	very cold	-phil-	loving
-crypto-	hidden, secret	-phon-	sound
-cyclo-	round	-photo-	light
-cyto-	cell	-plasm-	blood

*Many of the roots listed here may be used as prefixes and suffixes. Prefixes and suffixes may also appear as roots.

4   *Section One*

ROOT	MEANING	ROOT	MEANING
-proto-	first, original	-homo-	same
-rupt-	break	-hydro-	water
-schizo-	split, broken	-iatro-	medicine
-sci-	knowledge	-lith-	stone
-scop-	see	-luna-	moon
-scrib-, -script-	write	-macro-, -magn-	large, great
-seismo-	related to an earthquake	-man-	hand
		-meso-	middle
-eco-	environment	-solv-	loosen
-electro-	related to electricity	-spect-	sight, view
		-spiri-	breath
-erg-	energy	-sta-	stand firm
-flect-, -flex-	bend, twist	-strato-	horizontal
-frag-, -fract-	broken	-struct-	build
-gastro-	stomach	-tele-	distant
-gen-	birth, origin	-tend-	stretch
-geo-	earth	-terr-	earth
-gram-	drawn, written, seed	-therm-	heat
		-tort-	twist
-graph-	drawn, written	-tox-	poison
-gyn-	woman	-tract-	draw out
-gyro-	turn	-umbr-	shadow
-helio-	sun	-vert-	turn
-hemo-	blood	-viv-	life
-herb-	plant	-voc-, -vok-	voice
-hetero-	different	-zoo-	animal

Verbal Skills 5

TABLE 4:
*Some Common Suffixes**

MEANING	SUFFIX(ES)
capable of	-able, -ible, -ile
belonging to, pertaining to	-al, -ary
person who is doing something	-er, -ant, -ard, -eer, -ist
full of	-ful, -ous
having to do with	-ic
without	-less
like, resembling	-oid
study of	-ology, -ogy, -nomy
state of being, quality	-ance, -ity, -tion
inflammation	-itis
cut	-ectomy
act of	-ation
to cause to happen	-ize
death	-cide
belief in	-ism
result of an action	-ion, -ment

---

*Note that this table is arranged in reverse order from the prefix and root tables. The reason for this is that many suffixes have the same meaning.

A final suggestion: You may be able to invent a game that uses this method of word analysis. For example, one person could use these prefixes, stems, and suffixes to invent a term. Then he or she could ask another student to figure out the meaning of the term. (For example, can you guess what we are thinking of by using the imaginary term **retrographist**?) *WARNING:* Don't get too carried away with this game. Most of the terms you invent won't be real ones. The main benefit of the game will be to give you practice in learning prefixes, stems, and suffixes.

ACTIVITY PAGE 1 — RECOGNIZING PREFIXES, SUFFIXES, AND ROOTS

DIRECTIONS: For each of the following terms, 1.) write the meaning of the prefix, root, and suffix, and then, 2.) the meaning of the whole word:

1. barometer: _____

2. biographer: _____

3. circumspect: _____

4. cryobiology: _____

5. cycloid: _____

6. encephalitis: _____

7. epidermis: _____

8. hemisphere: _____

9. hydrocephalic: _____

10. isobar: _____

11. polychromatic: _____

12. transmission: _____

Verbal Skills 7

ACTIVITY PAGE 2   DEFINING WORDS IN SENTENCES

DIRECTIONS: Explain the meaning of the words in boldface in each of the following sentences:

1. The satellite went into a **heliocentric** orbit.

2. Bacteria live in a **microcosm**.

3. The book on Darwin included a very complete **bibliography**.

4. The red line on the map is an **isotherm**.

5. Mr. Johnson's plan looks much better in **retrospect**.

6. Gneiss is an example of a **metamorphic** rock.

7. The doctor used a **hypodermic** needle.

8. The professor is one of the world's outstanding **geomorphologists**.

9. All the **telephone** wires were sagging after the heavy snowstorm.

10. Many research scientists have need for an **ultramicroscope**.

Section One

11. Two important parts of the earth are the **hydrosphere** and the **lithosphere**.

12. We were told to find the circle's **diameter**.

13. The boys asked the movie star for his **autograph**.

14. The **astronomer** studies both meteors and **planetoids**.

15. Most school rules are **prescribed** by the principal.

ACTIVITY PAGE 3 MATCHING DEFINITIONS

___

DIRECTIONS: Match the definitions in Column B with each of the terms in Column A:

COLUMN A

1. post-mortem: ____
2. bipedalism: ____
3. postscript: ____
4. germicide: ____
5. microbiology: ____
6. homogeneous: ____
7. hydrophilic: ____
8. subterrestrial: ____
9. aviary: ____
10. seismograph: ____
11. paleoanthropology: ____
12. photometrist: ____
13. fractionate: ____
14. hyperschizoid: ____
15. orthopedics: ____

COLUMN B

a. the study of ancient human cultures
b. beneath the earth's surface
c. study done on a person after he or she has died
d. break apart into sections
e. a bird home
f. the study of very small organisms
g. the ability to move about on two legs
h. devices for correcting a person's feet problems
i. a machine for measuring earth movement
j. a substance that will kill harmful microorganisms
k. someone whose personality is severely broken up
l. something that is attracted to water
m. a note written at the end of a message
n. the same throughout
o. a person who measures the amount of light

2. Sentence Skills

Reading scientific materials is difficult for many students. There are three main reasons for this:

1. The math (formulas, equations, and graphs) is unfamiliar;
2. The vocabulary is new and difficult;
3. Reading **any** kind of material may be a problem.

Items one and two are dealt with in other parts of this text. We can do only a limited amount with item three. In this section, we will review some simple ideas and provide some simple exercises on the reading of scientific materials.

Topic Sentences are important parts of every reading selection. A topic sentence is a single sentence that summarizes the main idea of a paragraph. Every good paragraph contains one. You should always be able to find out what a paragraph is about simply by reading the topic sentence. The rest of the paragraph simply tells more about the main idea expressed in the topic sentence.

The topic sentence often comes first in a paragraph. It says, "This is what the paragraph is going to be about." Then you get more details about the idea in the rest of the paragraph. The topic sentence may come in the middle or even at the end of a paragraph. In the latter case, it may say, "Here's the main idea we've been leading up to."

A good technique for studying is to be sure that you can find the topic sentence in every paragraph you read. That means you've identified the main idea in every paragraph. By underlining the topic sentence, you will be able to emphasize the main idea of the paragraph. You will also be able to go back at a later time and review these ideas more efficiently.

Look at the paragraph below. See if you can find the topic sentence in this paragraph. Underline the sentence that you think tells the main idea of the paragraph. Then check your answer with the one we've given.

New Sources of Minerals: The Antarctic

> Imagine looking for minerals under three kilometers of ice and rock! Thirty years ago, no one would have taken that idea seriously. Today, mining in the Antarctic is a real possibility. So far, low-grade supplies of coal, iron, uranium, manganese, copper, nickel, gold, tin, and platinum have all been found in the Antarctic. Geologists also believe that oil can be obtained from offshore wells. Since no one nation owns the Antarctic, who has the right to mine these minerals?

Your teacher may want to have you try some additional problems on finding topic sentences. The reading selections on page 12 can be used for this purpose. When you think you are ready, turn to Activity Page 4, page 13. There you will find four selections for which you are to find the topic sentences. On a separate sheet of paper, write down any additional information the paragraph tells you about the topic sentence.

Verbal Skills

Selection A:

Food spoils because of physical, chemical, or biological deterioration and by the activities of microorganisms and insects. How a particular food spoils depends on its composition, the way it is stored, and the type of microorganisms that attack it. Microorganisms specialize in the kind of organic matter they decompose; only a few consume more than one kind of food. The result is, however, pretty much the same: All living tissues ultimately decay to the minerals, water, carbon dioxide, and ammonia from which their complex organic molecules are made.[1]

Selection B:

At the beginning of this booklet we said that the same power is used both in the atomic bomb and in the production of electricity. How is this possible? The atomic bomb and the nuclear reactor both use fission but under quite different conditions. In the reactor the fission chain is kept under careful control, but in the atomic bomb the chain is allowed to go completely out of control. In the atomic bomb exact timing and other special conditions are required for an explosion to take place. These conditions cannot occur in a nuclear power reactor, and so there is no danger that such a reactor would ever explode.[2]

Selection C:

Light travels in straight lines. You can demonstrate this by placing your hand in the beam of a flashlight. Your hand stops the beam and thus casts a shadow. All shadows are evidence that light travels in straight lines. Otherwise, the light would simply bend around any opaque (nontransparent) object that was in the way. You have probably noticed how the length of your own shadow changes as the sun moves across the sky. This also illustrates the straight-line path of light rays.[3]

Selection D:

What these figures all say is rather simple and straightforward. We're simply using up our energy resources at a faster and faster rate each year. But more than that, our resources are not increasing **at all**, or hardly at all. Certainly, there is little reason to believe that any more of the fossil fuels are being made in the earth right now, so that when we've used up our present supplies, that's the end of them. Period. How far away is that day? For coal, perhaps as much as 300 years or more, to be optimistic, but for oil and natural gas, perhaps as few as twenty-five years, to be pessimistic.[4]

---

[1] Grace M. Urrows, *Food Preservation by Irradiation* (Washington, D.C.: United States Atomic Energy Commission, 1968).

[2] Samuel Glasstone and S. Joe Thomas, *Atomic Energy and Your World* (Washington, D.C.: United States Atomic Energy Commission, 1970).

[3] From *Physical Science: A Problem Solving Approach,* Revised Edition, by Joseph L. Carter and others, ©, Copyright 1979, by Ginn and Company (Xerox Corporation). Used with permission.

[4] David E. Newton, *A Casebook in General Science* (Portland, ME: J. Weston Walch, Publisher, 1975).

ACTIVITY PAGE **4** RECOGNIZING TOPIC SENTENCES

DIRECTIONS: For each of the four reading selections on page 12, write first the topic sentence for the paragraph, and then the additional information contained in the paragraph. Use the spaces provided for these answers.

Reading Selection A:
    Topic Sentence: _____

    Additional Information:

Reading Selection B:
    Topic Sentence: _____

    Additional Information:

Reading Selection C:
    Topic Sentence: _____

    Additional Information:

Reading Selection D:
    Topic Sentence: _____

    Additional Information:

Verbal Skills

3. Understanding Skills

"But I really studied that chapter. I don't know how I could have failed the exam!" How often have you heard (or even said) something like this? It's very easy to confuse **studying** with **reading**. They aren't always the same. You may begin reading Chapter Seven with the first word in the first paragraph, and read to the last word in the last paragraph. That doesn't necessarily mean that you **understand** what you read.

There are lots of tricks to getting the most out of a reading (studying) assignment. Your teacher may want to review some of these with you. The most important point is to be **sure** you have understood a paragraph before going too far. There are a number of techniques that you may use to increase your understanding:

1. Underline topic sentences and other important ideas in a paragraph.*
2. Make notes—comments, ideas, questions, and so forth—in the margin of a book.
3. Check the meanings of words you're not sure of.
4. Do mathematical calculations to check results and ideas in the paragraph.
5. Examine photographs, drawings, graphs, and figures used in connection with the paragraph.
6. Use questions in the book (usually at the end of the chapter) to check your understanding of the paragraph.
7. Make up questions of your own on the topic of the paragraph . . . and then answer them.
8. Solve any mathematical problems given in the book and relating to the chapter.
9. Write a brief outline or summary of the paragraph you have just read.
10. Work with a classmate who can ask you questions and whom you can question about a chapter or a lesson.

See how many of these ideas you can use in the following selections. Read through each selection as many times as necessary. Use as many of the "gimmicks" listed above as you like. Do whatever you need to in order to be sure you understand each selection. Remember: mastery, not speed, is what you are aiming for. Then, when you think you understand the paragraph as well as you can, turn to Activity Pages 5 and 6, pages 28-31. These contain questions about each of the selections. Answer those questions as directed by your teacher.

SELECTION A

Avoid Too Much Sugar

The major health hazard from eating too much sugar is tooth decay (dental caries). The risk of caries is not simply a matter of how much sugar you eat. The risk increases the more frequently you eat sugar and sweets, especially if you eat between meals, and if you eat foods that stick to the teeth. For example, frequent snacks of sticky candy, or dates, or daylong use of soft drinks may be more harmful than adding sugar to your morning cup of coffee—at least as far as your teeth are concerned.

---

*It is very unfortunate that most students do not own their own textbooks today. It makes it much more difficult to study properly. If you are using the school's book, you will not be allowed to write in it, of course. You will have to do these things on a separate sheet of paper.

Obviously, there is more to healthy teeth than avoiding sugars. Careful dental hygiene and exposure to adequate amounts of flouride in the water are especially important.

Contrary to widespread opinion, too much sugar in your diet does not seem to cause diabetes. The most common type of diabetes is seen in obese adults, and avoiding sugar, without correcting the overweight, will not solve the problem. There is also no convincing evidence that sugar causes heart attacks or blood vessel diseases.

Estimates indicate that Americans use on the average more than 130 pounds of sugars and sweeteners a year. This means the risk of tooth decay is increased not only by the sugar in the sugar bowl but by the sugars and syrups in jams, jellies, candies, cookies, soft drinks, cakes, and pies, as well as sugars found in products such as breakfast cereals, catsup, flavored milks, and ice cream. Frequently, the ingredient label will provide a clue to the amount of sugars in a product.

TO AVOID EXCESS SUGARS

- **Use less of all sugars, including white sugar, brown sugar, raw sugar, honey, and syrups.**
- **Eat less of foods containing these sugars, such as candy, soft drinks, ice cream, cakes, cookies.**
- Select fresh fruits or fruits canned without sugar or light syrup rather than heavy syrup.
- Read food labels for clues on sugar content—if the names sucrose, glucose, maltose, dextrose, lactose, fructose, or syrups appear first, then there is a large amount of sugar.
- **Remember, how often you eat sugar is as important as how much sugar you eat.**[5]

SELECTION B

Volcanic Eruptions

When hot molten magma breaks through the earth's crust and pours out as lava, we say that a *volcanic eruption* has taken place. Such eruptions are classified as **quiet** and **explosive**. Quiet eruptions produce lava sheets. These are spread on the surface from vents. The vents from which the lava oozes are situated on deep faults. If the lava is very hot and contains dissolved water, it flows freely, and the solidified lava makes a relatively smooth land surface. On close examination, the flow may have a ropy appearance. The Hawaiian name for this kind of lava is **pahoehoe** (pähō′ē hōē). Cooler, dry lava is much rougher in texture. It breaks into blocks that tumble forward rather than flow. Such fragmented lava flows are called **aa** (ä′ä), another Hawaiian name.

In an active lava flow, the outer crust looks black and solid. Through cracks in it you can see the dull red glow of the plastic rock in the heart of the flow. It may not look hot, but the black shell of the flow is several hundred degrees Celsius. Whatever comes in contact with the advancing front of the lava smokes, chars, and bursts into flame. If this hot flow of lava reaches a shore and enters the sea or a large lake, the water boils and in doing so cools the lava. The rapidly cooled lava forms "pillows" of rock.

---

[5] "Nutrition and Your Health," Home and Garden Bulletin No. 232 (Washington, D.C.: Science and Education Administration, U.S. Department of Agriculture, Stock No. 001-000-03881-8).

Under some conditions, the surface of a lava flow hardens and forms a solid roof while the innermost lava is still fluid. As the eruption slows and no more lava joins the stream, the fluid rock may flow out from under the solid roof. When this happens a **lava tunnel** is left. A huge lava tunnel can be found at Rainbow Falls in Hilo, Hawaii. Rainbow Falls tumbles off the thick roof of the tunnel and splashes into a large pool that extends back into the tunnel.

In some places on the earth there have been dozens of quiet eruptions over thousands of years. The most spectacular have occurred in the Hawaiian Islands, where lava flows have piled one upon the other. They have built a pile that rises more than 9 km from the floor of the ocean. Such a broad conical pile of lava sheets is called a **shield volcano**. The slopes of these volcanoes are much gentler than those of other kinds of volcanoes.

Shield volcanoes, such as those that make up the Hawaiian Islands, are different from other quiet flows in that they have a **crater** (krā′ tər). A crater is a pit in which the lava wells up from deep within the earth. Sometimes this forms a fiery lake of molten rock. Sometimes the lava meets with water on its way up to the surface of the earth. Under pressure, the water dissolves in the molten rock. When the lava reaches the surface, the pressure is greatly reduced. The water than comes out of the rock as a red-hot stream. This blows drops of molten rock high into the air in a fountain. This kind of action does not occur in the truly quiet type of flow.

The most spectacular kind of volcano is the most dangerous This is the kind that produces an explosive eruption. Such volcanoes erupt periodically. During the quiet period, the floor of the crater cools and becomes solid rock. Very slowly, gas pressure builds up beneath the floor. In time the pressure is so great that the rock floor ruptures. The explosion of gases blows into the air chunks of the solid rock, gobs of molten rock, and vast amounts of molten drops of rock. Once the initial explosion has taken place, the volcano continues to erupt. It does so until the stress placed on the magma by dissolved gases is exhausted. This may be a matter of hours or months.

The material blown out of the volcano during an explosive eruption is given a variety of names. The general name given to these fragments is **pyroclasts** (pī rə klasts′). Another name that is becoming popular is **tephra** (tef′rə), the Greek word for "ashes." The finest particles are dustlike and called **ash**. Pebble-size particles usually are called **lapilli** (lə pil′ ī), an Italian word for "small stones." Larger particles are called **scoria** (skôr′ ē ə), an Italian word for "cinders." Gobs of red-hot lava blown into the air produce **bombs**. Some of these are elongated and have twisted tails.

When an explosive volcano quiets down, it leaves a cone of lapilli and scoria. These loose piles of material are called **cinder cones**. Sometimes large blocks of cooled lava are found in the bottom of the crater of a cinder cone. These, when originally blow out of the vent of the volcano, fell back into the crater.

A third kind of volcano is formed by alternate explosive and quiet eruptions. They are called **composite** (kəm poz′ it), or **strato** (strā′ tō) **volcanoes**. Mount Hood in Oregon is an example. After a long, quiet period, such a volcano explodes. For a time it ejects huge amounts of scoria. Then, when the gas pressures have subsided, a quiet flow occurs. Such a flow may originate from a crater filled to overflowing with lava. More often the molten rock finds a weak place in the side of the cone and leaks out through it. Thus the cone is made up of alternate layers of tephra and lava.[6]

---

[6] F. Martin Brown and Grace H. Kemper, *Earth Science* (Morristown, NJ: Silver Burdett Company, 1979). Reprinted by permission of the publisher.

SELECTION C

Radioactivity

Radioactivity (rā dē ō ak tiv′ə tē) is the giving off of particles and rays from the nucleus of the atom. Radioactivity was discovered in the late nineteenth century by Henri Becquerel (bek rel′), a French scientist. He was trying to determine whether any element gives of **X rays**. Earlier Wilhelm Roentgen (rent´gen) had discovered X rays when he bombarded a copper target with electrons. The X rays could be detected by using a photographic plate. When a plate was exposed to X rays and developed, it showed a certain amount of exposure to light. Roentgen also found that a new kind of picture could be taken using X rays. If a hand, for example, were placed between the source of the X rays and a photographic plate, a picture of the bonses in the hand could be obtained.

This discovery inspired other scientists. Roentgen had been able to produce X rays in the laboratory. Becquerel wondered if he could find a natural source of X rays. He knew that X rays would expose a photographic plate. He therefore placed different materials on wrapped photographic plates. After a period of time, he developed the plates. Most of them showed no exposure. There was one element, however, that caused a plate to be exposed. That element was U [*uranium*]. This discovery led Becquerel to other discoveries. He found that other elements give off rays similar to X rays. Two such elements are Th [*thorium*] and Ac [*actinium*].

Marie and Pierre Curie (kyùr′ē), using the property of radioactivity, discovered two new elements, Po [*polonium*] and Ra [*radium*]. The radioactivity of these two elements was different from X rays. It was caused by the breakdown of an atomic nucleus. There appeared to be three kinds of radiation coming from these elements. The radiation could be identified by passing it between the poles of a magnet. Two rays were deflected by the magnet. The third ray was not.

It was found that **gamma** (gam′ə) **rays** were not at all affected by the magnet. Gamma rays come naturally from the nucleus of the atom. They are similar to X rays, but they are more penetrating. **Beta** (bā′tə) **rays** were most affected by the magnet. Beta rays were found to consist of negative particles identical in charge and mass to the electron. **Alpha** (al′fə) **rays** were found to be positively charged particles. Alpha particles are helium ions [He^{+2}], made up of two protons and two neutrons. Alpha particles are less affected by the magnetic field than are beta particles.

Half-life

The amount of radioactivity present in a sample of material changes as time passes. Each time a nucleus gives off a radioactive particle the element changes. Uranium is one of the many radioactive elements. When a uranium nucleus gives off an alpha particle, a thorium nucleus remains. This process is known as **radioactive decay**. The amount of uranium remaining can be graphed against time. The period of time necessary for half of the atoms of a radioactive substance to decay into another element is called its **half-life**. Uranium has a half-life of 4.5 billion years. Each radioactive element has its own unique half-life. Radium has a half-life of 1620 years. Some elements have half-lives of less than a second. You will learn more about half-life in Activities 25 and 26.[7]

---

[7]Charles R. Barman, John J. Rusch, Myron O. Schneiderwent, and Wendy B. Hindin, *Physical Science* (Morristown, NJ: Silver Burdett Company, 1979). Reprinted by permission of the publisher.

SELECTION D

The Planet Venus

One of a series of NASA Facts about the exploration of Venus.

In 1978 NASA will send two spacecraft to Earth's nearest planetary neighbor, Venus. This is the Pioneer-Venus mission. One spacecraft will orbit the planet and send scientific information back to Earth for months. The other will carry four probes that will detach and plunge into the atmosphere of Venus to tell us about its meteorology, its composition, and its complex chemistry, but they are not designed to survive after impact.

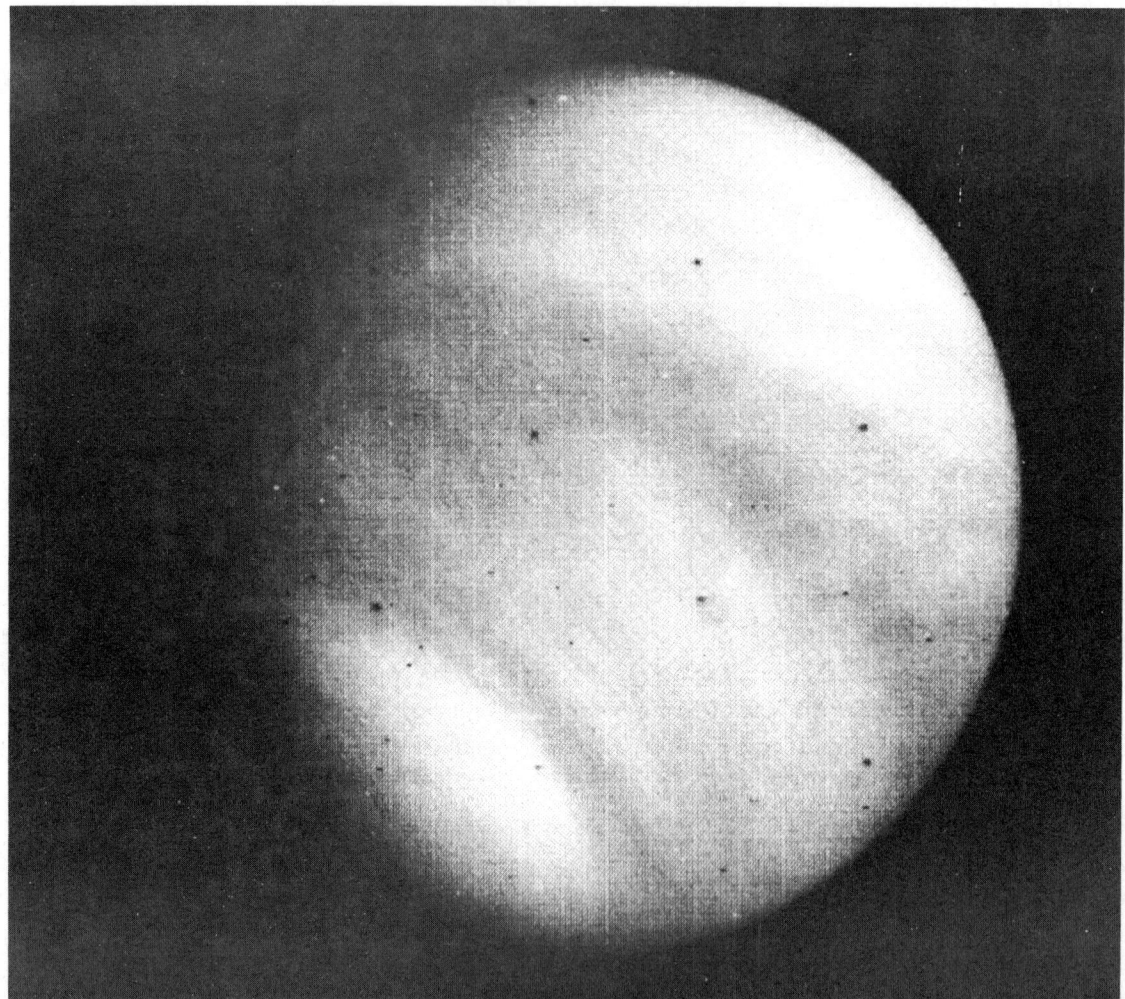

Venus is a fascinating planet because it is almost a twin of Earth, but has developed quite differently so that our type of life cannot live on its surface. Scientists want to find out why it developed the way it did, and in so doing, gain greater insight into the nature of the processes that have molded our Earth and brought it to the conditions of today.

Venus as a Member of the Solar System

After the Sun and the Moon, Venus is the brightest object in the sky. If you know where to look you can sometimes see Venus in broad daylight. Like other planets Venus appears to move through the constellations of the Zodiac, but it is never seen far from the Sun because it is an "inferior" planet. That is, it travels along an orbit within that of the Earth. Venus takes only 225 days to go completely around the Sun. The position of Venus east or west of the Sun is referred to as an elongation. At eastern elongation you can see it as a bright, star-like object in the evening sky. At western elongation you have to look for it rising before the Sun in the early morning sky (Figure 1).

When Venus passes between Earth and Sun, and thus comes closest to the Earth, it passes through what astronomers call inferior conjunction. On the far side of the Sun it passes through superior conjunction (see Figure 2). The positions of greatest elongation correspond to quadratures on the orbit.

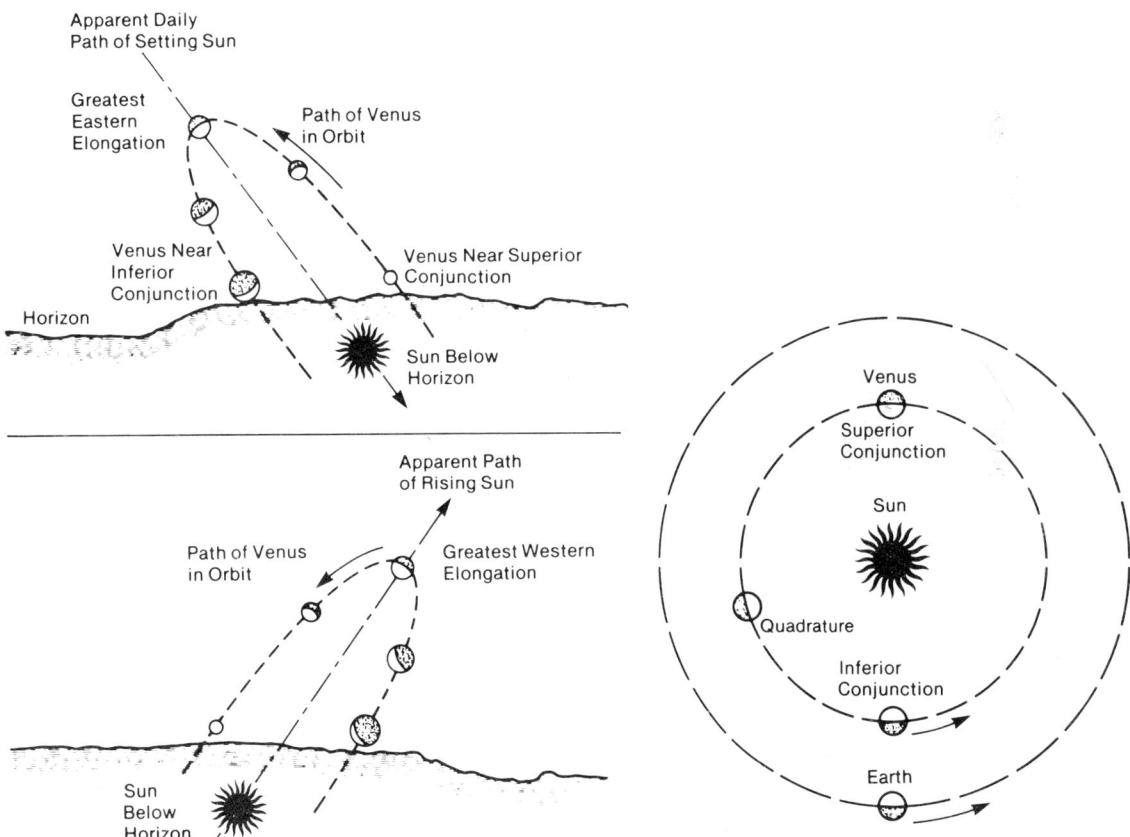

Figure 1. Venus moves from superior conjunction to the east of the Sun and thus appears as an evening star. As it progresses around its orbit, it passes through inferior conjunction between Earth and Sun and then becomes a morning star, rising before the Sun.

Figure 2. The orbits of Venus and Earth show the positions of the conjunctions.

Verbal Skills 19

Venus as a Planet

The mass, diameter, and density of Venus are all only slightly less than those of the Earth. But its surface is hotter, its atmosphere much denser, and its rotations much slower than those of the Earth. Venus is one of the three planets of the solar system that do not have satellites; the others are Mercury and Pluto. Also Venus does not have a significant magnetic field.

The diameter of Venus is 12,100 km (7519 mi) and its average density is 5.25 times that of water. This high density may imply that Venus has a core of nickel and iron like the Earth.

The surface of Venus cannot be observed visually from Earth because Venus is shrouded in a thick blanket of clouds. However, radar waves from Earth stations penetrate to the surface and astronomers have used them to map the surface of Venus. In addition, the surface emits radio waves—microwaves—which penetrate the clouds and can be received on Earth. Astronomers use these radio waves to estimate the temperature of the planet's surface.

In the early 1960's when these measurements were first made, astronomers were surprised to discover that the surface of Venus is extremely hot. The microwaves carry the message that it is about 430° C which is hot enough to melt zinc. They also told us that the temperature is the same both day and night on the surface of Venus.

The surface temperature of Venus is much higher than that of the Earth. This difference is attributed to the dense atmosphere of Venus which traps incoming solar radiation and prevents heat from being reradiated into space. This is termed the "greenhouse effect."

A telescope reveals no details in the yellowish clouds of Venus. However, if these clouds are photographed in ultraviolet light, dark shadings can be seen that rotate in a period of about 4 days. These shadings have also been seen more clearly in ultraviolet pictures of Venus taken from a passing spacecraft (Figure 3).

But the planet itself rotates much more slowly than its cloud tops. Again the discovery was made by radio waves. Transmitted from the Earth by a big antenna, these waves are reflected by Venus. Radar astronomers can tell from the form of the radio echo that Venus rotates once in 243.1 days, in a direction opposite to the rotation of the Earth. This is called a retrograde direction. A day (the time from one sunrise to the next) on Venus lasts about 117 Earth days (Figure 4).

Another peculiar fact about the rotation of Venus is that it seems to be linked to the Earth. Each time Venus passes closest to the Earth at inferior conjunction, the same face of Venus is turned towards the Earth. Most astronomers believe this is just a coincidence, but it may not be.

Astronomers do not know why Venus rotates so slowly. The other planets (except Mercury) rotate quickly on their axes. Mercury has been slowed by tidal friction because of its closeness to the Sun; but Venus is not only rotating slowly, it is also rotating in the "wrong" direction. The Sun could not have caused this. One possibility, proposed some years ago, is that Venus once had a big satellite that revolved around it in the retrograde direction. This satellite crashed into Venus and stopped the planet's rotation, or perhaps even pushed it a little into rotating the opposite way.

Astronomers looked at the spectrum of light reflected from the clouds of Venus and were able to find that its atmosphere contains much (97%) carbon dioxide. This again is a contrast to Earth which only has a small amount (0.03%) of carbon dioxide in its atmosphere. The reason there is so much carbon dioxide in the atmosphere of Venus is thought

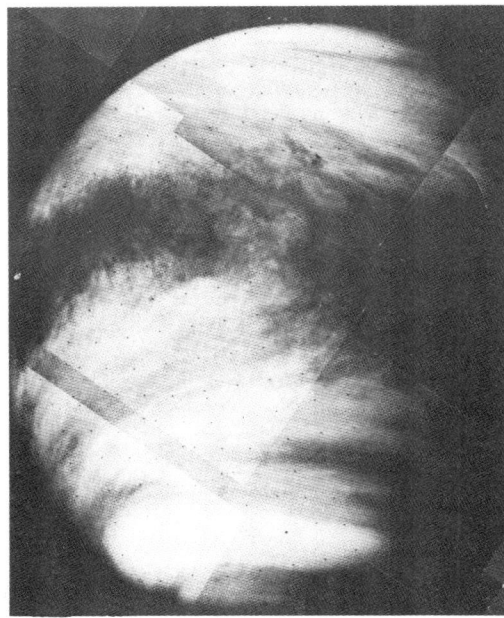

Figure 3. In visible light Venus is a featureless, bright, yellowish globe. In ultraviolet light the clouds of Venus have prominent patterns as shown in this mosaic of pictures taken by NASA's spacecraft, Mariner 10, as it flew by Venus on the way to Mercury.

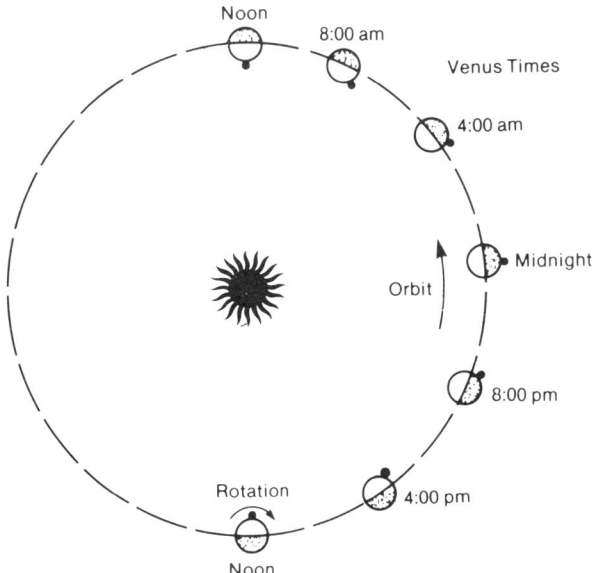

Axial Rotation: 243.1 Earth days
Orbital period: 225 Earth days (= Venus year)
Noon to Noon: 116.8 Earth days (= Venus day)
Venus year: 1.93 Venus days

Figure 4. A combination of retrograde rotation about its axis in 243.1 days and orbital revolution about the Sun in 225 days makes a day on Venus 116.8 Earth days long, as shown in this diagram.

to be because Venus is a dry planet. The presence of oceans of water on Earth allowed Earth's early atmosphere of carbon dioxide to react with the rocks and form carbonates. Today, most of Earth's carbon dioxide is bound up as carbonates in rocks. Also living things on Earth used carbon dioxide from the atmosphere to provide carbon for their bodies. Oxygen was released by plants to form Earth's oxygen-rich atmosphere of today.

Another big difference between Earth and Venus, as mentioned earlier, is that Venus does not have a magnetic field of any significance. As a consequence its atmosphere has no protection from the blizzard of high-energy particles—protons and electrons—known as the solar wind. These particles are held away from the Earth by our magnetic field. But they speed directly into the upper atmosphere of Venus.

The Surface of Venus

Details on the surface of Venus were virtually unknown until two Soviet Venera spacecraft landed on it in 1975 and returned pictures. Earlier speculations had ranged from steaming swamps to dusty deserts, from carbonated seas to oceans of bubbling petroleum. All were wrong, though the desert concept seems closest to what is now known. Photographs from the Venera spacecraft (Figure 5) revealed a dry rocky surface fractured and changed by unknown processes. There are rocks of many different kinds and a dark soil. Two spacecraft landed about 2000 km (1200 mi) from each other. One landed on an ancient

Figure 5. The first pictures of the surface of Venus were returned to Earth by two Soviet Venera spacecraft that landed on Venus in 1975. The top picture is from Venera 9 and the bottom from Venera 10. They show rocky terrains which are surprisingly different at the two sites, the Venera 10 site showing evidence of much greater age, inferred from the weathered nature of the rocks.

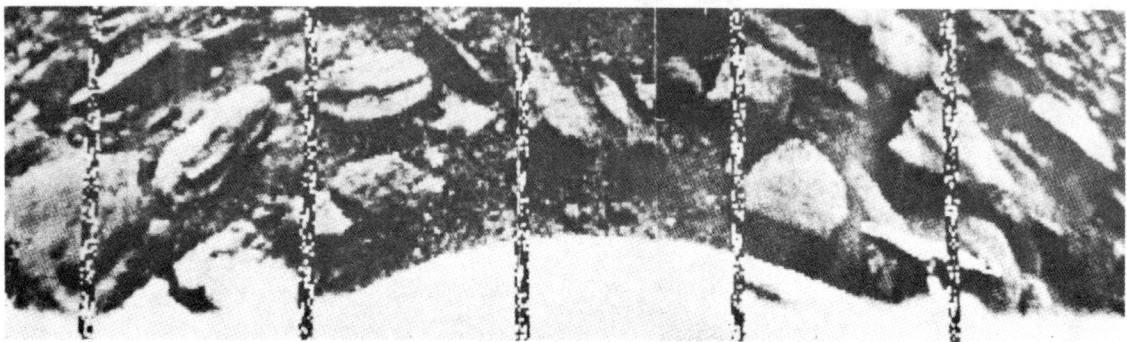

plateau or plains area. At this site there are rocky elevations interspersed with a relatively dark, fine-grained soil. This soil seems to have resulted from a weathering of the rocks, possibly by a chemical action. The rocky outcrops are generally smooth on a large scale, with their edges blunted and rounded. The dark soil fills some of the cavities in the rocks. By contrast the other Venera landed at a site where there are rocks which look younger and less weathered, with not much evidence of soil between them.

Measurements made by the Russian spacecraft showed that all these rocks on Venus have a density and radioactive content similar to terrestrial basaltic rocks.

In 1962, craters were discovered on radar maps of the planet (Figure 6).

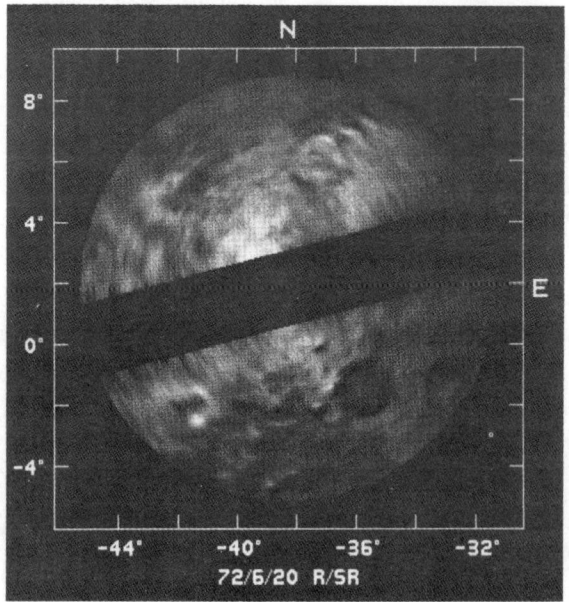

Figure 6. Radar scanning of the surface of Venus using the Deep Space Antennas of NASA's network, revealed craters as shown in this picture of an equatorial region. The dark band across the picture covers an area for which radar data were not obtained.

22 *Section One*

Subsequently, radar astronomers found evidence of large lava flows, great circular basins like those of the Moon, and even chasms and volcanoes like those on Mars. Generally, however, the surface of Venus is not so rugged as Earth and Mars. Radar measurements of altitude variation on Venus amount to only about 5 km (3 mi) compared with Earth's range of 20 km (12 mi) between the top of Mt. Everest and the bottom of the Marianas Trench, and Mars' range of 30 km (20 mi) between the top of Olympus Mons and the bottom of the Hellas basin.

The existence of craters and other features on the surface of Venus suggests that the planet had been subjected to a bombardment from space early in its history, just as the other inner planets of the solar system were bombarded, and that afterwards there were volcanic activities, lava flows, and possibly some mountain building. The evolution of Venus may have progressed to an even more Earth-like state than that of Mars. But the absence of water on Venus prevented it from becoming like the Earth is today.[8]

SELECTION E

Muscular System

You don't think about the muscles that move food along in your intestines. Those muscles are called **involuntary muscles**. Involuntary muscles are not under your conscious control. Other muscles in the body are voluntary. We direct the voluntary muscles to do things like write, play ball, and run. Both types of muscles receive their instructions from the nervous system. Both types of muscles work in the same way. Muscles tighten to move body parts or hold them in position. This tightening is called **muscle contraction**. A muscle does work or moves a body part by contracting.

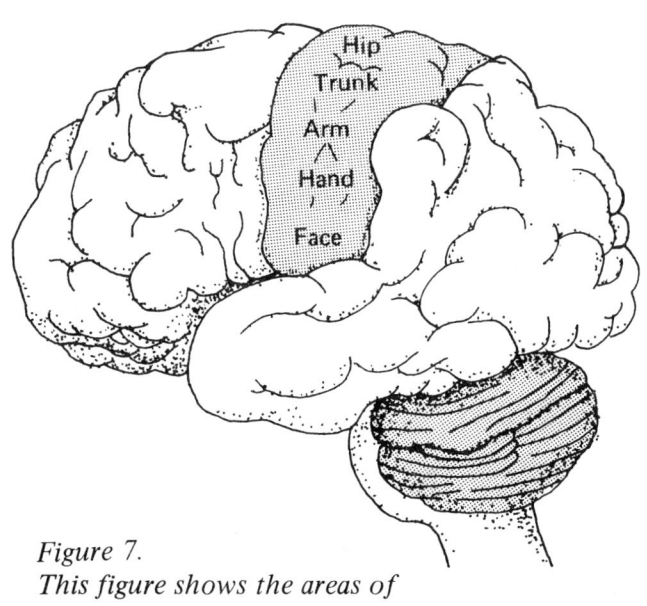

Figure 7.
This figure shows the areas of the brain that control the muscles in certain body areas.

Voluntary muscles are responsible for the movements that you can control. When you move your arms and legs, or chew food, you use voluntary muscles. Tendons attach voluntary muscles to bones. The muscles receive messages from the brain to contract. The right side of your brain controls the left side of your body. The left side of your brain controls the right side of your body.

Muscles are directed from specific areas in the brain called **motor areas**. Figure 7 shows the location of some of these motor areas. Passing an electrical current through these areas will cause certain muscles to contract.

---

[8] "The Planet Venus," *NASA Facts,* December 1977 (Washington, D.C.: National Aeronautics and Space Administration, 1977).

Sometimes voluntary movement is prevented due to damage to the nervous system. **Paralysis** (pə ral′ə sis) can make people unable to move. In paralysis, the muscles are not receiving instructions from the brain. Therefore, the person has no voluntary control over these muscles.

When we exercise our voluntary muscles regularly, the muscles grow larger. Under a microscope, muscle cells look long and thin. After you have exercised the muscles for several weeks, the muscle cells themselves increase in size. Most of the time there are unused muscle cells in a muscle. As the muscle is exercised, more muscle cells are used. Since the cells are larger and more cells are in use, the muscle is stronger. In Activity 14, you can investigate the effects of exercise.

Some of the movements of your voluntary muscles are automatic. When you walk through smog or dust-filled air, your eyes automatically blink. You don't have to think about it. Another word that is commonly used for this movement is **relfex** (rē′ fleks). In a reflex, a muscle reacts automatically.

There are several different types of reflexes. One type is the stretch reflex. When a muscle is stretched, the muscle tends to contract. This stretch reflex keeps your body standing straight. When your body starts to slump, the muscles stretch. The muscles send messages to the spinal cord. The spinal cord sends instructions to the muscles to contract.

Has a doctor ever tapped your knee and made your leg jerk? The tendon that was hit stretched the muscle in your upper leg. A message was sent to your spinal cord. The spinal cord sent instructions to the muscle to contract. The muscle contracted and pulled the lower leg up.

Breathing is an example of muscle action that can be voluntary or automatic. If you are going to dive into a swimming pool, you take a deep breath. If you are reading a book, you usually do not actively control your breathing. However, the brain automatically sends messages to the muscles that control breathing.

Some muscles are never under your conscious control. These muscles are called involuntary muscles. Muscles in the stomach and intestines keep food moving along as it is digested. These involuntary muscles receive instructions automatically from the nervous system. You do not have to think about directing these muscles. Involuntary muscles are also found in certain blood vessels.

The heart contains involuntary muscle called cardiac muscle. You do not consciously control your heartbeat. The rate of your heartbeat is automatically controlled by your nervous system.[9]

SELECTION F

The Gases Themselves

If you've made up your mind that chemistry is a dull subject, and want to continue to think so, you should not read this booklet. It will only upset your comfortable conviction. If that should happen, it will be quite traditional, by the way, because information about the "noble gases" has been shattering cherished beliefs with remarkable consistency for some years now.

---

[9] Jeanne Taylor Richardson, Anne F. Harris, and Oliver Crosby Sparks, *Life Science* (Morristown, NJ: Silver Burdett Company, 1979). Reprinted by permission of the publisher.

For over 60 years the 6 gases helium, neon, argon, krypton, xenon, and radon were the confirmed bachelors among the known elements. All the other elements would enter into chemical combination with one or another of their kind, irrespective of whether they were solids, gases, or liquids in their normal state. Not so helium, neon, argon, krypton, xenon, and radon. They were chemically aloof and would have nothing to do with other elements, or even with one another.

This behavior earned them a unique position in the Periodic Table of the Elements and they were called names like the "inert gases" or the "noble gases." They were also labeled the "rare gases," although helium and argon are not really "rare."

The inability of these gases to form chemical compounds was, until 1962, one of the most accepted fundamentals in chemistry. Then along came some scientists with what Philip Abelson, editor of the magazine *Science*, later called "a germ of skepticism." In the space of only a couple of months all the dogma relating to the inertness of xenon was overthrown—it had definitely become a "joiner." Radon and krypton began "mingling" chemically soon thereafter and, although the other three gases are still holding out, the damage to a firmly cherished belief was done.

Table I

ABUNDANCE OF NOBLE GASES IN AIR AT SEA LEVEL

Element	Symbol	Parts per Million (by volume)
Helium	He	5
Neon	Ne	18
Argon	Ar	9430
Krypton	Kr	1
Xenon	Xe	0.1
Radon	Rn	6×10^{-14}

Some idea of the excitement these discoveries caused among scientists can be gleaned from the fact that, less than a year after the first discovery of a xenon compound was announced, a conference on "Noble Gas Compounds" was held at Argonne National Laboratory near Chicago. Some 100 scientists discussed work they had done in the field, and almost 60 made formal reports! The proceedings of that meeting filled a 400-page book entitled *Noble Gas Compounds*. Not bad, considering that just a short time before not even one noble gas compound was known.

[We will now] attempt to show how these gases lost their bachelorhood, and why today they are called "helium group gases" or "noble gases" instead of "inert gases."

Discovery

The first indication of the existence of an inert constituent in the atmosphere came in 1785 when Henry Cavendish found that he could not convert atmospheric nitrogen completely to nitrous acid. He concluded that, "If there is any part of our atmosphere which differs from the rest . . . it is not more than 1/120 part of the whole." This result was apparently forgotten or neglected, and the problem arose again in studies on the density of nitrogen in the early 1890s. At that time Lord Rayleigh discovered that nitrogen obtained by removal of the then known gases from an air sample, or "atmospheric nitrogen," was denser than nitrogen prepared by chemical means—that is, "chemical nitrogen." A number of theories were advanced for the discrepancy in the densities of the nitrogen samples from the two sources. Either the "chemical" nitrogen was too light, or the "atmospheric" nitrogen too heavy, because of the presence of other gases. In 1894, however, Lord Rayleigh and William Ramsay showed that the "atmospheric" nitrogen was a mixture of nitrogen and a heavier, previously undiscovered, gas. This gas turned out to be a new element that was given the name "argon," on account of its chemical inactivity (from the Greek word, *argon*, meaning inactive, idle).

The discovery of the other 5 gases followed rapidly; by 1900 they had all been isolated and identified. Ramsay and his assistant, Morris Travers, in continuing their research on argon made use of newly developed methods for liquefying gases. The earth's atmosphere consists mainly of nitrogen (78%), oxygen (21%), and argon (1%), which have boiling points sufficiently different (-195.8°C, -182.96°C, and -185.7°C, respectively) that they can readily be separated by fractional distillation of liquid air. As Ramsay and Travers improved their techniques, they found that they could obtain several more fractions when distilling liquid air. Three of these fractions contained elements never before isolated, namely, neon (Greek, *neos*, new), krypton (Greek, *kryptos*, hidden), and xenon (Greek, *xenon*, stranger).

Ramsay was also instrumental in discovering the existence of helium (Greek, *helios*, the sun). This element had been noted in the sun's spectrum as early as 1868, but was only isolated as a terrestrial element in 1895 when Ramsay obtained it by heating the uranium-containing mineral cleveite. (The helium in this mineral was physically trapped and was not chemically combined.)

The final noble gas to be discovered was radon. In 1900 Friedrich Dorn, a German physicist, found that radium evolved a gas that he called "radium emanation." This gas was later given the name *nitron*, but since 1923 it has been known as *radon*. All isotopes of radon are radioactive.

Occurrence and Production

The atmosphere is our major source for neon, argon, krypton, and xenon, and these gases are now produced commercially as a by-product during fractional distillation of liquid air to produce liquid oxygen and nitrogen. Liquefaction of thousands of tons of air per day makes these 4 gases available in sufficient quantities for present needs.

Helium is the second most abundant element in the universe. About 76% of the mass of the universe, it is estimated, is hydrogen; helium makes up about 23%, and all the other elements together compose the remaining 1% of the mass. Helium is so light that it is continually escaping from the earth's atmosphere into interstellar space. The present concentration of helium in the atmosphere therefore probably represents a steady-state concentration, that is, the amount being released from the earth's crust is equal to the amount escaping from the atmosphere into space. The constant escape explains why there is so little to be found in our air. Helium *can* be obtained from the atmosphere in the same way neon, argon, krypton, and xenon are, but is more readily obtained from accumulations that have built up in the earth's crust.

This helium in the earth is continually being formed by radioactive decay. All radioactive materials that decay by emitting alpha particles produce helium, since an alpha particle is nothing more than a helium nucleus with a positive charge. Most of the helium in the earth's crust comes from the decay of uranium and thorium.

The helium is obtained by tapping natural gas wells, which yield an average helium content of about 2%. Most of these helium wells are in an area within 250 miles of Amarillo, Texas, although small amounts have been found in natural gas elsewhere in the U.S. Since the early 1950s helium-containing gases also have been found in South Africa, Russia, and Canada. In other parts of the world the helium content of natural gases and mineral springs is too low to make separation commercially attractive.

The helium is recovered from the natural gas by an initial liquefaction that leaves only helium and nitrogen in gaseous form. Further liquefaction, this time under pressure, causes most of the nitrogen to condense and leaves helium of about 98% purity in the gas phase. This can be further purified by passing it through a liquid–nitrogen-cooled trap containing charcoal, which absorbs the remaining impurities.

The final one of our noble gases, radon, is obtained from the radioactive decay of radium. . . .

Uses

Many of the uses of these gases are outgrowths of their inertness. The greater abundances, and hence lower costs, of helium and argon result in their use as inert atmospheres in which to weld and fabricate metals. The electrical and other properties of the noble gases make most of them ideal gases for filling numerous types of electronic tubes and in lasers. For this, the gases may be used singly or mixed with one or more of the others. Perhaps the best known use is in the familiar "neon" advertising signs. The glow produced by neon alone is red. The other gases produce less brilliant colors; helium (pale pink), argon (blue), krypton (pale blue), and xenon, (blue-green).

Helium, because of its lightness, finds use as a lifting gas for balloons and airships, although it is heavier than hydrogen. This weight disadvantage, however, is far overbalanced by the fact that helium is nonflammable. Recently, helium has been used as a cooling medium in nuclear reactors, and it is also a diluent for oxygen in breathing systems for deep-sea divers. Helium being less soluble in the blood than nitrogen, the helium-oxygen mixture is preferable to normal air for persons working under pressure, since its use tends to prevent "the bends," a serious condition caused by gas bubbles in the body fluids and tissues. Liquid helium, which is the only substance that will remain liquid at temperatures close to absolute zero (–273°C), is finding increasing use in low-temperature physics–*cyrogenics*. Radon has been used as a source of gamma rays for treatment of cancer, but more convenient gamma-ray sources produced in nuclear reactors now are more frequently chosen for medical therapy.[10]

---

[10]Cedrick L. Chernick, *The Chemistry of the Noble Gases* (Washington, D.C.: U.S. Atomic Energy Commission, 1967).

ACTIVITY PAGE 5 READING FOR UNDERSTANDING–I

DIRECTIONS: Answer each question for Reading Selections A, B, and C in the space provided.

Reading Selection A

1. What is the major health problem caused by eating too much sugar?

2. Name two ways to have healthy teeth, besides eating less sugar.

3. About how much sugar do Americans eat each year?

4. Name some foods—other than "sweets"—that contain sugar.

5. State two good rules for avoiding excess sugar.

Reading Selection B

1. Describe three types of volcanoes.

2. What is a volcanic eruption?

3. Name and describe three types of lava.

4. What is a cinder cone?

5. What are pyroclasts? Name some types of pyroclasts.

28 *Section One*

Reading Selection C

1. What is radioactivity?

2. How was radioactivity first discovered?

3. Describe three forms of radiation produced by radioactive materials.

4. Define the term *half-life*.

5. What discoveries in radioactivity were made by Marie and Pierre Curie?

ACTIVITY PAGE 6 READING FOR UNDERSTANDING–II

DIRECTIONS: Answer each question for Reading Selections D, E, and F in the space provided.

Reading Selection D

1. What method did NASA use for studying the planet Venus in 1978?

2. Explain the meaning of the following terms:

   a. elongation

   b. inferior conjunction

   c. quadrature

3. What is the biggest problem in studying the surface of Venus? How do scientists solve that problem?

4. Tell one strange fact about the way Venus rotates.

5. Describe the surface of Venus.

Reading Selection E

1. What is the difference between voluntary and involuntary muscles?

2. What are motor areas in the brain?

3. Define the term *paralysis*.

30 *Section One*

4. Describe some kinds of reflex actions.

5. What happens to muscle cells when you exercise?

Reading Selection F
1. Name the six noble gases.

2. Why are these gases called "noble"?

3. How was the first noble gas discovered?

4. What is the source of most noble gases?   How are they obtained from this source?

5. Name three uses for noble gases.

Verbal Skills 31

Section two

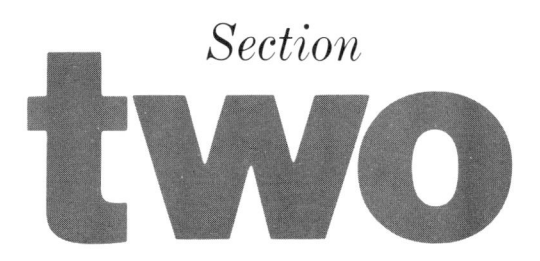

Library Skills

The best source of information about libraries is your own school librarian. He or she will be able to tell you everything you need to know about using your library. A few essential tools that you should be familiar with are described in this section.

1. The Card Catalog

The card catalog is your road map to the library. It lists every book contained in the library. It may also list magazines, films, pamphlets and other non-book resource materials—or they may be listed in a catalog of their own. Check with the librarian to see what system your library uses.

The card shown below is like the ones you will find in the card catalog:

```
            SCIENCE — SOCIAL ASPECTS

Q         Newton, David E.          comp.
175.5           Science and society [ by ] David E. Newton. Boston, Hol-
.N48            brook Press [ 1974 ]

                x. 306 p. illus. 23 cm.
                Includes bibliographies.


                1. Science—Social aspects.  2. Technology—Social aspects.
                1. Title.
                Q175.5.N48              301.24'3              73-87650
                                                                MARC

                Library of Congress          74 [ 4 ]
```

Notice the information contained on this card:

1. The topic of the book: Science — Social Aspects

2. The author of the book: David E. Newton

3. The name of the book: *Science and Society*

4. The "call number": Q
   175.5
   .N48

This tells you where the book can be located in the library. There are two major cataloging systems now in use: the Dewey Decimal System and the Library of Congress System. Some very large libraries may have other systems of their own for cataloging some materials. Ask your librarian which system is used in your library. Then have him or her show you how the system works.

5. The place, publisher, and date of publication: Boston, Holbrook Press, 1974.

6. The number of pages: "x" means 10 pages in the introduction. There are 306 pages in the main body of the text. The abbreviation "illus." means that there are illustrations. The entry "23 cm" tells the length of the book. Although this information is usually not very important to a reader, it can be to a librarian. Do you see why? Compare your answer with the one given on page 273.

7. Other headings under which this book can be located in the card catalog: "Technology-Social Aspects" and by the title.

   Notice that every book can always be found listed under the author's name. This book could also be found under the heading "Newton, David E." in the card catalog.

8. The card may also contain a short description of the content of the book, although this card does not.

The card shown here is called a **subject card**. It would be found in the card catalog under the letter "S" or the section that contains words beginning with "SCI." The same book would be classified under its title and its author. These cards are called the **title card** and the **author card**. They contain the same kind of information as that given on the subject card. The title card and author card for this book are shown below and on the opposite page.

```
Q         Newton, David E.          comp.
175.5         Science and society [by] David E. Newton. Boston, Hol-
.N48          brook Press [1974]

              x. 306 p. illus. 23 cm.
              Includes bibliographies.


                1. Science–Social aspects. 2. Technology–Social aspects.
              1. Title.
              Q175.5.N48              301.24′3              73-87650
                                                                MARC
              Library of Congress      74 [4]
```

34 *Section Two*

```
              Science and society

    Q       Newton, David E.           comp.
    175.5         Science and society [by] David E. Newton. Boston, Hol-
    .N48     brook Press [1974]

                 x. 306 p.  illus.  23 cm.
                 Includes bibliographies.


                 1. Science—Social aspects.  2. Technology—Social aspects.
              1. Title.
              Q175.5.N48              301.24′3                 73-87650
                                                                  MARC

              Library of Congress          74 [4]
```

The card catalog can be used in two major ways. If you already know the name of a book you want to use—but not where it's located in the library—look in the card catalog under the title of the book or under the author's last name (if you know it). The title or author card will give the call number for that book. Then, use the call number to locate the book on the shelves.

Perhaps you have a different problem. You have a topic to research, but don't know of any books. You want to find materials that will tell you about your topic. Let's assume the topic is **mammals**. Go to the card catalog and look under the heading MAMMALS. There will probably be a few books whose titles begin with the word "Mammals." There will also be other books **about** mammals that may not have that word in the title. The subject cards will tell you what the names of those books are and where they are located on the shelves.

Activity Page 7, pages 36-37, will help you become better acquainted with the card catalog.

Library Skills

ACTIVITY PAGE 7 — USING THE CARD CATALOG

DIRECTIONS: Answer the following questions by referring to the card catalog.

1. List the titles, authors, publishers, and dates of publication for any four books on the following topics.

    a. botany

      1. _____
      2. _____
      3. _____
      4. _____

    b. the solar system

      1. _____
      2. _____
      3. _____
      4. _____

    c. plastics

      1. _____
      2. _____
      3. _____
      4. _____

2. Give the titles, subjects, publishers, dates of publication, and any other information you can find for **two** books by the author Isaac Asimov:

    a. First book: _____
    _____

    b. Second book: _____
    _____

36 *Section Two*

3. Locate each of the following titles in the card catalog. Give as much information on each book (author, publisher, etc.) as you can find. (If these books are not available in your library, your teacher will suggest other titles to look up.)

   a. *The Intelligent Man's Guide to Science*

   _____

   _____

   b. *Beyond Earth: The Search for Extraterrestrial Life*

   _____

   _____

   c. *Colonies in Space: The Next Giant Step*

   _____

   _____

   d. *Drifting Continents, Shifting Seas*

   _____

   _____

2. Reference Books

Your library contains many kinds of reference books. You are already familiar with some, like dictionaries, encyclopedias, atlases, and almanacs. Reference books are usually placed together in a single part of the library. Here are some reference books with which you should be familiar:

a. **Encyclopedias** usually consist of many volumes, although one-volume encyclopedias also exist. An encyclopedia contains a short amount of information on almost any topic you can think of. When you don't know where to start on a research topic, try an encyclopedia. However, encyclopedias have their limitations. Since they discuss so many topics, they can't give much detail on any one. You should usually research other sources to get depth on a subject.

b. **Dictionaries** give the definitions of words. Many dictionaries provide other useful information, such as word origins, pronunciation, antonyms, synonyms, and alternative spellings.

c. **Atlases** give geographical information about a country or the world. They contain maps, population information, and other data about the places listed.

d. **Almanacs** are issued each year. They give current information on many different topics, such as election results, population figures, manufacturing data, and sports statistics.

e. There are many kinds of **science reference books** too. Ask your librarian to show you the ones your library has and to explain the kind of information in each.

Some practice exercises using reference books are found on Activity Page 8, pages 39-40.

ACTIVITY PAGE **8** USING REFERENCE BOOKS

1. *DIRECTIONS:* List the titles of the following reference books found in your library: (The answer might be "none.")

   a. A one-volume encyclopedia: _____

   b. One or more dictionaries: _____

   c. One or more almanacs: _____

   d. One or more atlases: _____

   e. One or more multi-volume encyclopedias: _____

   f. A book of mathematical tables: _____

   g. A book on scientific biographies: _____

   h. A book telling about chemicals: _____

   i. A book telling about stars: _____

   j. A book telling about rocks: _____

   k. A book telling about plants: _____

Library Skills 39

2. *DIRECTIONS:* Where would you find information about each of the following topics? Give the title of the reference book, the volume, and the page number. (There can be more than one answer.)

   a. The population of Grand Rapids, Michigan: _____

   b. The element xenon: _____

   c. viruses: _____

   d. The meaning of the word **xenophobia**: _____

   e. The process of making steel: _____

   f. United States exports of oil in 1981: _____

   g. Farm products that come from Georgia: _____

   h. A general description of mammals: _____

   i. The life history of Joseph Drew: _____

   j. The history of the Manhattan Project: _____

3. The Readers' Guide to Periodical Literature

Many times you will need very recent information. Books are usually not good for the latest information on a subject. It takes a year or more for a book to be written and published. The information it contains will always be a little out of date by the time it gets to the bookstore or the library. Magazines are better sources for current information.

The *Readers' Guide to Periodical Literature* is something like a card catalog for current magazines. The *Readers' Guide* comes out about every month. Then, at the end of the year, an annual edition is printed. Check the monthly edition for the very latest information. For information in magazines from a year ago or more, use the yearly edition.

Remember that the *Readers' Guide* is much like the card catalog. It has entries listed under topics, titles of articles, and authors. Suppose, for example, that you wanted to find an article you remember reading by Isaac Asimov on mushrooms. One way to find the article would be to look under **Asimov, Isaac** in the *Readers' Guide*. All of the articles written by this author in the last few months would be listed.

If the titles of the articles don't sound familiar, then look under the topic heading, **mushrooms**, to see if you can locate the article. If it appeared during the past few months, it would be listed here.

Once you've found the listing, what information will be given about the article? A sample page from the *Readers' Guide* is reproduced on page 42. Look at the article indicated within the box. Here is the information contained in the entry:

1. The subject of the article: Internal structure of the earth

2. The title of the article: Deep-earth-gas hypothesis

3. The authors of the article: T. Gold and S. Soter

4. The magazine in which it appeared: *Scientific American* (Each magazine has a special abbreviation. These abbreviations are explained at the front of the *Readers' Guide*.)

5. An indication of any visual material in the article: The abbreviations "il" and "map" tell that there are illustrations and maps in this article.

6. The volume of the magazine in which the article appeared: 242

7. The page numbers on which the article is found: 154-161

8. The date of the magazine: June 1980

9. The final note ("Discussion. 243:6+ D '80") tells you that someone responded to the original article in a later issue of the magazine. This could have been a "letter to the editor" or a short note about the original article. The response appeared in the December 1980 issue (volume 243) of the magazine, beginning on page 6. The "+" means that the response continued on a later page, but **not** on the following page (which would have been "7").

Any other symbols used in the *Readers' Guide* are explained in the first few pages of each issue.

Library Skills 41

READERS' GUIDE TO PERIODICAL LITERATURE*

EARTH
See also
Atmosphere
Creation

Age
See also
Geological time

Figure
Geoidal change and shore-level tilt along Holocene estuaries: Sénégal River area, West Africa. H. Faure and others. bibl f il map Science 210:421-3 O 24 '80

Internal structure
Deep-earth-gas hypothesis. T. Gold and S. Soter. il map Sci Am 242:154-61 Je '80; Discussion. 243:6+ D '80

Observations from space
Planet discovered! D. Lago. il Sci Digest 89:22 Ja/F '81

Ring system
End of a serene era [ring system cause of end of Eocene period] Sky & Tel 60:363-4 N '80

Rotation
See also
Foucault's pendulum

Shape
See Earth—Figure

Surface
See also
Continents
Earth's active crust:
Time: the fourth dimension. R. M. Pearl. Earth Sci 33:108 Summ '80

Temperature
See Earth temperature

EARTH movements. *See* Geology, Structural
EARTH Resources Company
Bidding up the price for Earth Resources. por Bus W p44-5 N 24 '80
Success proves costly at Earth Resources [proxy battle] por Bus W p36-7 N 10 '80

EARTH scientists
See also
Geologists
Petroleum engineers

EARTH temperature
Comparison of thermal observations of Mount St. Helens before and during the first week of the inital 1980 eruption. W. St Lawrence and others. bibl f il Science 209:1526-7 S 26 '80

EARTHQUAKE prediction
Hydrogen may flag fault movement [study of the Yamasaki Fault] Sci News 118:280 N 1 '80
Hydrogen release: new indicator of fault activity [measurements around the Yamasaki Fault] H. Wakita and others. bibl f il maps Science 210:188-90 O 10 '80
Predicting earthquakes: imperfect science. il U.S. News 89:9 D 8 '80
Predicting quakes: a shaky art. F. Golden and P. Faflick. map Time 116:69 D 8 '80
Stress anomaly accompanying the 1979 Lytle Creek earthquake: implications for earthquake prediction. B. R. Clark. bibl f il map Science 211:51-3 Ja 2 '81
Tectonics-torn Italy. map Sci News 118:376 D 13 '80

EARTHQUAKES
See also
Seismology
Deep-earth-gas hypothesis. T. Gold and S. Soter. il map Sci Am 242:154-61 Je '80; Discussion. 243:6+ D '80
What causes earthquakes [plate tectonics theory] J. K. Footlick and others. il map Newsweek 96:53-4 D 8 '80

Alaska
Rupture zones of great earthquakes in the Alaska-Aleutian arc, 1784 to 1980. L. R. Sykes and others. bibl f map Science 210:1343-5 D 19 '80

Algeria
Death is thick in the air. D. Baird. il map Macleans 93:33-4 O 27 '80
Killer quake at Al Asnam. B. Levin and E. Behr. il Newsweek 96:52 O 20 '80
Sifting through quake ruins. il Time 116:70 O 27 '80
Tragedy of El Asnam. il Time 116:46 O 20 '80

California
Stress anomaly accompanying the 1979 Lytle Creek earthquake: implications for earthquake prediction. B. R. Clark. bibl f il map Science 211:51-3 Ja 2 '81

Italy
Aftershocks may be political. R. Wright. il Macleans 93:4 D 15 '80
Black Sunday's terrible toll. T. Lurie. il maps Macleans 93:27-8 D 8 '80
Chaos of digging out. J. Nielsen and R. Flamini. il Time 116:47 D 15 '80
Death in the Mezzogiorno. J. Nielsen and others. il map Time 116:38-40+ D 8 '80
Earthquake. V. S. Kearney. America 143:431 D 27 '80
Ex-skyjacker who survived an earthquake himself rushes aid to Italy's homeless [work of R. Minichiello] L. Dodsworth. il pors People 14:46-7 D 15 '80
Predicting earthquakes: imperfect science [November 23 quake outside Naples] il U.S. News 89:9 D 8 '80
Quake: the end of the world. J. Brecher and others. il map Newsweek 96:50-2 D 8 '80
Tectonics-torn Italy. map Sci News 118:376 D 13 '80
Temblors in Rome. C. Marzani. Nation 231:629-30 D 13 '80

EARTHWORK
See also
Filling (earthwork)

EARTHWORM culture
Self-sufficient energy/livestock system [work of C. McCutcheon] il por Mother Earth News 66:132-4 N/D '80

EASON, Yla
Battle of the beauticians. il Black Enterprise 11:32-4+ N '80

EAST TIMOR. *See* Timor (island)

EASTABROOK, William
Food photography—an interview with Bill Eastabrook [interview by R. Long] il Peter Phot Mag 9:31+ N '80

EASTCOTT, John. *See* Momatiuk, Y. jt auth

EASTERBROOK, Gregg
English, si Spanish no. Wash M 12:37-44 D '80
How to end it: natural gas. Wash M 12:20-2+ O '80

EASTERLIN, Richard A.
Young will fare better economically [interview] por U.S. News 89:82 D 29 '80-Ja 5 '81

EASTERN Air Lines, Inc
Deregulation breeds an East Coast air war [New York Air and Eastern] il Bus W p30 Ja 26 '81
Eastern's fare play [coupon war with New York air] il Newsweek 97:66 Ja 26 '81

EASTERN Air Lines, Inc-Braniff Airways, inc merger. *See* Airlines—Acquisitions and mergers

EASTERN Mountain Sports Climbing School, North Conway, N.H. *See* Mountaineering—Study and teaching

EASTERN States petroleum industry. *See* Petroleum industry

EASTPORT, Me.
Bad idea that won't go away [proposed refinery of Pittston Company] M. Sullivan. il maps Nat Wildlife 19:41-3 D '80/Ja '81

EATING. *See* Gastronomy

EATING, Psychology of
Boys munch what they watch [study of TV commercials influencing eating preferences by D. Balfour Jeffrey] B. Rice. Psychol Today 14:27 D '80
Connection between sex and food. H. Zehner. il Mademoiselle 86:82-3 D '80
Why love makes us fat. B. J. Raphael. Glamour 78:248-9+ N '80

EATON, Charles Warren
Charles Warren Eaton. C. T. Clark. bibl il por Antiques 118:1242-50 D '80

EAVESDROPPING, Electronic. *See* Electronics in criminal investigation, espionage, etc.

EBER, Ronald. *See* Scharlin, P. J. jt auth

EBERHART, Jonathan
Sighting in on Saturn. il Sci News 118:282-3 N 1 '80

EBERSOLE, Christine
Glamour people. il pors Glamour 79:99+ Ja '81

EBERSTADT, Nicholas
Malthusians, Marxists, and missionaries. Society 17:29-35 S/O '80

EBERSTADT Asset Management, Inc. *See* Investment advisers

EBERSTADT Energy-Resources Fund. *See* Investment trusts

EBERT, Alan
(int) *See* Hepburn, Katharine. Katharine Hepburn speaks up

EBERT, Roger
Not being there. il Atlantic 246:88-91 D '80

EBONY (periodical)
Ebony years [reprint from November 1965 issue] L. Hughes. il Ebony 36:104-6+ N '80
35th anniversary special issue [with editorial comment by J. H. Johnson] il Ebony 36:6-7 N '80

EBY, Sheila Mary
Physical self-confidence: can you improve your agility? Vogue 170:210+ O '80

Readers' Guide to Periodical Literature, Copyright © 1981 by the H. W. Wilson Company. Material reproduced by permission of the publisher.

You can also use the *Readers' Guide* as you do the card catalog even if you don't have a specific article in mind. You might just want to do a report on "the earth," for example. In that case, you would begin by looking under this heading. As you can see, there are specific topics under the general heading "EARTH" to which you are referred. You might want to read about the "Age" of the earth, the earth's "Ring system," or some other aspect of the earth. Articles are also listed here by these sub-topics.

You may be referred to other headings for more information. For example, the first entry under "EARTH" is a "see also" reference. This means that you may be interested in related topics, such as "Atmosphere" or "Creation." There are "see also" references under sub-topics too. To what you are referred under the sub-topics of the earth's age and the earth's temperature? (Compare your answer with the one given on page 273.)

There is one problem with the *Readers' Guide*: there are thousands of magazines in publication, and the *Readers' Guide* can summarize only a few of them. There are other guides, indexes, and digests that do the same thing for special areas of interest. Your library, for example, may carry the *Education Index* or the *Book Review Digest*. If so, look at one or the other and see how it is like the *Readers' Guide*. Ask your librarian if there are other research aids like the *Readers' Guide* in your library. Then turn to Activity Page 9, pages 44-45, for some practice exercises on the use of the *Readers' Guide*. Lastly, complete Activity Page 10, page 46, which lists some typical errors found in references with a few ideas about finding the correct reference.

ACTIVITY PAGE 9   USING THE *READERS' GUIDE*

DIRECTIONS: Consult the most recent annual or monthly issue of the *Readers' Guide* to answer the following questions:

1. Find three articles on nuclear power plants. Write down the author, title, magazine, issue, date, pages, and any other information for these three articles.

    a. _____

    b. _____

    c. _____

2. Under what related headings could you look for information on **nuclear power plants**? _____

3. Find three articles on insecticides. Write down the author, title, magazine, issue, date, pages, and any other information for these three articles.

    a. _____

    b. _____

    c. _____

4. Under what related headings could you look for information on **insecticides**?

---

44   *Section Two*

5. Which of the following authors has written at least three articles on a scientific topic in the last year? For each person who has, list the titles of the articles, the magazines, volumes, pages, and any other information.

Philip Abelson _____

_____

Paul Ehrlich _____

_____

Kendrick Fraser _____

_____

Constance Holden _____

_____

Lawrence Lessing _____

_____

ACTIVITY PAGE 10   CHECKING FALSE REFERENCES

DIRECTIONS: Sometimes the references you find contain errors—it's easy to get a book title confused, an author's name wrong, or an incorrect volume, date, or page number. Suppose you find that each of the following references is wrong. Where else would you look in order to check out the incorrect reference? (We've given some hints for a few of these.)

1. Incorrect reference:

    vol. IV, p. 363

    Also look under:

    vol. VI, p. 363

    vol. IV, p. 636

2. Incorrect reference:

    vol. XVI, p. 447

    Also look under:

3. Incorrect reference:

    James Williams, *Biography of the Earth.*

    Also look under:

4. Incorrect reference:
    Ref.
    Z321
    .Y194
    1969

    Also look under:

    Ref.   Z123   .Y14   1969

    Ref.   Z321   .Y41   1969

5. Incorrect reference:

    Science, **223**, 615, January 5, 1981

    Also look under:

6. Incorrect reference

    Anatomy and Physiology of Cats, P. J. Morris

    Also look under:

    Anatomy and Physiology of Cats, P. J. Maurice

46   Section Two

Section three

Writing Reports

Record-keeping is an important part of any scientific research. It doesn't do much good to design wonderful experiments and carry them out with great skill unless there is a good record of that research. Being able to write laboratory reports is, therefore, another important scientific skill.

There are actually two parts to this skill. The first is the actual recording of data taken in the laboratory. The second is the formal report of the research. We'll consider these one at a time.

Most scientists have notebooks with them at all times in the laboratory. These provide a place to record everything of importance about research: the equipment and materials used, the procedures carried out, and the results observed in the experiment. The exact method by which this is done is not important. Each scientist has a system that works best for him or her. The important thing is to have a written record that can be understood and used later.

Think back on experiments that you have done in this course or at some other time in your life. What kind of information would you have recorded (or did you record) about those experiments? Make a list in the space provided below. We'll help you get started by showing the kind of responses you might give.

Data Recorded in Lab:

1. Temperature of water at two minute intervals.

2. Time required for a certain chemical solution to change color.

3. Weight of a piece of copper.

4. Size of a plant seedling on ten consecutive days.

5. Weight of a hamster during each of the days in a month that it was being studied.

6.

7.

8.

9.

10.

11.

12.

The notes taken in a laboratory are mainly for **your** benefit. After an experiment has been completed, you will have to write another kind of report: One that will tell other people about your research. This is a formal laboratory report. Since nearly all scientists have to write formal reports, there are some standard forms for them. You might be interested in looking at some scientific journals to see what a "real" scientific report looks like. They will be somewhat different in the field of biology, chemistry, physics, geology, astronomy, and other sciences.

The format we describe below is a little artificial. Most scientists would not write a formal report like the one you will (on Activity Page 11). Why use it at all, then? The reason is simple. The report form we show here will help you to recognize and think about the **elements** that should appear in any formal report. If and when you become a great nuclear physicist, you won't turn in laboratory reports with sections headed "Purpose," "Materials," "Procedures," "Observations," and so forth. However, the article you write about your research **will** contain these kinds of information.

Writing a laboratory report is not like writing a short story or novel. You don't have to worry about "entertaining" anyone. What you **do** have to think about is providing a clear, accurate, brief description of your work. The outline we suggest below will do that. It is not the **only** way to write a laboratory report, and your teacher may prefer to have you use another **model**.

Parts of a Formal Laboratory Report

1. The TITLE should give a brief, precise description of what your research is about.

2. The PURPOSE should state in a few sentences what the main objective(s) of the experiments was (or were).

3. A DIAGRAM (or set of diagrams) may be included to show the apparatus used in the experiment.

4. A list of MATERIALS tells the name of the equipment and materials (chemicals, organisms, rocks, or other substances) used in the experiment. Quantities used should also be listed.

5. The PROCEDURE section describes, step by step, the **things you did** in carrying out the experiment.

6. The section on OBSERVATIONS mentions the **things you saw, smelled, tasted, felt, or heard** in the experiment. You should include everything and anything that might have been important, even if it was not directly related to the primary objective of the experiment. This is a critical section of the report since it really summarizes the results of your research.

7. The section called CONCLUSIONS is the place in which you can make some inferences about the results of the experiment. This includes NOT what you have done or what you have observed, but **how you interpret** your observations. It is often useful to try drawing at least one conclusion for each observation you've made. This isn't always possible or even useful, but thinking along these lines will help you decide whether an observation is important or not.

8. The ERRORS section provides you with an opportunity to think about mistakes that were made in the experiment. Some of these, of course, will be **your** errors—human errors. Others will be caused by equipment or conditions beyond your control—inherent errors. Try to think of all possible kinds, sources, and amounts of errors in your work. Then, try to mention ways in which such errors might be avoided in the future.

Activity Pages 11 and 12, pages 50-51, are set up according to the above outline. Use them to report the results of an experiment you have done in this class, or one your teacher assigns to you. If you need more space, use additional sheets of paper.

ACTIVITY PAGE 11 WRITING A FORMAL LABORATORY REPORT–I

Title:

Purpose:

Diagram:

Materials:

Procedure:

Observations:

Conclusions:

Errors:

ACTIVITY PAGE 12 — WRITING A FORMAL LABORATORY REPORT–II

Title:

Purpose:

Diagram:

Materials:

Procedure:

Observations:

Conclusions:

Errors:

Section four

Math Skills with Hand Calculators

Many kinds of hand calculators are available today. The instructions for working with each kind are different from each other. If you own a hand calculator, refer to the instructions that came with it to answer the following questions. When you have completed these questions, turn to Activity Page 13, page 57. There you will find practice problems that can be solved with your hand calculator.

1. Answer each of the following questions for your own calculator.

   a. How do you turn the calculator on?

   b. How do you turn the calculator off?

   c. If your calculator has a memory function, how do you clear it?

   d. If your calculator has a memory function, how do you display it?

   e. How do you correct an incorrectly entered number?

   f. How do you know when the batteries are running low on your calculator?

2. Write down the steps you must follow in order to perform each of the following operations. The first step in every case, of course, is to turn the calculator on. We have shown the answer for the first operation as an example. Does **your** calculator work in exactly the same way for addition?

   Note: Operations 7-12 require use of a calculator with a memory function. If you do not have access to one, you will have to skip to Operation 13.

   Operation 1:   Addition: 45 + 83
   1. Enter first number: push "4" button, then "5" button.
   2. Push "+" key.
   3. Enter second number: push "8" button, then "3" button.
   4. Push "=" key.
   5. Read answer shown on display.

Math Skills with Hand Calculators 53

Operation 2:* Subtraction: 769 − 482

Operation 3: Multiplication: 4.58 x 39.4

Operation 4: Division: 45.9 ÷ 3.57

Operation 5: Finding a square: $(45.8)^2$

Operation 6: Finding a square root: $\sqrt{59.43}$

Operation 7: Adding a number to memory: Add 87.43 to memory.

Operation 8: Subtracting a number from memory: Place 609.4 in memory; then subtract 487.99 from memory.

Operation 9: Subtract a number in memory from some other number: Place 58.3 in memory; then subtract this number from 104.2.

Operation 10: Multiplying a number times something stored in memory: Place 3.4 in memory; then multiply this by 14.0.

Operation 11: Divide a number by a number in memory: Place 5.87 in memory; then divide 81.04 by memory.

---

*Compare your answers for Operations 2-14 with those given in the answer section.

Operation 12: Divide a number in memory by some other number: Place 14.58 in memory; then divide this by 8.9.

Operation 13: Find the percentage of a number: Find 4.5% of 1300.

Operation 14: Multiply a number by pi (π): Find 4.5 π.

3. Many problems in science require that you carry out a series of operations. An example is the problem shown here:

$$V = 35 \times \frac{760}{679} \times \frac{275}{273}$$

You may or may not have to use memory storage for some of these problems. If your calculator has no memory, write down intermediary steps on a piece of paper as a form of memory storage. Your instruction booklet may have some suggestions for solving problems like these. It will also help you to review some simple mathematical ideas. They are listed below.

a. Always simplify expressions within parentheses first.

Example: $(4.5)^2 + 3.8$

Solution:

Simplify within parentheses first:

$(4.5)^2 + 3.8 = 20.25 + 3.8$

Then complete other operations:

$20.25 + 3.8 = 24.05$

b. In expressions that do not contain parentheses, always do multiplication and division before addition and subtraction.

Example: $3 + 8 \times 4 - \frac{18}{4}$

Solution:

1. Do multiplication and division first:

   $3 + 8 \times 4 - 18/4 = 3 + 32 - 4.5$

2. Then do addition and subtraction:

   $3 + 32 - 4.5 = 35 - 4.5 = 30.5$

Math Skills with Hand Calculators

c. Problems involving multiplication and division can be arranged in a variety of ways.

Example: $V = 35 \times \dfrac{760}{679} \times \dfrac{275}{273}$

Solution:

For convenience of working with a calculator, this problem can be rearranged in a number of ways. For example:

1. Multiply 35 x 760
2. Divide by 679
3. Multiply by 275
4. Divide by 273

Or

1. Multiply 679 x 273
2. Store answer in memory
3. Multiply 35 x 760 x 275
4. Divide answer by memory

Or

1. Multiply 35 x 760 x 275
2. Divide answer by 679
3. Divide answer by 273

Now turn to Activity Pages 13 and 14, pages 57-58, for some practice exercises with a hand calculator.

ACTIVITY PAGE **13** WORKING WITH A HAND CALCULATOR—I

DIRECTIONS: Use a hand calculator to find the answer to each of the following problems. In problems 5-14, write down the steps you performed in order to get the answer. Problems that require memory storage are indicated with an asterisk. If your calculator has no memory, write down intermediary steps on a piece of paper as a form of memory storage.

1. 583 + 422 = _____

2. 6243 − 5995 = _____

3. 8.34 x 0.157 = _____

4. 16.1 ÷ 0.0482 = _____

5. $\dfrac{3}{4} \times \dfrac{5}{8} =$ _____

6. $\dfrac{2}{7} \times 0.439 =$ _____

7. $\dfrac{3.2 \times 4.1 \times 0.9}{8.3 \times 5.5} =$ _____

8. $\dfrac{63}{4} \times \dfrac{125}{439} \times \dfrac{8}{9} =$ _____

9. $\dfrac{\sqrt{3}}{4} =$ _____

10. $(3 + 6.4)^2 =$ _____

11.* $\dfrac{4 \times \sqrt{7}}{9} =$ _____

12.* $\dfrac{(3.3)^2}{\sqrt{7}} =$ _____

13. $\dfrac{-3.85}{14} =$ _____

14.* 3 (4.2) + 3 (8.6) + 3 (6.5) + 3 (1.58) = _____

Note: If your calculator has no square root function, you may have to omit these problems. However, some calculators lacking a square root function may be able to do a square root problem with this procedure: Enter number; enter ÷, enter =.

Math Skills with Hand Calculators 57

ACTIVITY PAGE **14** WORKING WITH A HAND CALCULATOR–II

DIRECTIONS: Use a hand calculator to find the answer to each of the following problems. In problems 5-14, write down the steps you performed in order to get the answer. Problems that require memory storage are indicated with an asterisk. If your calculator has no memory, write down intermediary steps on a piece of paper as a form of memory storage.

1. $4.362 + 18.954 =$ _____

2. $16.42 - 38.855 =$ _____

3. $483 \times 1.569 =$ _____

4. $3.87 \div 142.8 =$ _____

5. $\dfrac{6}{7} \times \dfrac{2}{5} \times \dfrac{3}{4} =$ _____

6. $\dfrac{14}{17} \times 3.085 =$ _____

7. $\dfrac{14.2 \times 6.8 \times 130.4}{28 \times 1.73} =$ _____

8. $\dfrac{5.3\pi}{4} =$ _____

9. $26.8\pi^2 =$ _____

10.* $\sqrt{\dfrac{8.4}{7.3}} =$ _____

11.* $7.6 + 3(1.4) + \dfrac{8.6 - 5}{2.4} =$ _____

12. $\dfrac{(6.42)^3}{3.8} =$ _____

13.* $-2.8\sqrt{13.5} =$ _____

14.* $5.5\pi + 4.1(3.6)^2 + \dfrac{3}{8} =$ _____

Note: If your calculator has no square root function, you may have to omit these problems. However, some calculators lacking a square root function may be able to do a square root problem with this procedure: Enter number; enter ÷; enter =.

58 *Section Four*

Section five

Math Skills with Measurement

> I often say that when you can measure what you are speaking about, and express it in numbers, you know something about it; but when you cannot express it in numbers, your knowledge is of a meager and unsatisfactory kind; it may be the beginning of knowledge, but you have scarcely, in your thoughts, advanced to the stage of **Science**, whatever the matter may be.

These words were written by one of the great physicists of the nineteenth century, William Thompson, Lord Kelvin. He was expressing an idea that most scientists would agree with: the skill of measuring is at the very heart of scientific research. Some people would even argue that the major difference between science and other kinds of study is the skill of measurement. You can easily see how important this section is, then.

The section is divided into five parts, as follows:

1. Measuring length
2. Measuring weight
3. Measuring volume
4. Measuring temperature
5. Derived measurements: density

1. Measuring Length

For most people, measuring length is no problem. We have all had experience in measuring a piece of cloth, finding the length of a room, or measuring our own height, for example. It seems like a simple skill: place a measuring stick next to the thing to be measured. Then read off the length.

That's just about correct; finding a length really is a simple matter. Since it **is** so simple. we will use the skill to demonstrate some ideas about measuring you may not have thought about. Let's start with a simple exercise.

a. **Uncertainty of a Measurement**

On the next page, we've constructed three different measuring devices for you. The top one is a metric ruler that measures in decimeters. The middle one is accurate to a centimeter. The bottom one can be read to a millimeter. Carefully cut out or trace these three rulers. Then use the first one (the decimeter ruler) to find the length of the line below. Write down the answer as exactly as you can here. _____

_____

Your answer is probably somewhere between 1 and 2 decimeters. An answer of 1.3 or 1.4 dm would probably be reasonable for the length. Let's think about that answer for a moment. For our discussion, we'll assume you wrote down 1.4 dm. Notice that there are two digits in the measurement, a "1" and a "4." (We can ignore the decimal point for now.) There is something **very different** about these two digits (**besides** the fact that one is a "1" and the other is a "4"!) How sure are you that the first digit really is a "1" and not a "2" or "3" or "4" or some other digit? Actually, you can be very certain about the "1." The measuring device you used has a "1" marking and a "2" marking. The line is longer than 1 dm, but shorter than 2. There is no question about that.

Is that also true of the "4"? No, it is not! There are no ".1," ".2," ".3," ".4," ".5" markings, and so forth, on this metric ruler. If you said "4" for the second digit (or "3" or "5"), that was only a guess. It was a good guess—you probably didn't say "7" or "8" or "9"—but it was still a guess.

However, this measurement can't be a very good one if it contains some guessing in it, right? Wrong! What would you write down if you had **not** guessed? Simply "1 dm"? That wouldn't be very smart. It's very clear that the line is not 1 dm; it's more than that. In fact, by making your guess—remember, it was a good guess—you expressed the length of this line as accurately as you possibly could. You made the very best possible report of this length that you knew how. In fact, a measurement of 1.4 dm (or 1.3 dm or 1.5 dm) is a good result for this problem.

Now take the second ruler you cut out (the centimeter ruler) and repeat this process. Write down the length of the same line, this time by measuring with the centimeter ruler:

_____ .

Now look back at the answer you've just written. Does it contain any digits that you guessed? Does it contain any digits you know for sure? In the space below, write down the **known** digits and the **estimated** (guessed) digits. Tell how you know whether a digit is known or estimated.

  Known digits:

  because:

  Estimated digits:

  because:

Math Skills with Measurement 61

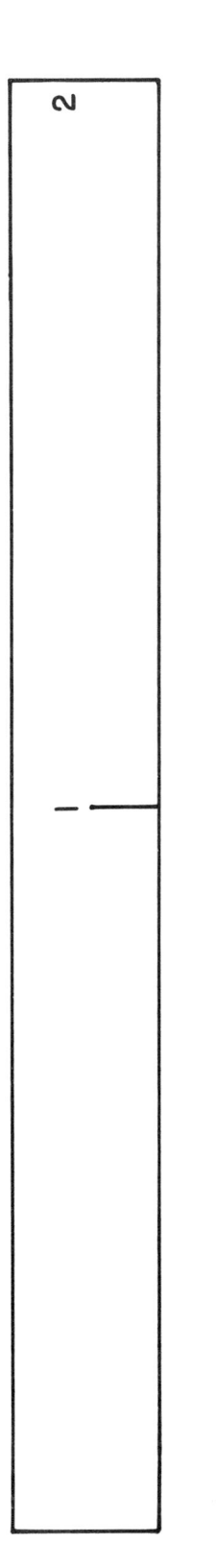

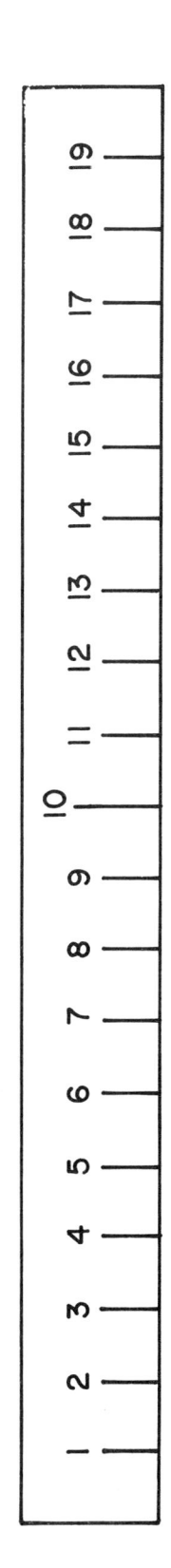

Finally, take the third ruler (the millimeter ruler) and measure the line a third time. Write down the length and the other information asked for below:

Length (with millimeter ruler): _____

Known digits:

    because:

Estimated digits:

    because:

Suppose you could get better and better rulers. Would there ever be a time when there would be **no** estimated digit? Write down your answer and compare it with the one given.

Suppose you measured a line that seemed to be **exactly** 1.54 cm long. That is, the end of the line came **exactly** to the 0.04 cm mark on your ruler. Would there be any estimated digit in this measurement? Write down your answer before checking it.

When you have finished this exercise, you will understand a basic rule about making measurements:

EVERY GOOD MEASUREMENT CONTAINS ONE—AND ONLY ONE—UNCERTAIN (ESTIMATED) DIGIT.

Notice the extra phrase "... and only one" in this rule. Why would it not be good to have two estimated digits? If one estimated digit makes for a good measurement, why wouldn't two make it twice as good? Write down your answers to these questions before comparing with the one given.

The rule we've described here came from making length measurements, but the idea applies to other kinds of measurements, too: volume, temperature, weight, and time, for example. The rule comes from the fact that **every measuring device we use has a certain built-in limitation to it.** We could measure only so precisely with the decimeter ruler because it was

Math Skills with Measurement

marked off ("graduated") to only a certain extent. We could do better with the centimeter ruler because it was graduated more precisely. We could do even better with the millimeter ruler because its smallest units were even more precise.

As you go on to measuring other qualities, the first step will always be to look at the measuring device you have to work with. In finding the volume of a liquid, for example, look first at the graduated cylinder you have to work with. If the smallest units on the cylinder are 0.1 ml, that tells what the limitation is with this measuring device. You can read precisely ("for sure") to tenths of a milliliter, but you can estimate one digit beyond that, to 0.01 milliliter in this case. ALWAYS keep in mind the uncertainty of a measurement when you are weighing, finding temperatures, timing an event, or taking any other kind of measurement.

b. Errors of Measurement

Look back at the best measurement you were able to make for the line on page 60. How "good" is that measurement? Is it perfect? We already know that **that** isn't the case. Since every measurement contains an estimated digit, there is at least **some** uncertainty in the result we write down. Are there any other reasons for thinking the measurement you wrote down might **not** be totally correct? See if you can think of any other **possible sources of error** in your measurement. Write down anything you can think of in the space provided below. Do this before going on with your reading.

Some possible sources of error might be:

If you look back at the list of errors you've just made, you'll probably find they are of two kinds. Some are errors that you, the measurer, might make. For example, maybe you didn't line the ruler up exactly with both ends of the line you were measuring. Also, you might have nudged the ruler as you were making the measurement. Finally, you might not have looked straight down on the line while you were measuring it. Your eyes might have been to one side or the other of the end of the ruler. Errors like these—called human errors—**can** be prevented if a person is very, very careful while making a measurement.

There are other kinds of errors, too. For example, was the "1 dm" marking on the ruler you used **really** and **exactly** 1.00000 decimeters long? Or could it have been a little more or less than exactly 1.00000 decimeters? You really don't know that. Unless you have some perfect measuring device of your own, there's no way you can check to see. You have to believe in the ruler-maker that the first section of the ruler is really 1.00000 dm. This is an error over which you have no control. No matter how carefully you measure, any error in the measuring device will still cause some error in the final result you write down. Errors of this kind are called **inherent errors**. Go back to the list you made on page 64 and tell which ones are human errors and which are inherent errors.

Now we can summarize the special ideas about measurement we have introduced in this section.

1. Every measurement that's made will contain some errors in it. Some of these are human errors, which can be reduced by being very careful. Others are inherent errors that cannot be eliminated, no matter how carefully you work.

2. The quality of a measurement is limited by the device you have to measure with. You can never get a **better** answer than your measuring device allows you.

3. Points 1 and 2 demonstrate that every measurement contains some uncertainty. A really good measurement contains some known (certain) digits and **one** estimated (uncertain) digit.

These points should be kept in mind as you continue with the following exercises on measuring. Think about them anytime you have to make a measurement of **any** kind. You are now ready to try the exercises on measuring length on Activity Page 15, page 66.

ACTIVITY PAGE **15** MEASURING LENGTH

DIRECTIONS: Measure the length of each item listed below. Before you begin measuring, decide how precisely your measuring device reads. Write that answer in the space provided. Then, for each measurement of length, put a check (✓) over the estimated digits in your result.

1. Precision # (smallest unit) of your measuring device: _____

2. Find the length of each of the following:

   a. Length of this page: _____

   b. Width of this page: _____

   c. Length of the lines at the right:

   A: _____ B: _____ C: _____

   D: _____ E: _____ F: _____

   d. Your height: _____

   e. Height of your teacher's desk: _____

   f. Thickness of your science book: _____

3. Some additional measuring problems:

   a. Find the circumference of any water glass: _____

   b. Find the thickness of this page: _____

   c. Find the height of your school building: _____

   d. Find the distance from your school to the ocean or Great Lake nearest you: _____

   e. Find the height of a MacDonald's Golden Arch: _____

Section Five

2. Measuring Weight

Measuring weights is another skill you might already know. Most of us have weighed ourselves, a bag of candy, or some pieces of fruit, for example. Weighings in science, however, are usually much more exact than weighings we do in everyday life. The balances in your science laboratory may be of two general types: "rough" balances and "analytical" balances. Both kinds work on the same general principle, but the exact instructions for using them will differ. Since there are so many different models of balances, we will not try to explain the operation of a balance. Instead, your instructor will show you how to use the ones in your classroom. There are some general rules of weighing that should be followed with any balance, however. The most important of these include the following:

1. The object to be weighed is always placed on the left pan of any double-pan balance.

2. Chemicals should never be placed directly on the pan of a balance. Instead, use a small square of paper or glass container in which to place the chemical during weighing.

3. Never weigh an object that is warm or hot.

4. Always be sure that the balance is clean before you begin weighing and again after you have completed the weighing.

After your instructor's explanation, turn to Activity Page 16, page 68, and do the weighing exercises given there.

ACTIVITY PAGE 16 — MEASURING WEIGHT

DIRECTIONS: Find the weight of each item listed below. Before you begin measuring, decide how precisely your measuring device reads. Write that answer in the space provided. Then, for each measurement of weight, put a check (✓) over the estimated digit in your result.

1. Precision # (smallest unit) of your balance: _____

2. Find the weight of each of the following:

   a. A U.S. or Canadian nickel (are they the same?): _____

   b. A glass beaker: _____

   c. Your hand calculator: _____

   d. A piece of fruit (apple, orange, etc.): _____

   e. A 100 g weight (Does it really weigh 100.0 g?): _____

   f. Any object(s) given to you by your instructor (record object and weight):

   1. _____ _____   *3.* _____ _____

   2. _____ _____   *4.* _____ _____

3. Here are some additional weighing problems:

   a. 50 ml of water: _____

   b. One page of your *Basic Skills in Science* text: _____

   c. $100 in pennies: _____

   d. The weight of a stamp on a postcard: _____

68 *Section Five*

3. Measuring Volume

Finding the volume of a substance can be more complicated than any of the measuring you've done so far. In the first place, the procedure can differ depending on whether you have a solid or a liquid. Then, it makes a difference what kind of solid you're working with. We'll discuss these possibilities one at a time.

a. Finding the Volume of a Liquid

A number of devices can be used to find the volume of a liquid. Your instructor will show you the ones you have to work with. These may include any or all of the ones shown below and on page 71. Notice that each one contains a tube that is marked off (the scientific term is "graduated") in some unit.

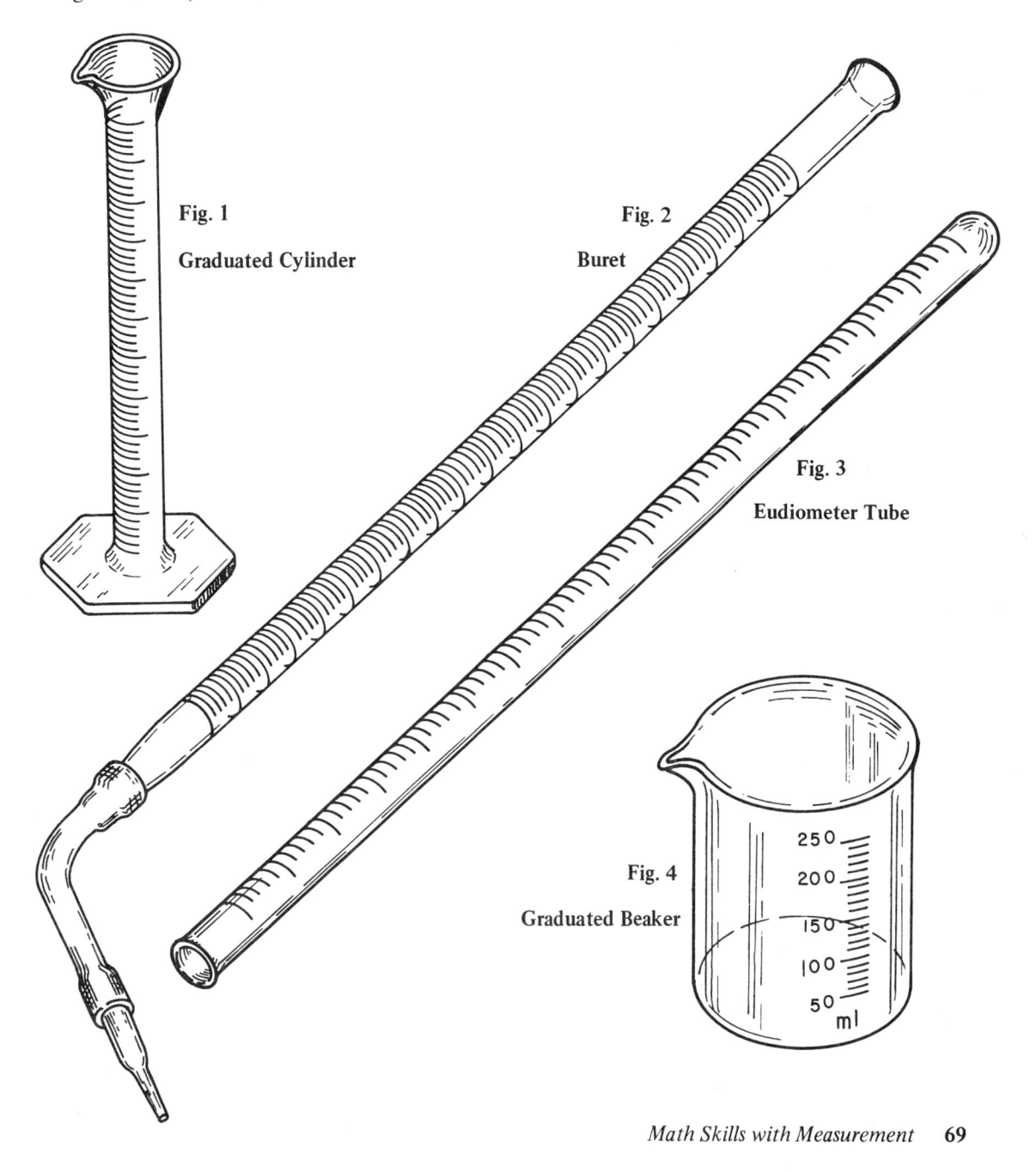

Fig. 1

Graduated Cylinder

Fig. 2

Buret

Fig. 3

Eudiometer Tube

Fig. 4

Graduated Beaker

Math Skills with Measurement 69

The unit could be milliliters, ("ml"), cubic centimeters, ("cm^3" or "cc"), tenths of a milliliter (or cubic centimeter), or some other unit. Look carefully at this smallest unit before you do anything else.

The graduated cylinder is the most common device for measuring the volume of liquids. So that's what we'll use for the rest of this explanation. Place enough water in your graduated cylinder to make it about a third full. Then, try to read the volume of water. Write down your answer here: _____ .

Before you go very far with this exercise, you'll notice a small problem. The water in the graduated cylinder does not have a flat surface, like Fig. 5 (page 71). Instead, the surface of the water is curved, as shown in Fig. 6 (page 71). This curved surface is called the **meniscus** of the liquid. Of course, it will make a difference as to whether you read the top of the meniscus or the bottom. By common agreement, scientists read the lower part of the meniscus when finding the volume of water and most other liquids. That means you should look along the dotted line shown in Fig. 7 (page 71). Do that and see if you are still satisfied with the answer you wrote above. If not, put down your new measurement here: _____ .

There are some special suggestions for measuring liquid volumes. Here are three of them:

1. Keep your eye on the same level as the bottom of the meniscus when you read the graduated cylinder. Do not look down or up at it.

2. Place the graduated cylinder on a flat surface when you read the volume.

3. Place a white sheet of paper behind the graduated cylinder as you read the volume.

b. Finding the Volume of a Solid

The volume of a **regular** solid can be found in two ways. A **regular** solid is one that has a definite geometric shape: a cube, pyramid, sphere, or cone, for example. Some drawings of regular solids are shown in Fig. 8 (page 72). The volume of any regular solid can be calculated mathematically by using a geometric formula. The formula used for each solid is written below its name in Fig. 8. (Compare your answers with those given in the answer section.)

To determine the volume using the formula:

1. Find all the length measurements required by the formula.

   What measurements would you need to find the volume of:

   a. a cube? _____

   b. a sphere? _____

   c. a rectangular parallelepiped? _____

   d. a cylinder? _____

2. Then, substitute these numbers in the correct formula.

3. The volume can then be found mathematically.

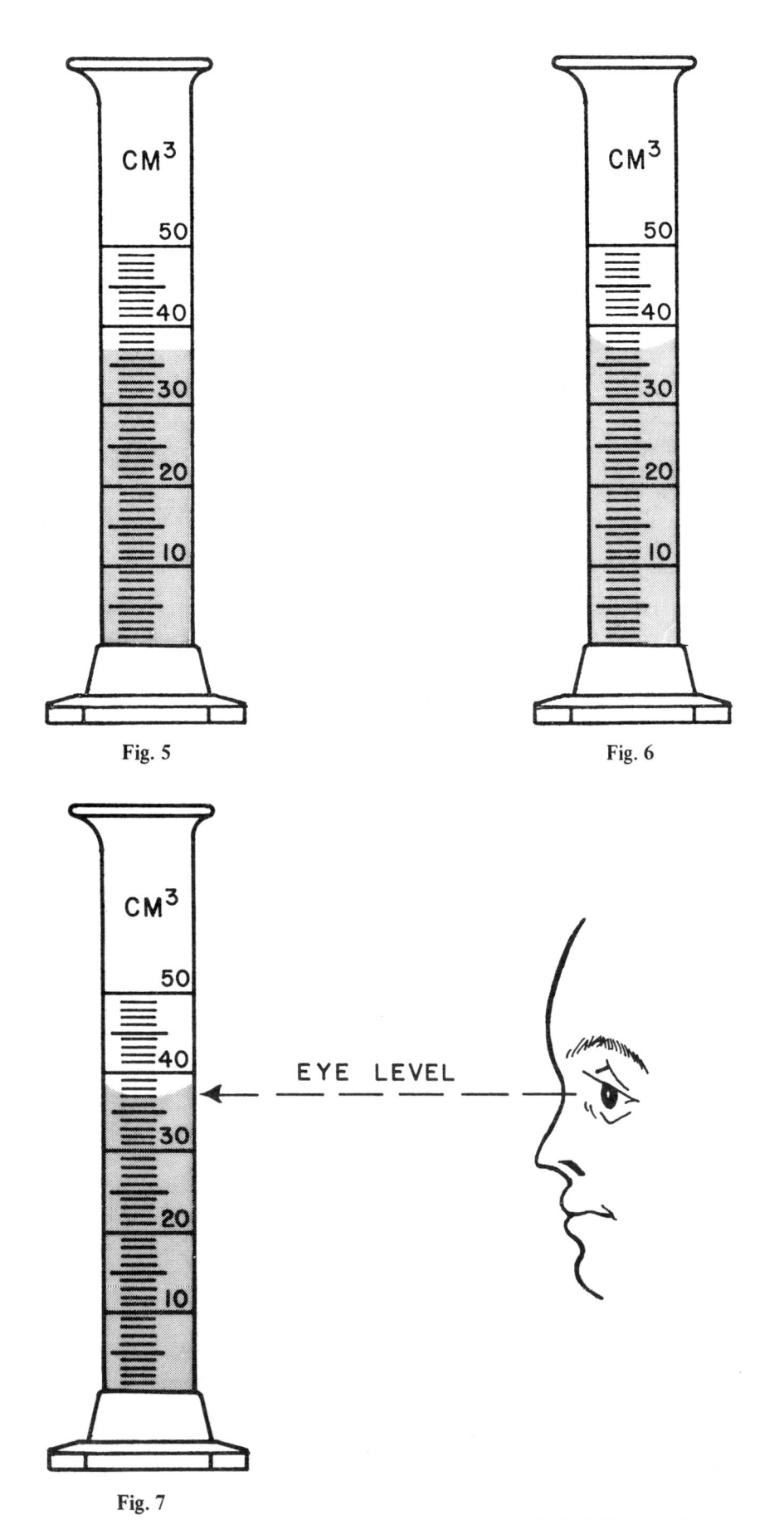

Fig. 5

Fig. 6

Fig. 7 ← EYE LEVEL

Math Skills with Measurement 71

CUBE
$V = Bh$

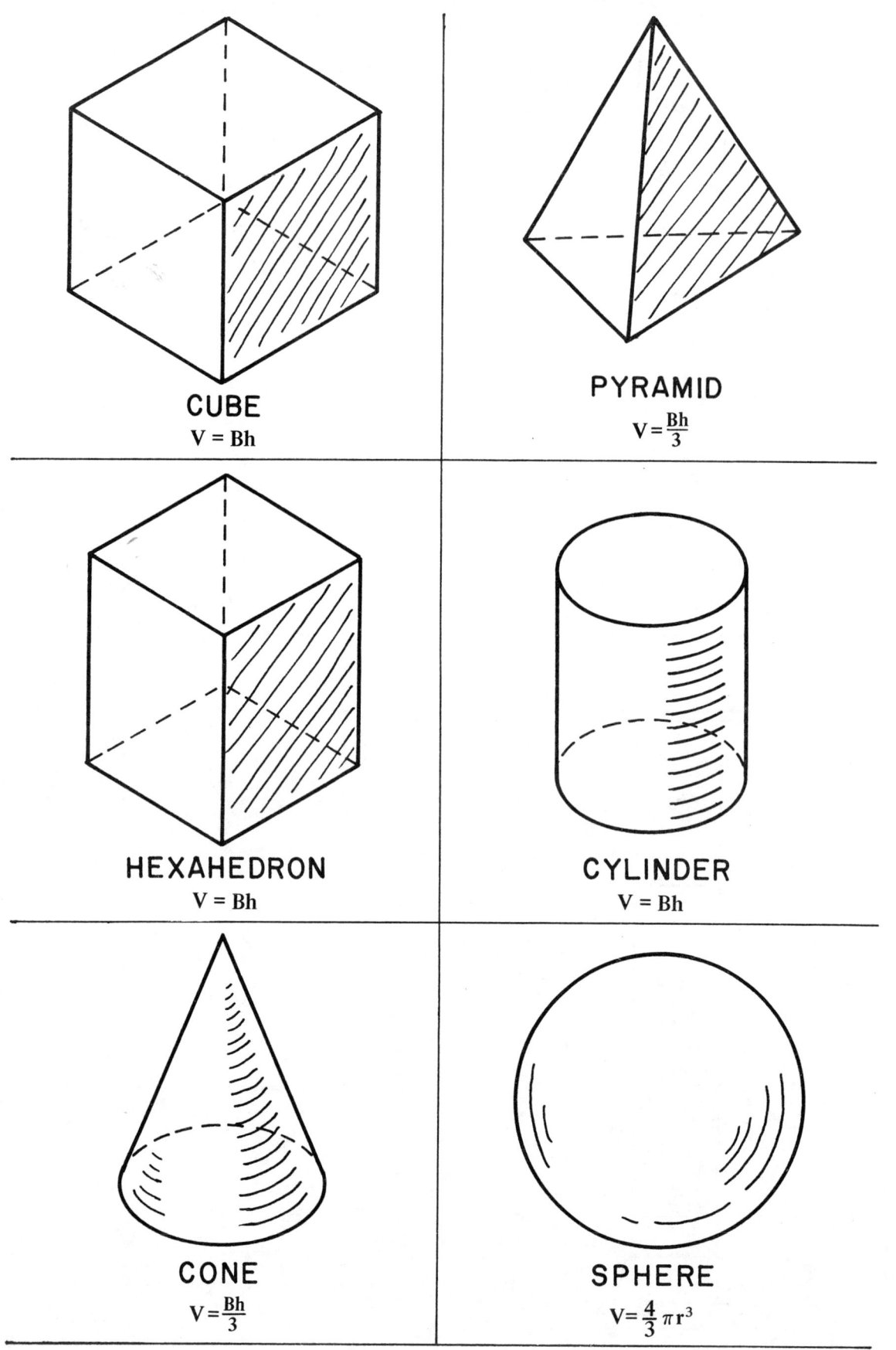

PYRAMID
$V = \dfrac{Bh}{3}$

HEXAHEDRON
$V = Bh$

CYLINDER
$V = Bh$

CONE
$V = \dfrac{Bh}{3}$

SPHERE
$V = \dfrac{4}{3}\pi r^3$

Fig. 8　Regular solids

The practice problems below contain the length measurements you need to determine the volume of each solid. Calculate the volume for each before checking your answers.

a. Cube   length of one side: 3.54 cm

b. Cylinder   radius of one end: 2.8 cm
                  length: 14.5 cm

c. Sphere   diameter: 47.8 cm

d. Rectangular   length: 8.42 cm
   parallelepiped: width: 3.24 cm
                  height: 5.90 cm

e. Cone: radius of base: 46.8 cm
                  height: 70.1 cm

A second method of finding the volume of a solid is by water displacement. This method works for **any** solid, whether it is a regular solid or not. The steps to follow in this procedure are these:

a. Find a graduated cylinder that is large enough to place the solid into.

b. Add water to the cylinder. Use enough water so that the solid object will be covered when it is added later.

c. Read, as accurately as possible, the volume of water in the graduated cylinder.

d. Add the solid object to the water in the graduated cylinder.

e. Read the new level of water in the graduated cylinder.

f. Find the volume of the solid by subtraction:

   Final level of water in graduated cylinder: _____

   − Original level of water in graduated cylinder: _____

   = Volume of solid: _____

(Can you think of any solids for which this method will not work? Check your answer against the one given.)

Activity Page 17, page 74, contains a number of exercises that will help you test your skill of finding volumes of both regular and irregular solids.

ACTIVITY PAGE **17** MEASURING VOLUME

DIRECTIONS: Find the volume of each item listed below. Before you begin measuring, decide how precisely your measuring device reads. Write that answer in the space provided. Then, for each measurement of volume, put a check (✓) over the estimated digit in your result.

1. Precision # (smallest unit) of your measuring device: _____

2. Find the volume of each of the following objects given you by your instructor (record object and volume):

   a. _____ _____   d. _____ _____

   b. _____ _____   e. _____ _____

   c. _____ _____   f. _____ _____

3. Extra problems:

   a. One drop of water: _____

   b. Volume of any water pipe in your science classroom: _____

   c. Volume of mercury in your thermometer: _____

74 *Section Five*

4. Measuring Temperature

Carefully examine the thermometer your instructor gives you. Decide how accurately you can measure temperatures with it. Will it read to one degree Celsius? To 0.5°C? To 0.2°C? To 0.1°C? To 0.05°C? Record the smallest unit shown on this thermometer in this space _____ .

To practice using the thermometer, set up a beaker of ice water, as shown in Figure 9, below. Be sure that everything is firmly in place before starting any heating. Have your instructor check your apparatus and sign in this space: _____ . That will tell you that you may begin heating.

Place about a half cup of ice and about 50 ml of water in the beaker. Heat the bottom of the beaker with a moderate flame. Record the temperature at the end of every minute on the chart on Activity Page 18, page 76.

When the ice is completely melted, arrange the flame so that the temperature rises about 2°C every thirty seconds. Continue to record the time and temperature every minute for an additional five minutes. Your teacher may ask you to graph the results you obtain.

In all of your time and temperature measurements, remember to read your watch and your thermometer as accurately as you can!

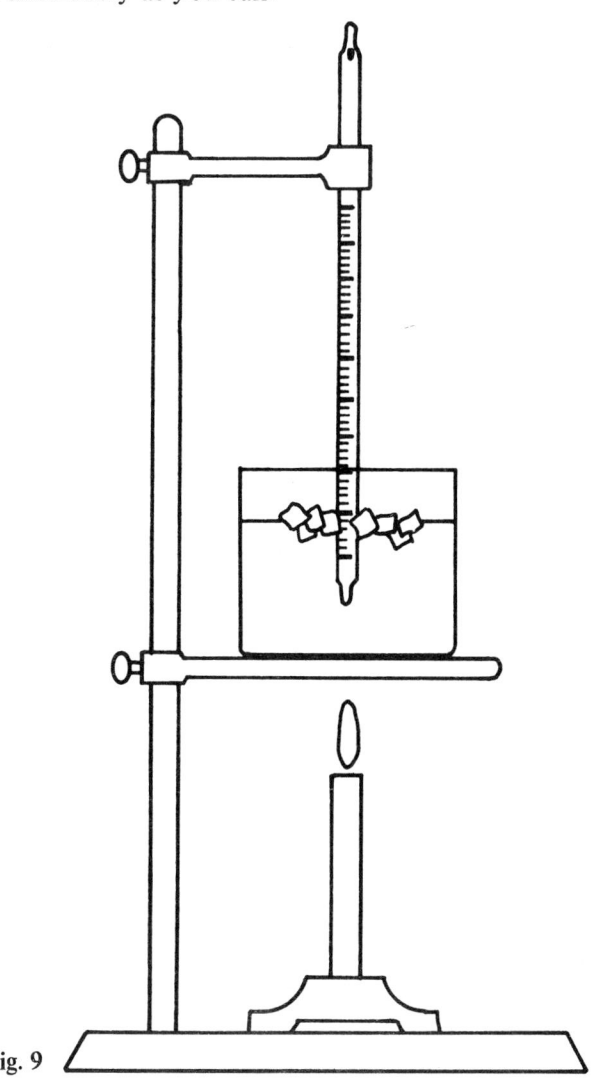

Fig. 9

Math Skills with Measurement

ACTIVITY PAGE 18 MEASURING TEMPERATURE

DIRECTIONS: In the space provided below, record the results of your experiment on heating of water.

DATA

Time	Temperature	Time	Temperature	Time	Temperature

Graph of results:

Temperature

Time

5. Derived Measurements: Density

A **derived measurement** is one that depends on other measurements and is not a basic quantity itself. For example, volume is really a derived measurement. The volume of a cube is determined by the length of the sides of the cube. The volume of a sphere depends upon the radius of the sphere.

Speed is another derived measurement. In order to find the speed of an object, you have to know two other measurements first. What are they? Write your answer here before comparing it with the answer given.

Density is still another derived measurement. Density is defined as the weight of a unit volume of something. The word "unit" means "one" of something. So density is the weight of one cubic centimeter, one milliliter, one liter, etc. of something. The density of water, for example, is the weight of one cubic centimeter of water; the density of air is the weight of one liter of air; and so forth. In order to find the density of an object, you need to make two measurements first: the weight of the object and the volume of the object. Then, you can find the density by dividing the weight by the volume. Here's an example to illustrate that process:

What is the density of a piece of marble whose volume is 31.2 cm³ and whose weight is 84.2 grams?

Weight = 84.2 g

Volume = 31.2 cm³

Density = $\dfrac{\text{weight}}{\text{volume}}$

= $\dfrac{84.2 \text{ g}}{31.2 \text{ cm}^3}$

= 2.7 g/cm³

The label for this answer is read: "grams per cubic centimeter." It means that each cubic centimeter of marble weighs 2.7 grams ... the definition of density.

Activity Page 19, page 78, contains some practice exercises on finding the density of objects. You will have to find the weight and the volume of each object first. You have already learned the procedures for making these measurements. Then, when you know the weight and the volume of each object, you can calculate the density. The mathematical procedures are exactly like the ones used in the sample problem above.

Math Skills with Measurement

ACTIVITY PAGE **19** FINDING DENSITY

DIRECTIONS: Use any procedure for finding the density of each of the following:

1. **water**

   weight: _____ volume: _____ density: _____
   calculations:

2. **alcohol**

   weight: _____ volume: _____ density: _____
   calculations:

3. **lead**

   weight: _____ volume: _____ density: _____
   calculations:

4. **glass**

   weight: _____ volume: _____ density: _____
   calculations:

5. **wood**

   weight: _____ volume: _____ density: _____
   calculations:

6. **air** (optional)

   weight: _____ volume: _____ density: _____
   calculations:

Section six

Math Skills with Graphs

Graphs are a way of expressing mathematical ideas visually. They show us a "picture" of an equation, a formula, or a relationship. Sometimes we can understand an idea better by looking at a graph than by looking at numbers and letters. Graphs are used in all sciences.

1. Types of Graphs

Many kinds of graphs are used. Here are some types you may see:

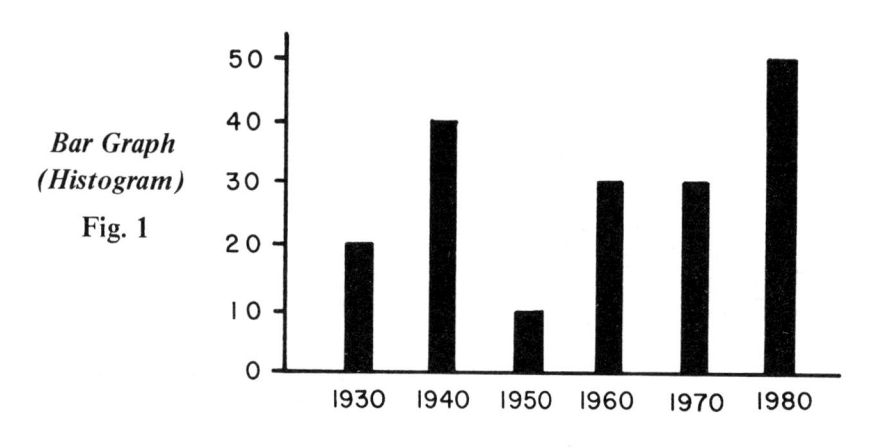

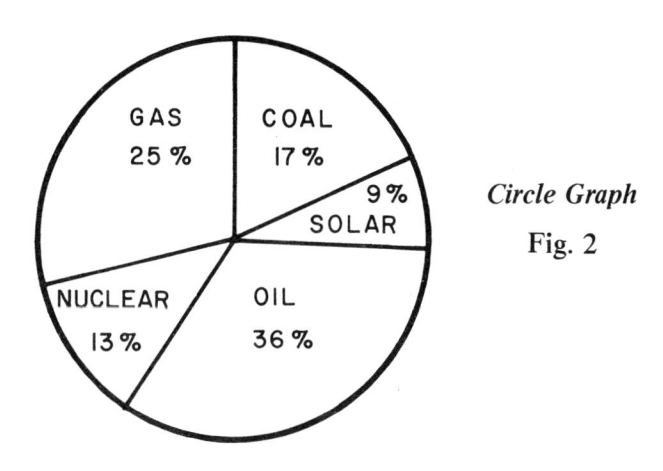

Bar Graph (Histogram)

Fig. 1

Circle Graph

Fig. 2

Continued

Math Skills with Graphs

Pictogram
Fig. 3

Line Graph
Fig. 4

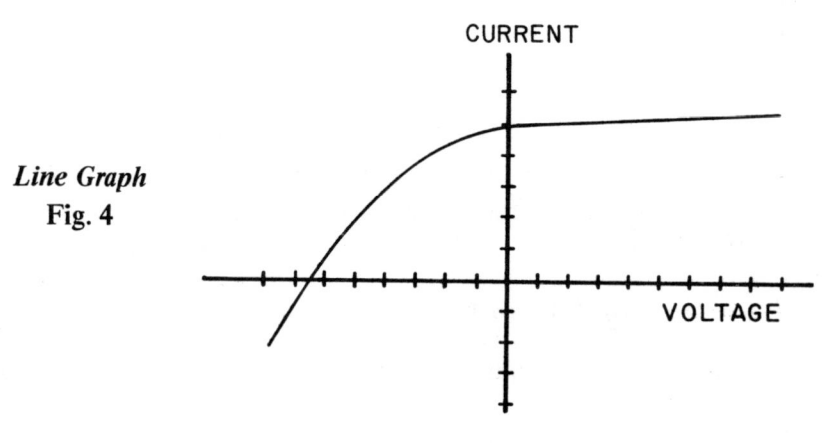

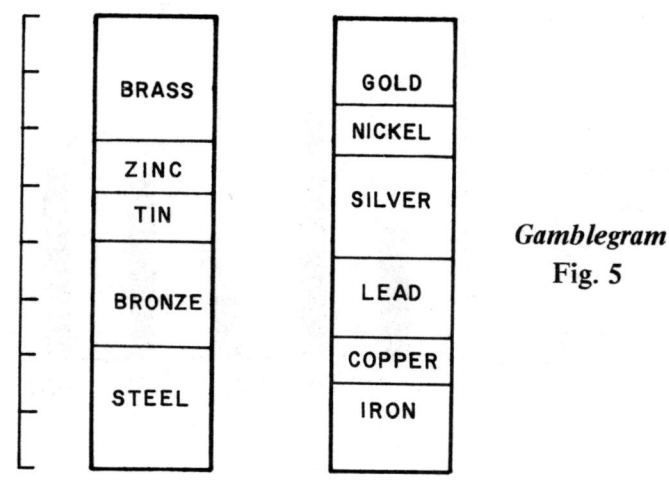

Gamblegram
Fig. 5

Two kinds of graphs are used in science more often than the others. They are **bar graphs** (or **histograms**) and **line graphs**. These are the two we will study in this book. In this section, you should learn:

1. How to construct a histogram.

2. How to interpret ("read") a histogram.

3. How to construct a line graph.

4. How to interpret ("read") a line graph.

80 *Section Six*

2. Histograms (Bar Graphs)

A histogram shows how much there are of various kinds of things. It could show:

a. The number of students in grades 7 through 12 in your school.

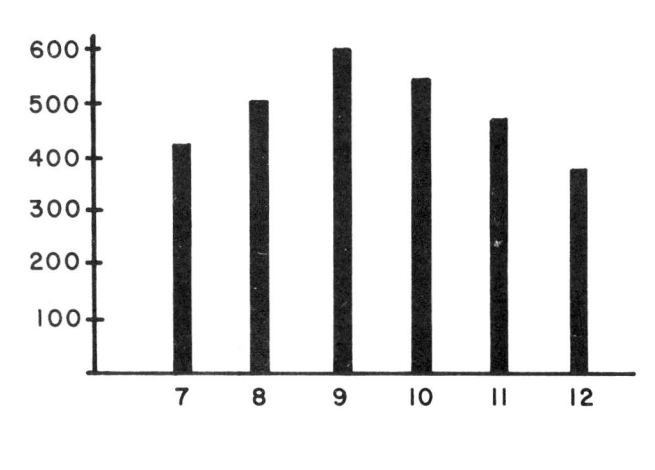

Fig. 6

b. The number of people in various age groups in your county.

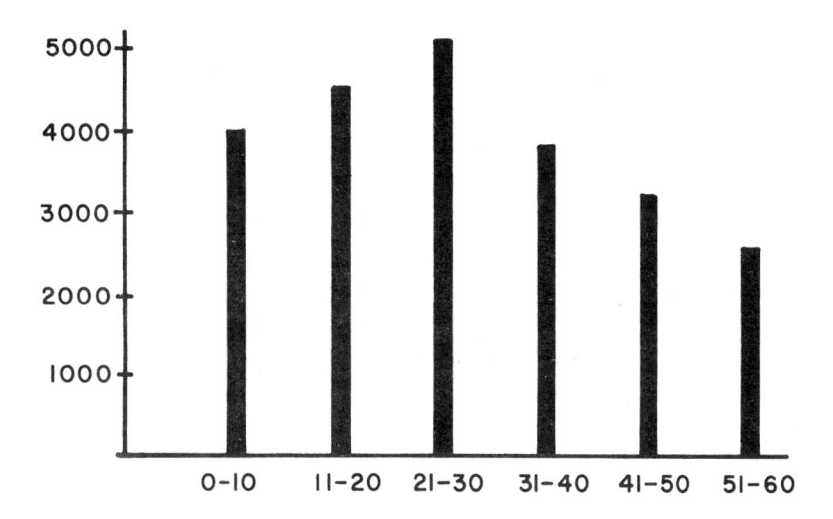

Fig. 7

Math Skills with Graphs 81

c. The number of pea plants of various colors.

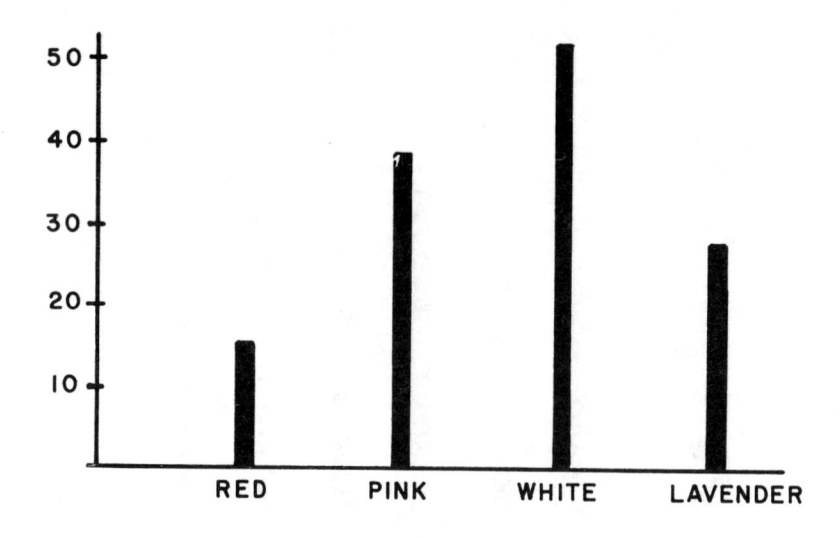

Fig. 8

d. The number of pebbles of various sizes in a stream.

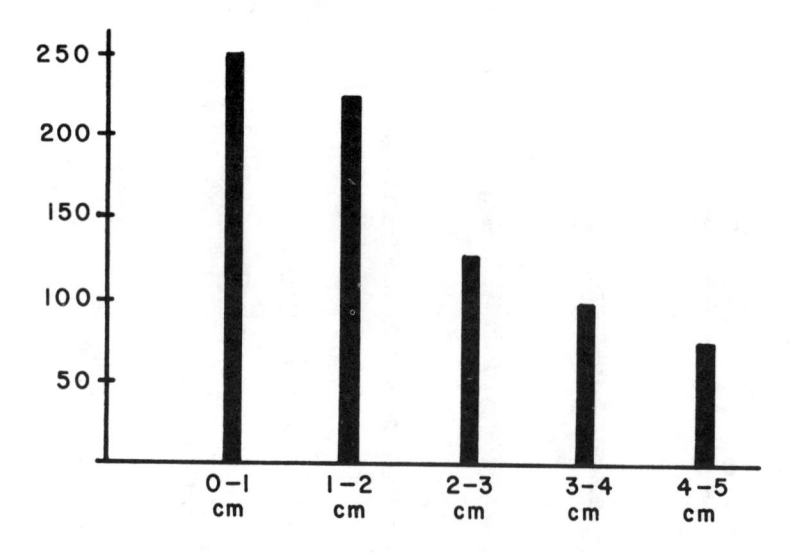

Fig. 9

e. The number of molecules traveling at various speeds in a gas.

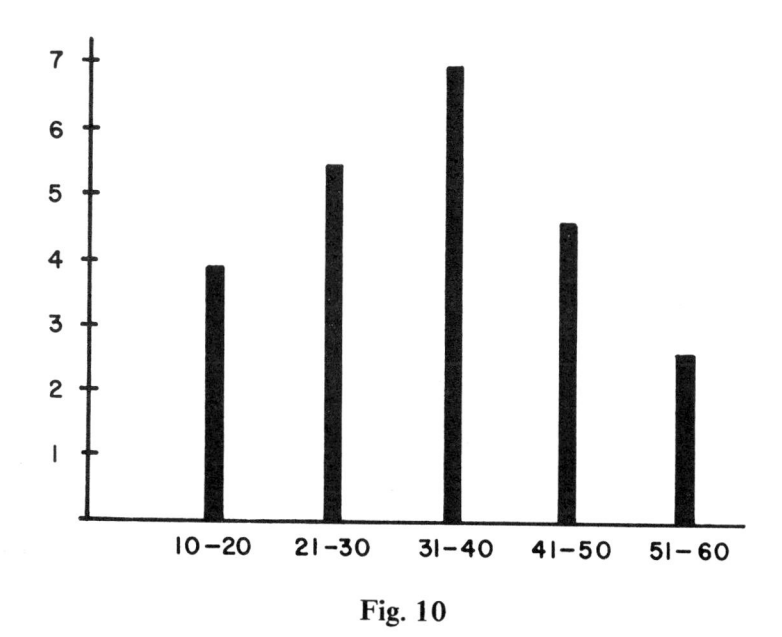

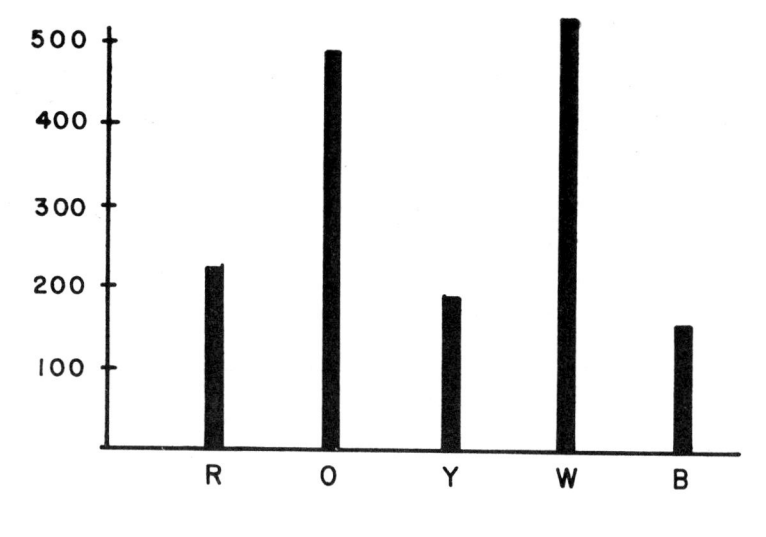

Fig. 10

f. The number of stars that have certain colors.

Fig. 11

Math Skills with Graphs 83

In order to make a histogram, you need to know:

1. The groups of things you want to count (students, people of various ages, pea plant colors, pebble sizes, speeds of molecules, or colors of stars, for example). These go on the horizontal axis (line) of the graph.

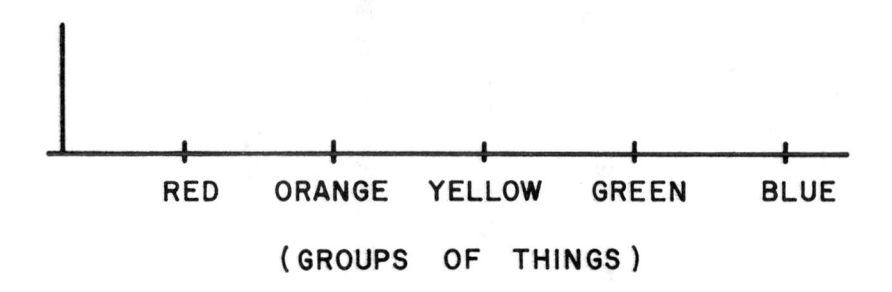

```
        |
        |
        |
        +------+------+------+------+------+
           RED  ORANGE YELLOW GREEN   BLUE

              ( GROUPS   OF   THINGS )
```

Fig. 12

2. The number of items in each group. This determines how long each bar will be. We show the "number of things" on the vertical axis.

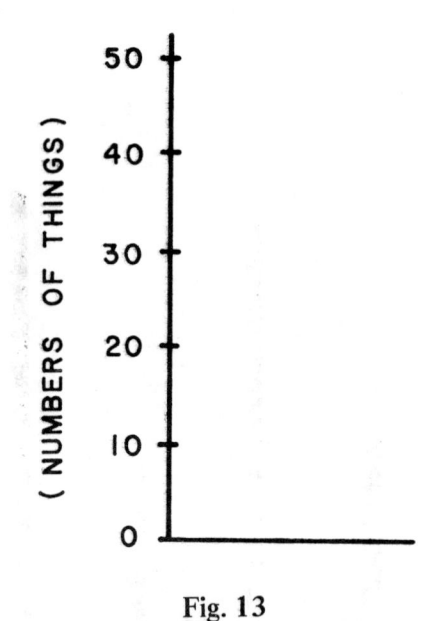

```
( NUMBERS OF THINGS )

  50 +
  40 +
  30 +
  20 +
  10 +
   0 +-------------------
```

Fig. 13

As an example of the way to make a histogram, suppose we measure the amount of rain that falls in the school weather station for six weeks, from March 5 through April 9. Suppose this is what you find out:

March 5:	1.2 cm	March 26:	1.4 cm
March 12:	0.8 cm	April 2:	2.1 cm
March 19:	0.0 cm	April 9:	0.3 cm

84   *Section Six*

To make a histogram for this information:

a. Draw and label the horizontal and vertical axes:

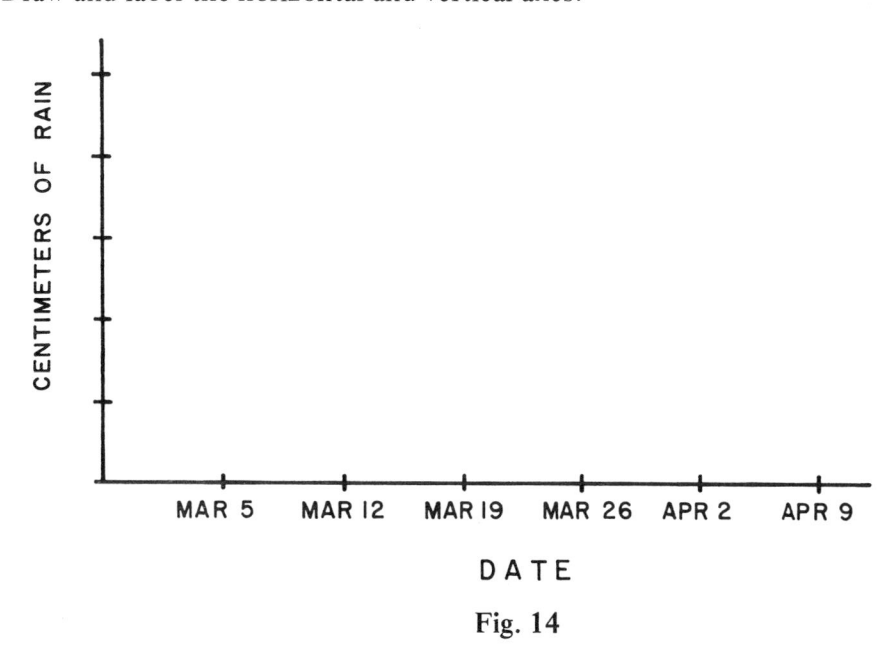

Fig. 14

b. Leave one space on the horizontal axis for each week you made an observation.

c. On the vertical axis, mark off a scale for the number of centimeters of rain that fell each week. Be careful here! You should make the scale "just right" in order for the histogram to be most useful. Which of the following scales do you think is "just right"?

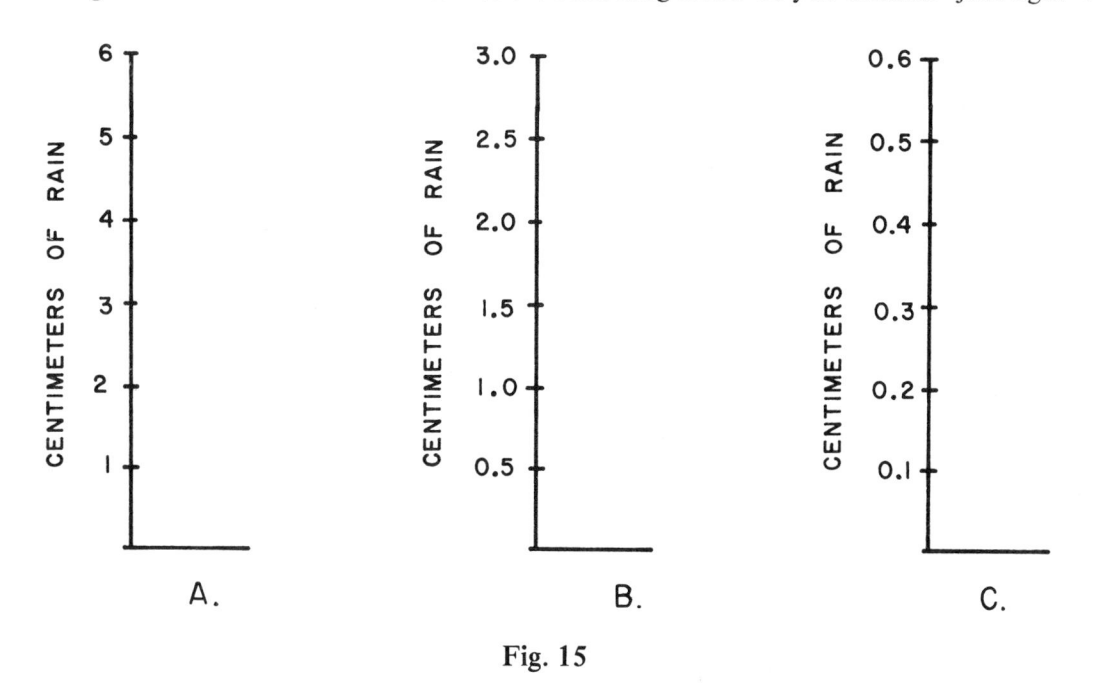

Fig. 15

Math Skills with Graphs 85

If you chose "B," you'd be correct. On this scale, the data you have will just about fill the graph. It will be squeezed near the bottom of graph A or go way off the top of graph C. You should always choose a scale so that your graph will just about fill up the space you have.

d. Also notice that the difference between lines on the vertical axis is the same all the way up. In graph A, each vertical space stands for "1 centimeter of rain." What does each space represent on:

   Graph B? _____

   Graph C? _____

e. Now, make a dot above each week that shows the number of centimeters of rain measured for that week.

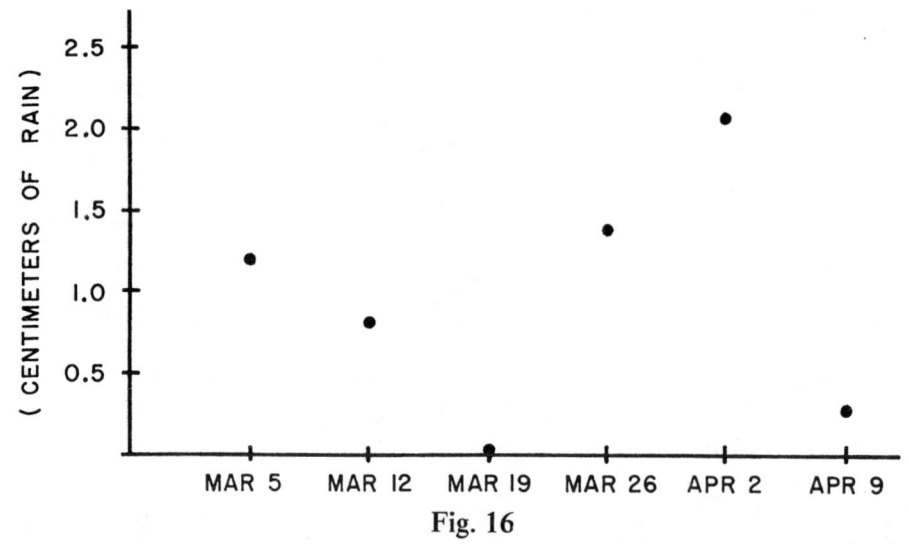

Fig. 16

f. Finally, draw a line from each dot to the horizontal axis. You could leave the graph in this form . . .

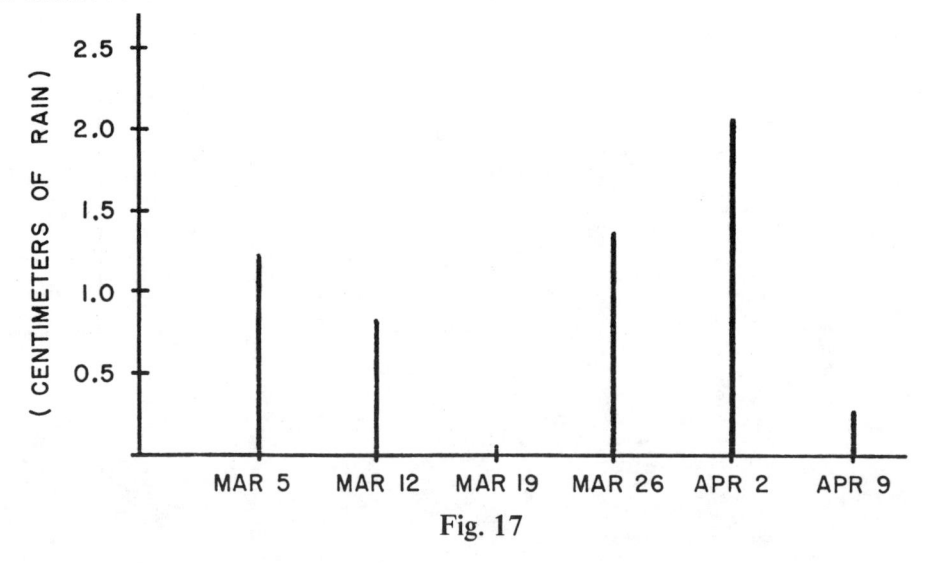

Fig. 17

86   Section Six

... or you could make a full "bar" out of each line, like this:

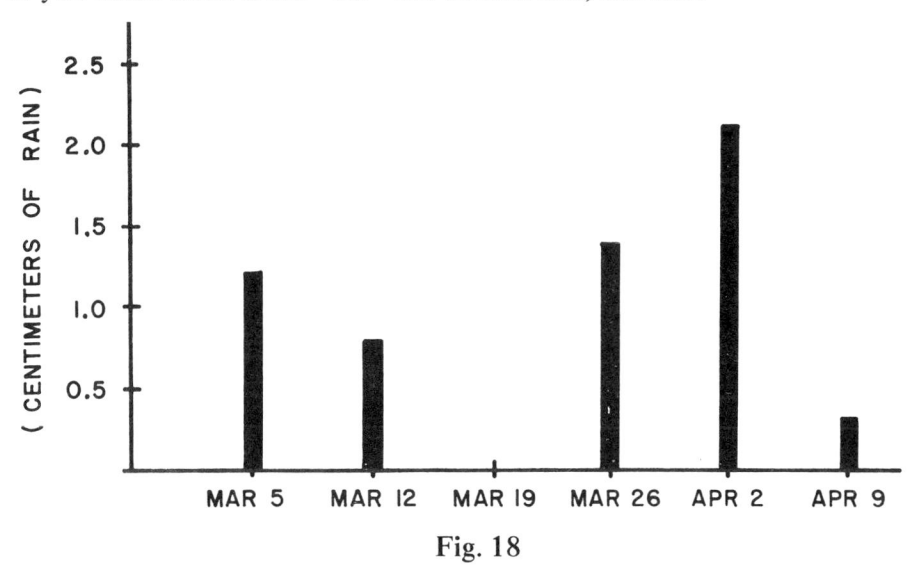

Fig. 18

Activity Page 20, page 89, and Activity Page 21, page 93, give you practice in making and reading histograms. The data you need for Activity Page 20 is given below and on the following page. The histograms you need to answer the questions on Activity Page 21 are given on pages 90-92.

Data for Activity Page 20

1. Forest Acres Burned in the U.S., 1955-1976[1]

Year	Acres Burned (thousands)
1955	8,069
1958	3,280
1961	3,036
1964	4,197
1967	4,659
1970	3,279
1973	1,915
1976	5,110

---

[1] *Environmental Quality: The Tenth Annual Report of the Council on Environmental Quality* (Washington, D.C.: Government Printing Office, 1979), Table A-23.

2. Life Expectancy in the United States (Females), 1900-1977[2]

Year	Life Expectancy
1900	51
1910	54
1920	59
1930	63
1940	67
1950	72
1960	74
1970	75
1977	78

3. Isotopes of the Element Tin[3]

Mass Number	Natural Abundance
112	0.95%
114	0.65%
115	0.34%
116	14.24%
117	7.57%
118	24.01%
119	8.58%
120	32.97%
122	4.71%
124	5.98%

4. Causes of Death in the United States in 1979[4]

Cause	Number of Deaths (per 100,000 persons)
Heart disease	330.4
Motor vehicle accidents	23.6
Other types of accidents	23.4
Pneumonia	19.7
Tuberculosis	0.9
Cancer	183.5
Influenza	0.3
Syphilis	0.1
Nephritis and nephrosis	7.3

---

[2] *Information Please Almanac* (New York, NY: Simon & Schuster, 1981), page 815.

[3] *Lange's Handbook of Chemistry*, 12th edition. Table 3-7. (New York, NY: McGraw-Hill Book Company, 1979).

[4] *Information Please Almanac* (New York: NY: Simon & Schuster, 1981), page 811.

ACTIVITY PAGE **20** MAKING HISTOGRAMS

DIRECTIONS: Use the information contained on pages 87 and 88 to make histograms for each of the situations given there.

1. **Forest Fires**

2. **Life Expectancy**

3. **Isotopes of Tin**

4. **Causes of Death**

Math Skills with Graphs

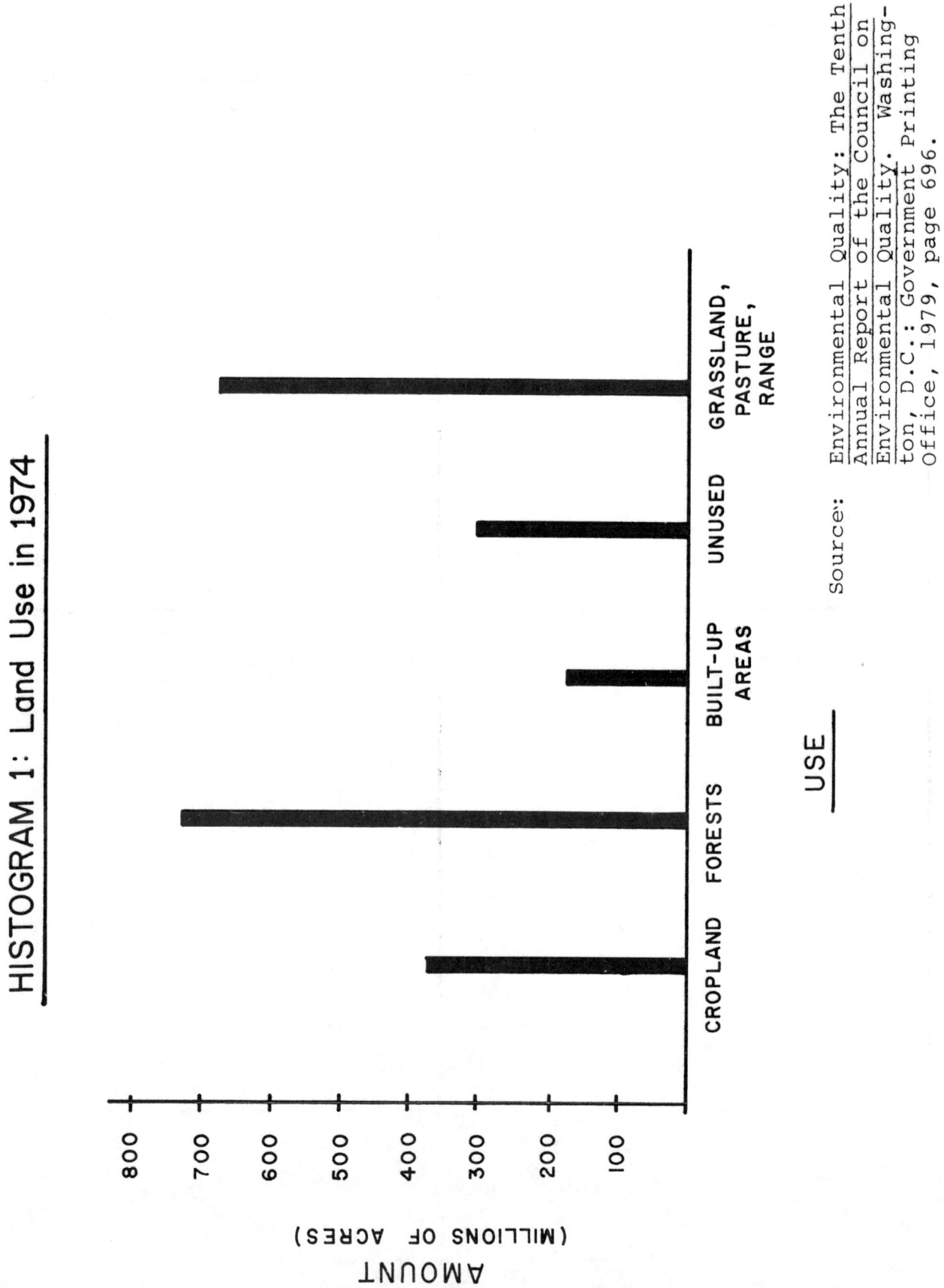

HISTOGRAM 1: Land Use in 1974

USE	Amount (Millions of Acres)
CROPLAND	~380
FORESTS	~720
BUILT-UP AREAS	~170
UNUSED	~290
GRASSLAND, PASTURE, RANGE	~680

Source: Environmental Quality: The Tenth Annual Report of the Council on Environmental Quality. Washington, D.C.: Government Printing Office, 1979, page 696.

90 *Section Six*

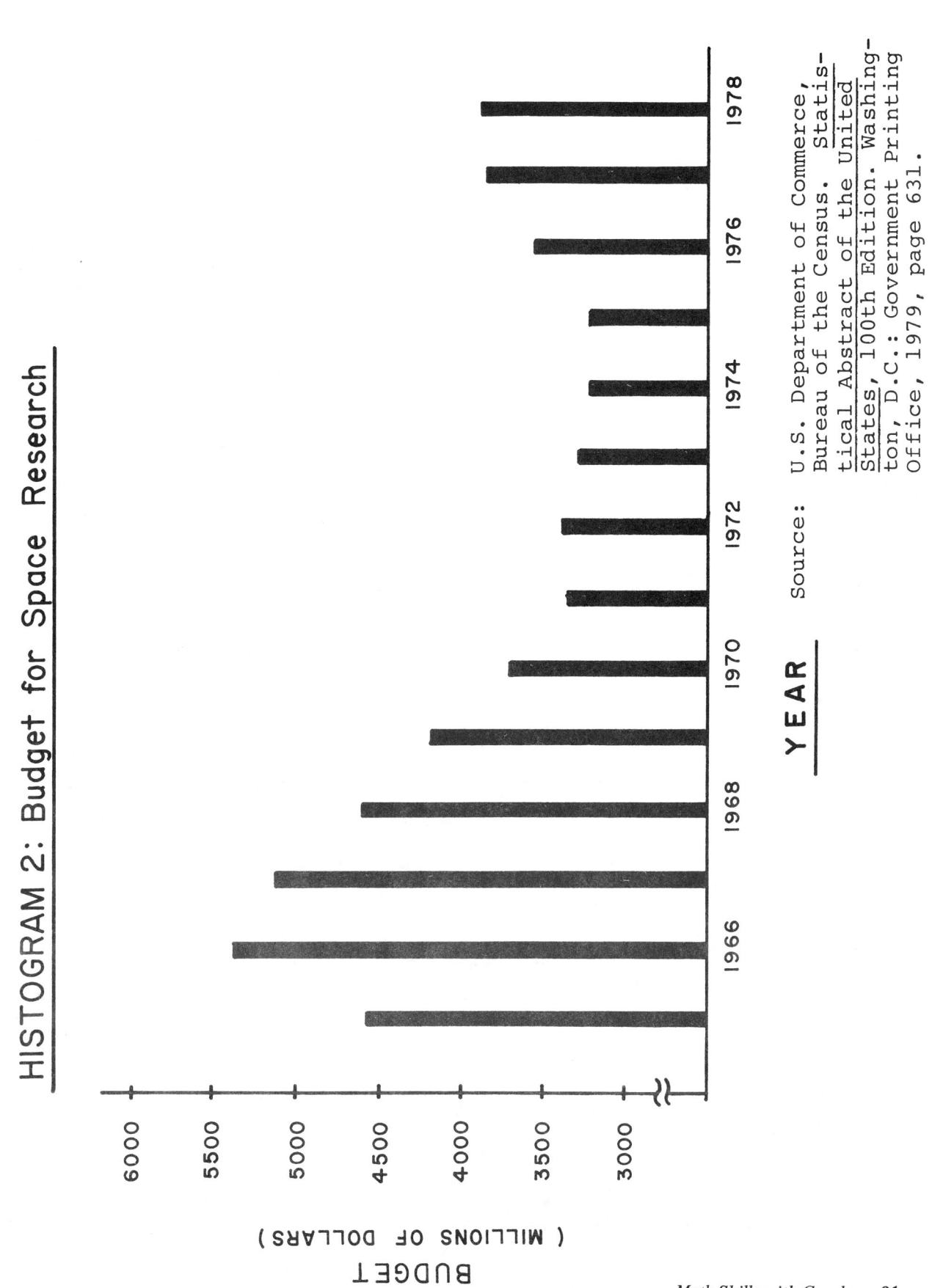

HISTOGRAM 2: Budget for Space Research

YEAR

BUDGET (MILLIONS OF DOLLARS)

Source: U.S. Department of Commerce, Bureau of the Census. *Statistical Abstract of the United States*, 100th Edition. Washington, D.C.: Government Printing Office, 1979, page 631.

Math Skills with Graphs 91

HISTOGRAM 3: Intercity Transportation, 1977

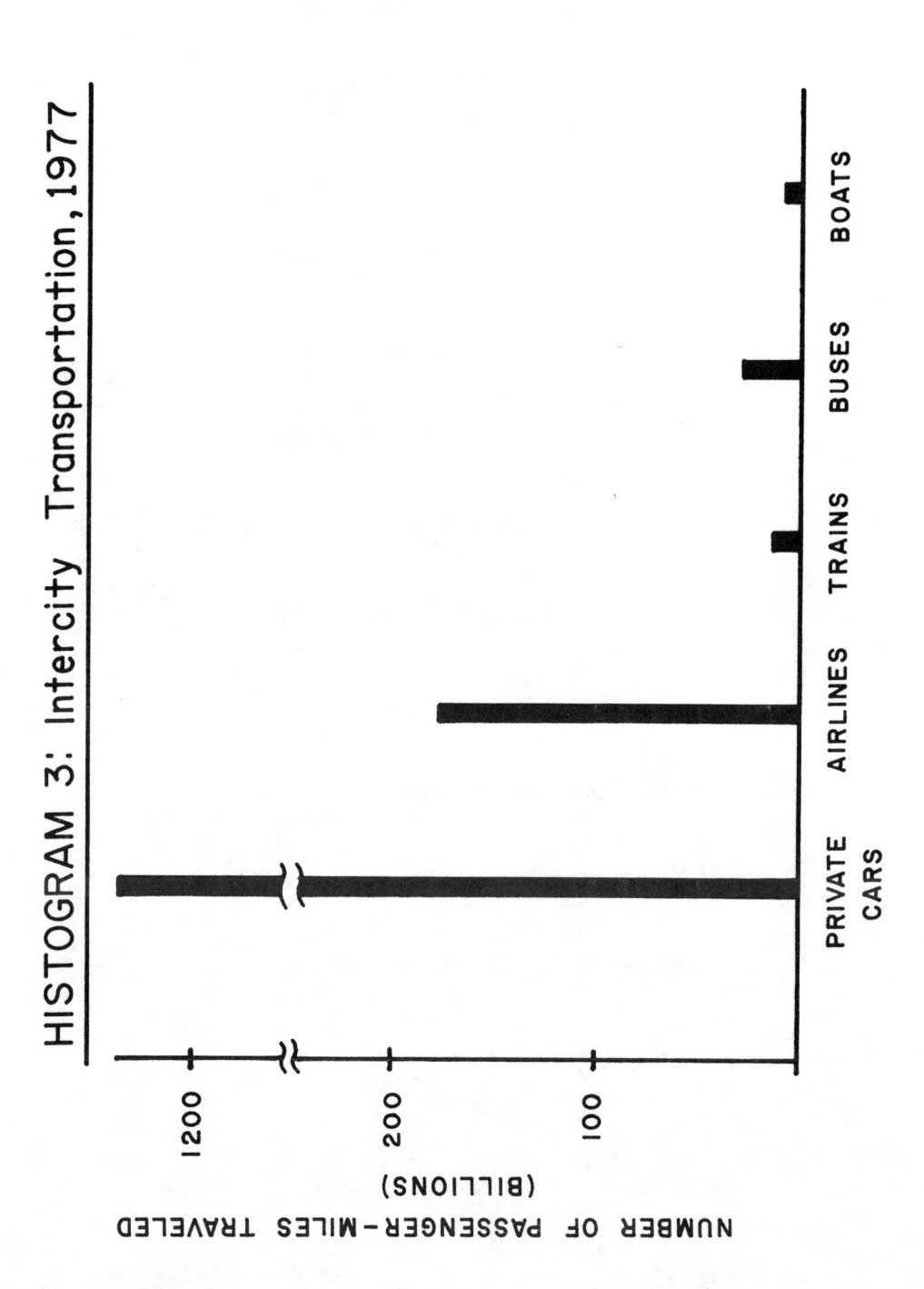

NUMBER OF PASSENGER-MILES TRAVELED (BILLIONS)

- 1200
- 200
- 100

MODE of TRANSPORTATION

PRIVATE CARS | AIRLINES | TRAINS | BUSES | BOATS

Source: U.S. Department of Commerce, Bureau of the Census. *Statistical Abstract of the United States*, 100th Edition. Washington, D.C.: Government Printing Office, 1979, page 635.

92 *Section Six*

ACTIVITY PAGE 21 INTERPRETING HISTOGRAMS

DIRECTIONS: The questions below are based on the histograms on pages 90-92. Answer each question in the space provided.

Histogram 1: Land Use in 1974

1. Which of the land uses in this chart took up the largest amount of land in 1974? _____

   How much land area was used in this way? _____

2. How much land area was occupied by cropland in 1974? _____

3. What is the total amount of land accounted for in this chart (approximately)? _____

Histogram 2: Budget for Space Research

1. In what year was the largest amount of money spent for space research? _____

   How much was spent that year? _____

2. In what year was the least amount of money spent on space research? _____

   How much was spent that year? _____

3. How much money was spent on space research in 1965? _____

   1975? _____

4. What was the total (approximate) amount of money spent on space research from 1965 to 1970? _____

Histogram 3: Intercity Transportation, 1977

1. What form of travel did most people use in getting from city to city in 1977? _____

   How many passenger-miles were traveled by this means in 1977? _____

2. How many passenger-miles were traveled by domestic airlines in 1977? _____

   By railroads? _____

3. What percentage of intercity travel in 1977 was conducted by private automobiles?

   _____

Math Skills with Graphs

3. Line Graphs

a. Variables

Line graphs are probably the most common kind of graph used in science. They also show how two different things are related to each other. The two "things" are also called **variables**. A variable is something that can have different values at different times. For example, your weight is a variable. When you were born, you weighed only a few kilograms. At the age of six, you may have weighed about fifteen kilograms. Now your weight may be thirty or forty kilograms. Your weight **varies** from time to time.

Notice that your age is a variable, too. When you were first born, your age was only a few minutes. Later, your age was four years, seven years, and ten years. Now it is twelve, fourteen, or sixteen years.

Now notice that these two variables go together. A person's **age** and **weight** are often (but not always) related to each other. You could probably guess the weight of a person if you know his or her age. Try doing that. In the list at the left below, tell which weight listed at the right belongs with each age.

1 year old: _____

4 years old: _____   30 kg; 8 kg;

11 years old: _____   14 kg; 75 kg;

20 years old: _____   55 kg

40 years old: _____

You might not guess correctly every time in this game, but you could recognize silly answers. A one year old, for example, would **not** weigh 75 kg, and a forty year old would not weigh 8 kg. You **know** that age and weight are related to each other.

We're saying that age and weight are more than simply related to each other—weight **depends on** age (to some extent). During the first part of life, the older a person gets, the more he or she weighs. Since weight is a variable that depends on age, we call it a **dependent variable**. Age, in this case, is called an **independent variable**. It does not depend on weight. See if you can pick out the dependent and independent variables from each of the following pairs. Compare your answers with the ones given.

  1. a person's height   2. a person's age
  3. amount of food a person eats   4. a person's weight
  5. time spent in the sun   6. amount of sunburn
  7. years spent in school   8. how many facts a person knows
  9. amount of jogging each day 10. size of one's leg muscles

b. Tables of Data and Formulas

Line graphs show the relationship between two related variables. One is the dependent variable; the other, the independent variable. To make a line graph, we must begin with either an equation or formula OR with a set of data for the related variables.

94 Section Six

For example, suppose that one of your classmates planted a seed on March 1. Then, on noon of each of the next ten days, she measured the height of the plant that grew from that seed. Suppose that this is the data she collected:

Time (in days)	1	2	3	4	5	6	7	8	9	10
Height (in cm)	2	4	6	8	10	12	14	16	18	20

One thing we **could** do (but don't **have** to) is to write a mathematical formula that shows how these two variables are related. This is a very easy example. You can easily see what the formula will be. The height of the plant (in centimeters) is always twice as great as the time (in days) it has been growing. Therefore, we can write:

$$height = 2 \times time$$

In math, we always abbreviate variables with letters. In this example, we can let:

h stand for the height of the plant, and

t stand for the time it has been growing.

A better way to write the relationship we found is:

$$h = 2 \times t$$
or $$h = 2t$$

Working the other way around, you can make a table of data from a formula. For example, suppose that our student had found that the relationship between height and time was:

$$h = t + 2$$

In other words, the height of the plant was equal to the number of days **plus** 2 cm. We could use this formula to make a new table of data. For example, on day 1 (that is, t = 1), the height of the plant would be:

$$h = t + 2$$
or $$h = (1) + 2$$
$$h = 3 \text{ cm}$$

We could start a table that would look like this:

t (in days)	1
h (in cm)	3

t (in days)	1	2
h (in cm)	3	4

t (in days)	1	2	3
h (in cm)	3	4	5

Calculate the rest of this table from t = 4 days up to t = 10 days. Fill in the values in the spaces provided below.

t (in days)	1	2	3	4	5	6	7	8	9	10
h (in cm)	3	4	5							

Now turn to Activity Page 22, page 97, where you are asked to derive formulas from given tables of data. Activity Page 23, page 98, asks you to make tables of data from given formulas.

ACTIVITY PAGE **22** WRITING FORMULAS FROM DATA

DIRECTIONS: Write a formula for each set of data reproduced below.

1.
n	1	2	3	4	5	6	7	8
s	5	6	7	8	9	10	11	12

s = **n+4**

2.
x	1	2	3	4	5	6	7	8
y	3	6	9	12	15	18	21	24

y = **3x**

3.
z	1	2	3	4	5	6	7	8
a	1	4	9	16	25	36	49	64

a = **z^2**

4.
c	1	2	3	4	5	6	7	8
e	3	5	7	9	11	13	15	17

e = **2c+1**

5.
t	1	2	3	4	5	6	7	8
s	2	6	10	14	18	22	26	30

s = _____

6.
r	1	2	3	4	5	6	7	8
Q	-2	1	6	13	22	33	46	61

Q = _____

7.
a	1	2	3	4	5	6	7	8
B	6	13.5	21	28.5	36	43.5	51	58.5

B = _____

8.
e	1	2	3	4	5	6	7	8
L	2	3.5	5	6.5	8	9.5	11	12.5

L = _____

Math Skills with Graphs

ACTIVITY PAGE 23 MAKING DATA TABLES FROM FORMULAS

DIRECTIONS: Make a table of data for each of the following formulas.

1. $a = c + 3$ ($c = 1$ to $c = 8$)

c								
a								

2. $z = 6y$ ($y = 1$ to $y = 8$)

y								
z								

3. $w = 2x + 5$ ($x = 1$ to $x = 8$)

x								
w								

4. $q = r^2 + 1$ ($r = 1$ to $r = 8$)

r								
q								

5. $k = 3n - 8$ ($n = 1$ to $n = 8$)

n								
k								

6. $y = 4x^2 - 3$ ($x = 1$ to $x = 8$)

x								
y								

7. $A = a^3 - 1$ ($a = 1$ to $a = 8$)

a								
A								

8. $y = 2^n$ ($n = 1$ to $n = 6$)

n						
y						

Section Six

c. **Plotting Points**

Now we are ready to make a line graph from either a table of data or a mathematical formula. The first step in this process is called **plotting points**. The term means finding a way to represent the relationship of the values for two variables. Look back at the data table on page 95, for example. How do we show on a graph the situation when the plant was four days old and 8 centimeters tall? That is, how do we plot the formula h = 2t when t = 4 and h = 8?

To do that, we begin with a "blank graph." This consists of two intersecting lines (axes) and a scale on each axis. The point at which the two axes intersect is called the **origin**. The horizontal axis is reserved for the **independent** variable, and the vertical axis for the **dependent** variable. In our example, t is the independent variable, so it goes on the horizontal axis. The dependent variable is **h**; it goes on the vertical axis.

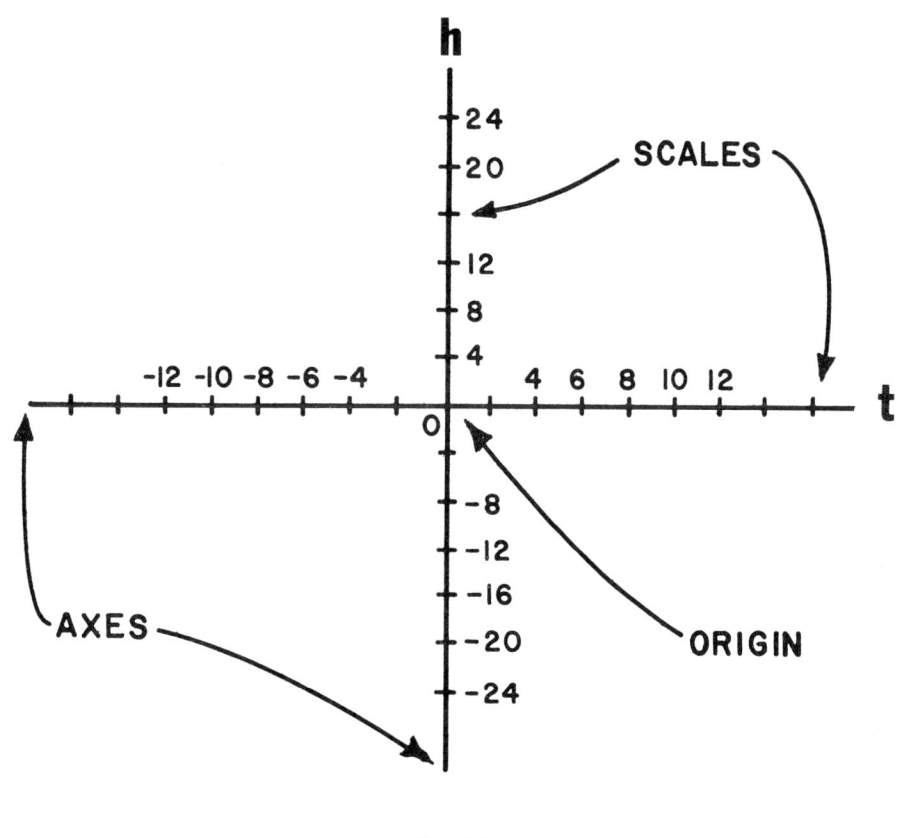

Fig. 19

Numbers **above** and **to the right** of the origin are positive. Those **below** and **to the left** are negative. As with histograms, make sure the scale makes sense. The values of t go from 0 to 10 in our example. This tells you how big to make the scale so that you use up all the space on the graph. In the same way, h goes from 0 to 20, so the spaces on the vertical axis will have to be about half as large as those on the horizontal axis. Look at Fig. 19 to see what this means.

Now stop reading. Go back through the last two paragraphs and make sure you understand all of the new terms used. Then check yourself by looking at the formulas and data tables below. Set up a "blank graph" for each of these practice problems on Activity Page 24, page 101. Label all parts of the graphs as we showed on page 99.

Practice Problem 1

$a = 3b$ ($b = 1$ to $b = 8$)

Practice Problem 2

$x = 2y - 4$ ($y = 1$ to $y = 8$)

Practice Problem 3

r	1	2	3	4	5	6
A	4	7	10	13	16	19

Practice Problem 4

s	0	1	2	3	4	5	6
z	-5	-3	-1	1	3	5	7

ACTIVITY PAGE 24 — SETTING UP GRAPHS AND PLOTTING POINTS

DIRECTIONS: Set up graphs for Practice Problems 1-4 from page 100. Finish reading the section on plotting points before completing this Activity Page.

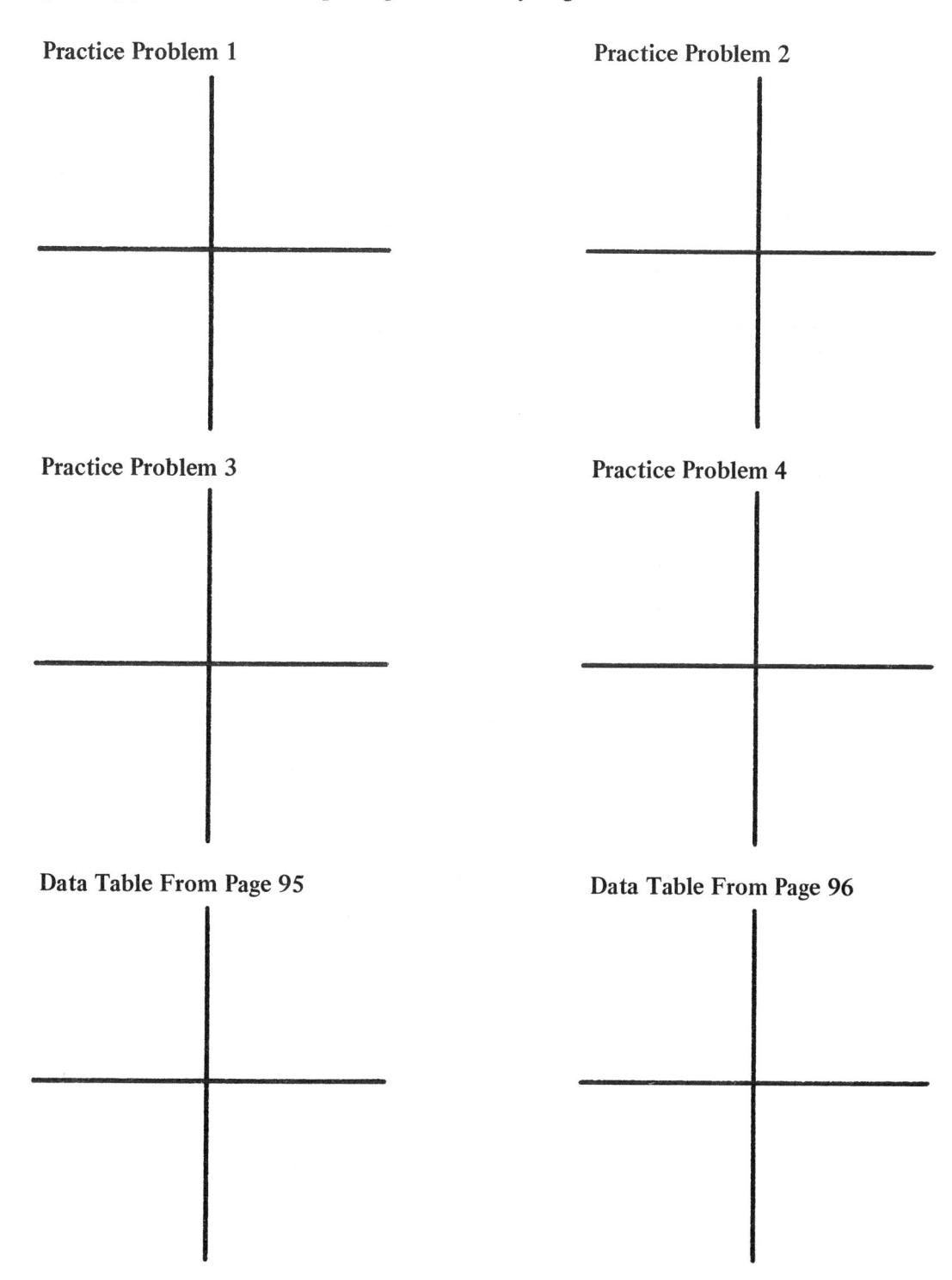

Practice Problem 1

Practice Problem 2

Practice Problem 3

Practice Problem 4

Data Table From Page 95

Data Table From Page 96

Math Skills with Graphs

Now you are ready to start plotting points. Look at Practice Problem 3, for example. The first pair of data points in this table is:

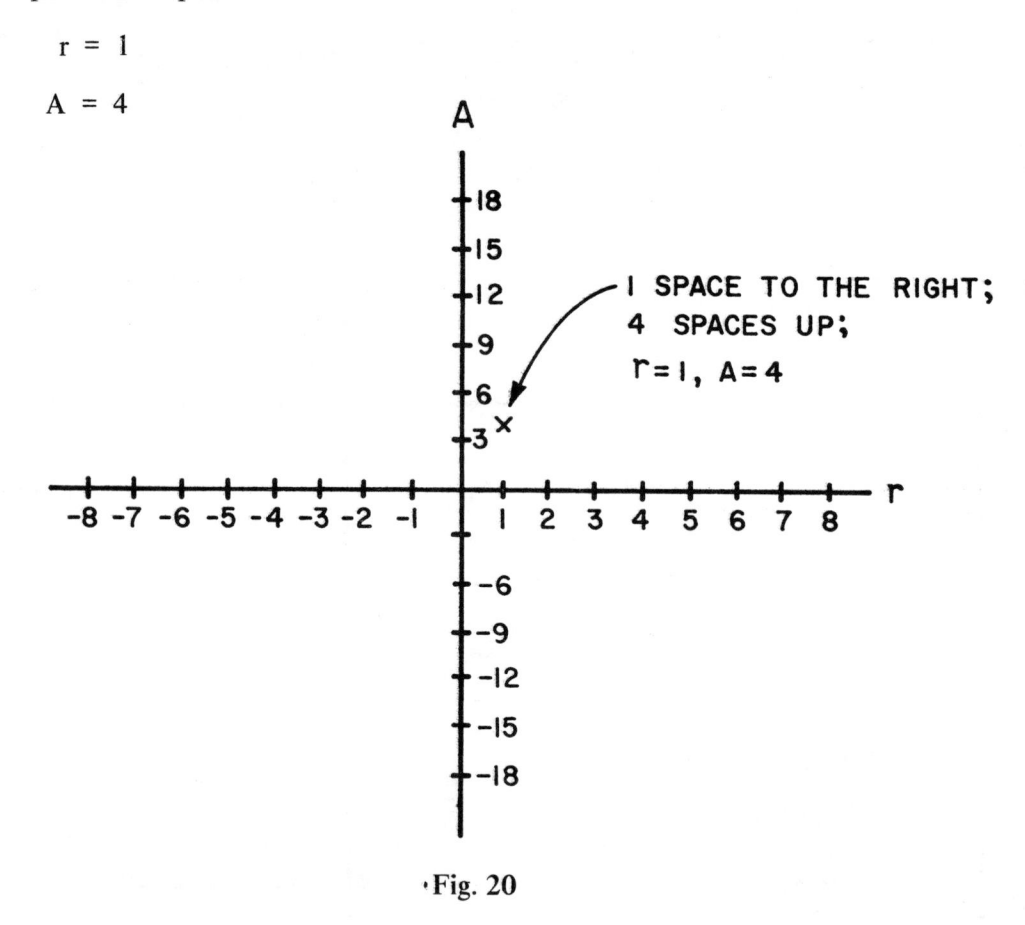

r = 1

A = 4

·Fig. 20

We can "picture" these on the graph by moving one space over on the "r" axis (r = 1) and four spaces on the "A" axis. A small cross ("x") marked at this point represents the pair of values, r = 1; A = 4. The point on the graph, in other words, is a graphical "picture" of the pair of data points, r = 1, A = 4.

Can you see that the graph is something like a street map? The data table always tells you to go so many streets to the right or left, and then so many streets up or down from the center of town.

We have plotted points for the next two pairs of data in Practice Problem 3. Look at the graph to be sure you see how we got them. Then plot the remaining points on the blank graph on Activity Page 24, page 101. If you have any problems with this technique, ask your teacher for help.

Have your answers to this assignment checked by your teacher. Then plot all of the data points given in Practice Problems 1, 2, and 4 on their corresponding graphs on Activity Page 24. Lastly, plot the points for the data tables on pages 95 and 96. Additional problems of this kind are found on Activity Page 25, page 104.

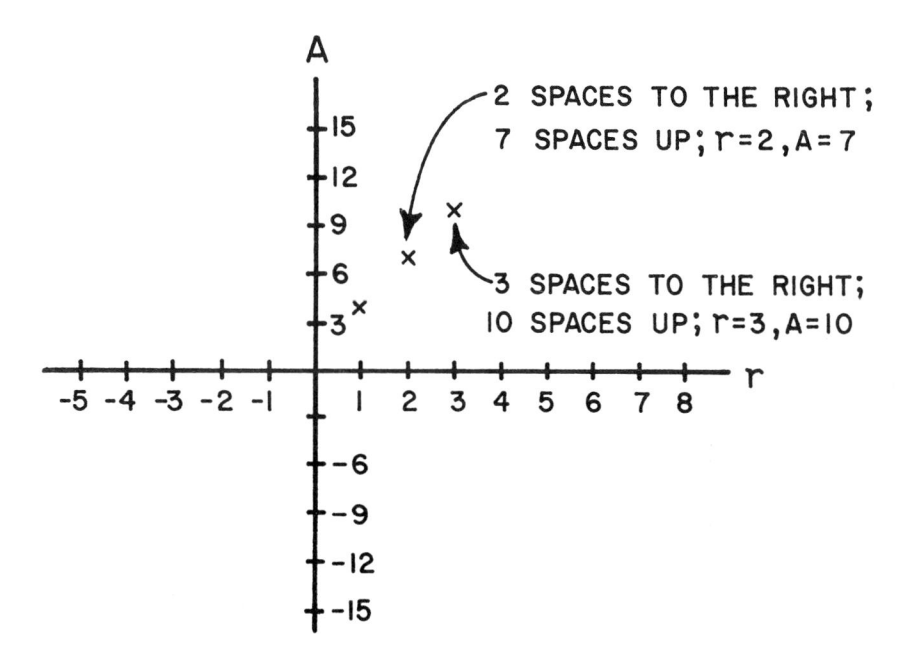

Fig. 21

ACTIVITY PAGE 25 PLOTTING POINTS

DIRECTIONS: On the axes below, plot points for the corresponding problems from Activity Pages 22 and 23, pages 97-98.

Problem 22:1

Problem 22:4

Problem 22:5

Problem 23:1

Problem 23:3

Problem 23:5

104 *Section Six*

d. Drawing Curves

Look back at the data table on page 95. In some ways, that table tells only part of a story. It gives the height of a plant at only ten times in ten days ... at noon on each day. The plant also had different heights at other times during the ten days. What do you think the height of the plant might have been:

        at midnight between day two and day three? _____

        at 6 p.m. on day six? _____

        at 8 a.m. on day eight? _____

When you try to guess the value of a variable **between** two known values like this, you are said to be **interpolating**. All that means is that we know there are values for the relationship between **t** and **h other** than the ones in the table. We could measure those other values directly. We could find the height of the plant for every hour for ten days. Or for every minute. Or for every second.

However, that really isn't necessary. In the last two cases (minutes and seconds), it would be a huge waste of time and effort. How do we know? Look at the points you plotted for this data table on Activity Page 24, page 98. Notice that the points all lie in a straight line. It looks very much as if the height of the plant is changing in a regular, orderly, predictable way. There are no sudden spurts of growth ... no periods of slow growth ... no unexpected changes.

We can show that idea in a simple way—connect the points we have plotted with a straight line. This line tells us what the height of the plant will be for every possible time during the ten days. Of course, we're not absolutely positive about this—we really **didn't** measure at every possible time—but we are quite certain that the line shows how the plant is growing.

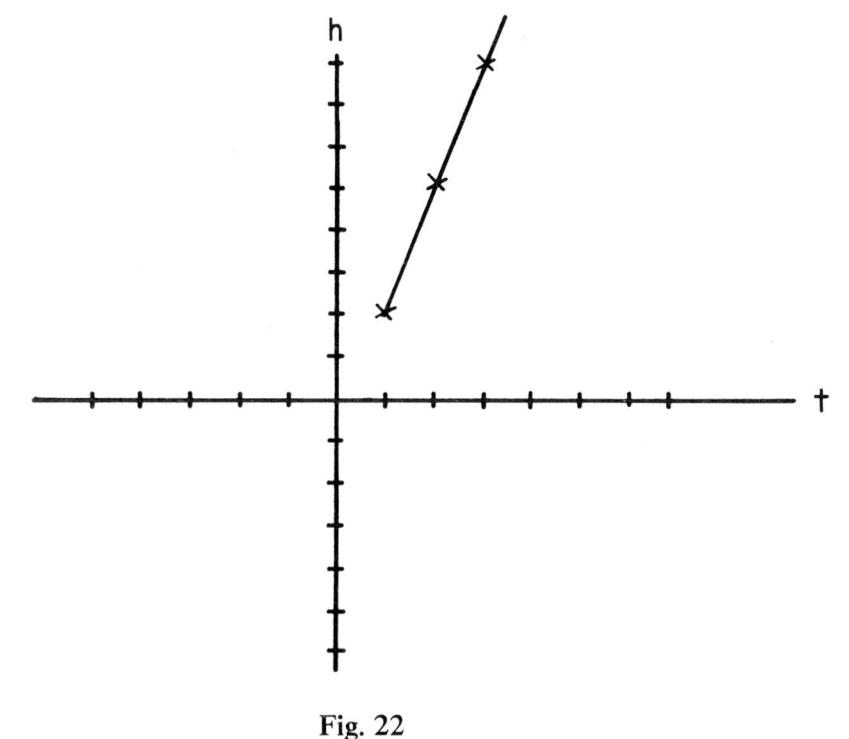

Fig. 22

Now you can use this line to check the guesses you made on page 105. For example, what is the height of the plant at midnight between days two and three? To find out, read over on the horizontal axis to day two. Midnight will be halfway between day two (noon) and day three (noon). Move your pencil halfway from two to three.

Now draw a line **straight up** until it crosses the growth line. Finally, draw another line straight across to the **h** axis. The value you read here is the height of the plant at midnight on day two. Does it come close to your guess?

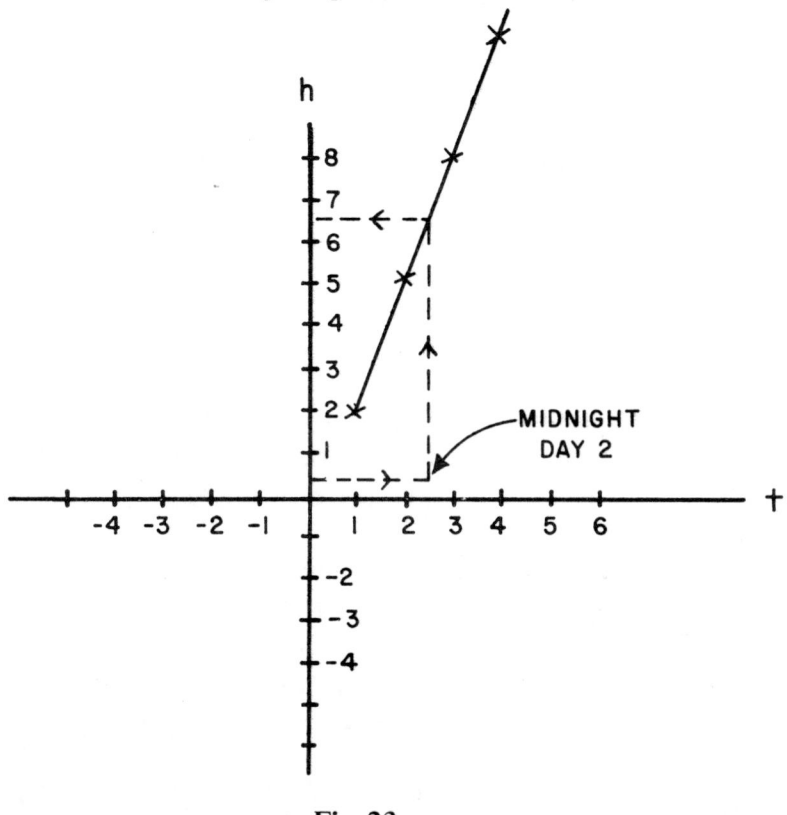

Fig. 23

Check your other two guesses on the graph above. How close were you to the correct answer?

Go back to Activity Page 24, page 101, and Activity Page 25, page 104, and draw in straight lines that fit the points you plotted there.

e. **Curves That Are Not Straight Lines**

The title of the last section may mystify you. It was called "Drawing **Curves**," but we talked about **straight lines**, not "curves." In mathematics, any line that connects points in a regular, orderly way is called a **curve**. Figures 24, 25, and 27 all show mathematical curves. Figure 26 shows something that is not a curve.

106 *Section Six*

Fig. 24 **Fig. 25** **Fig. 26** **Fig. 27**

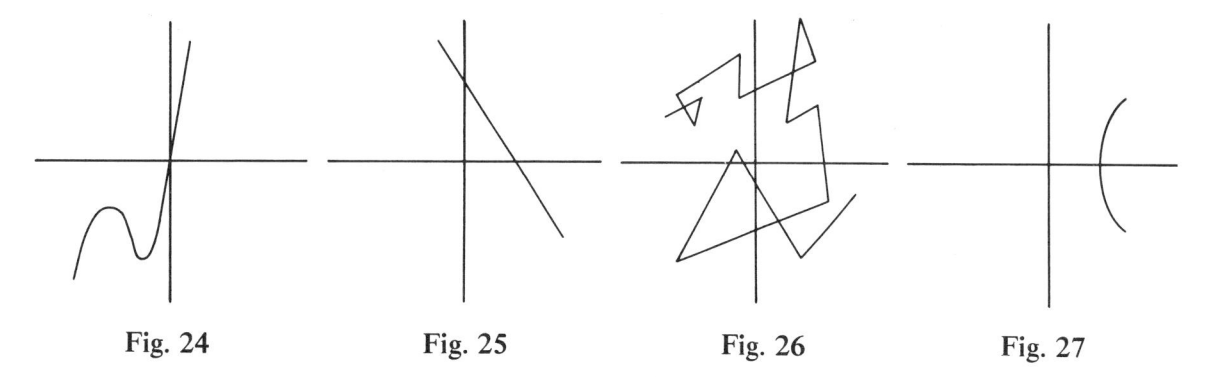

Straight lines are one kind of curve we get when we study scientific data, but other kinds of curves are also possible. Some common curves other than straight lines are shown below:

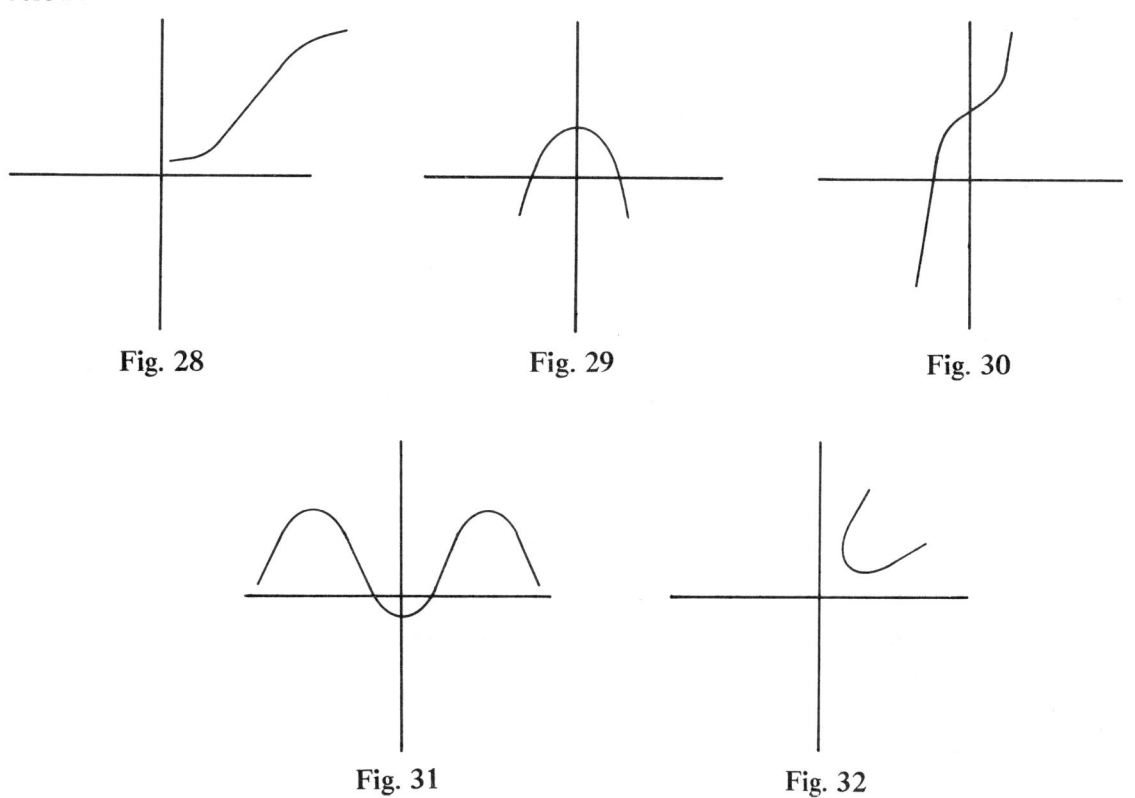

Fig. 28 **Fig. 29** **Fig. 30**

Fig. 31 **Fig. 32**

Each of these curves represents a relationship found in nature. For example, Figure 30 shows the way in which a population of organisms grows over time. Figure 29 describes the way objects travel when thrown into the air. Each curve shown above corresponds to many kinds of events in the real world.

It is sometimes difficult to know exactly what kind of curve to draw to connect a set of points. For example, look at the set of points in Figure 33. One way to connect those points is shown in Figure 34.

Math Skills with Graphs 107

Fig. 33   **Fig. 34**

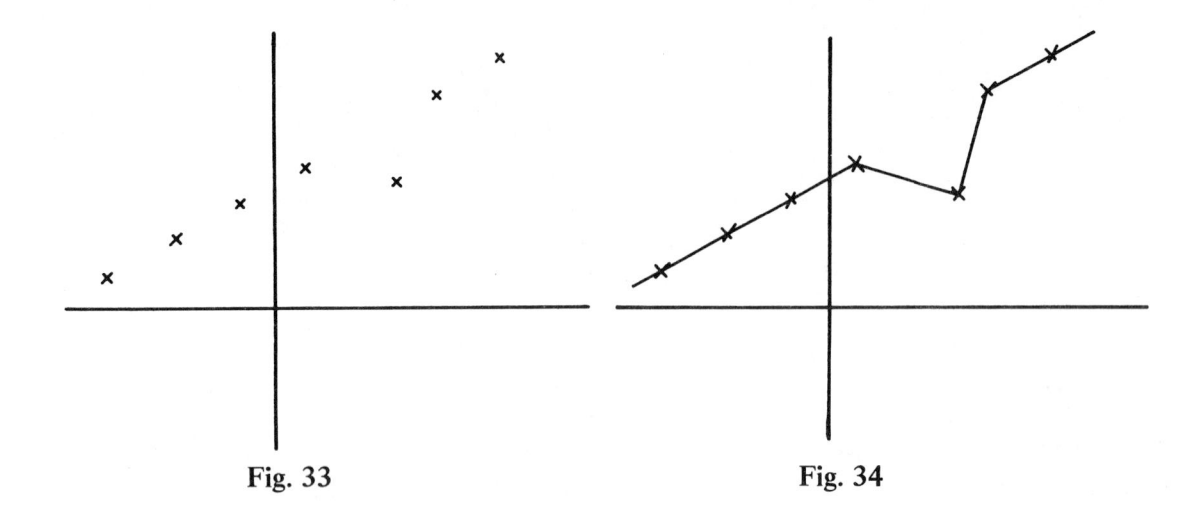

This graph would bother a scientist. It doesn't look like any of the curves commonly encountered in science. What's the problem?

The answer is easy. The points on the graph are pictures of data collected in an experiment. Experiments are performed by humans. Humans can always make a mistake. Maybe one point on the graph represents a mistaken set of data. What point do you think that might be?

Small errors are common in scientific experiments. In fact, they are to be expected. The data we've given you so far in this section have been "perfect." The points you plotted have all lined up in a perfect line. You would **never** expect that to be true in the real world. You would expect one or more measurements to be "off" by a little bit.

What this means in practice is that a scientist never looks for a curve that will fit **every** data point exactly. He or she looks for a familiar curve that will fit all points as well as possible. This process is known as "fitting a curve to a set of data."

Sometimes the task is very easy. Sometimes it is quite difficult. That's what you'll find when you try the problems on Activity Page 26, page 109. You should have no trouble choosing a curve on some of the problems. You may have a good deal of trouble on others. You should compare your answers with those of other students to see how much you agree with each other.

ACTIVITY PAGE **26** DRAWING CURVES

DIRECTIONS: On the axes below, plot points and draw curves for the corresponding problems from Activity Pages 22 and 23, pages 97-98.

Problem 22:3

Problem 22:6

Problem 23:2

Problem 23:4

Problem 23:7

Problem 23:8

Math Skills with Graphs **109**

f. Interpreting Graphs

There will probably be times in your life when you have to make line graphs . . . in this class, for example. There are likely to be many more occasions on which you have to interpret a graph. Newspapers and magazines, technical reports, business communications, political news . . . all make frequent use of graphs. In order to be well-informed, you should be able to read and understand graphical information.

At this point, you have learned all the skills you need for interpreting graphs except one: **extrapolation**. Remember that interpolation means figuring out the value of a variable **between** two given points (page 105). To **extrapolate** means to figure out the value of a variable **beyond** the last given point. An example should help.

Look at the graph below. What do you think the population of Yokum County will be in the year 2000?

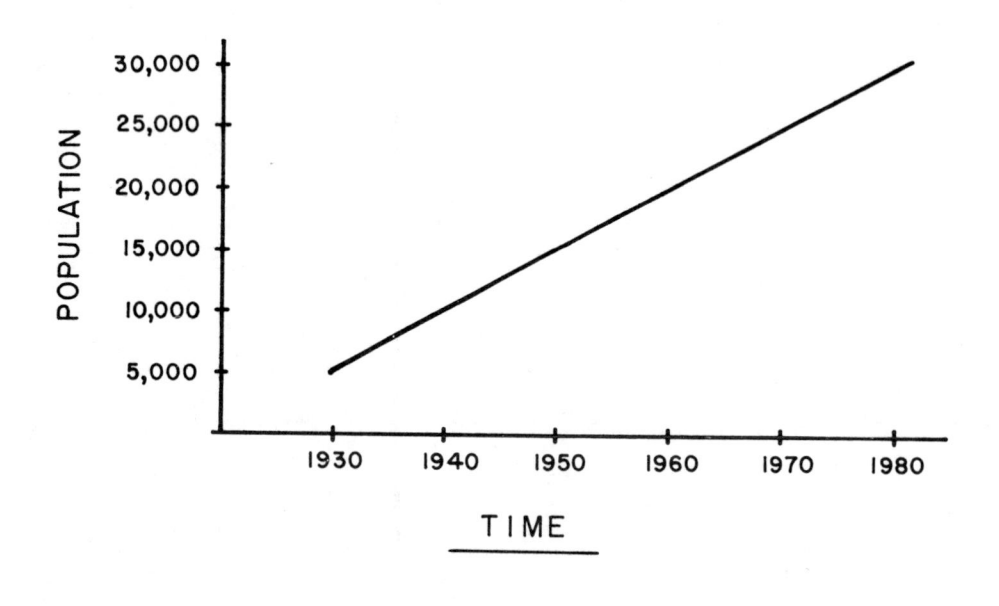

Fig. 35

It should be easy to make a guess. The population seems to increase regularly in a predictable, straight-line way. It would be reasonable to assume that it will continue to do so. We can show that graphically simply by extending the population/time line a bit further. The graph would then look like the one in Figure 36, on the following page.

110 Section Six

Fig. 36

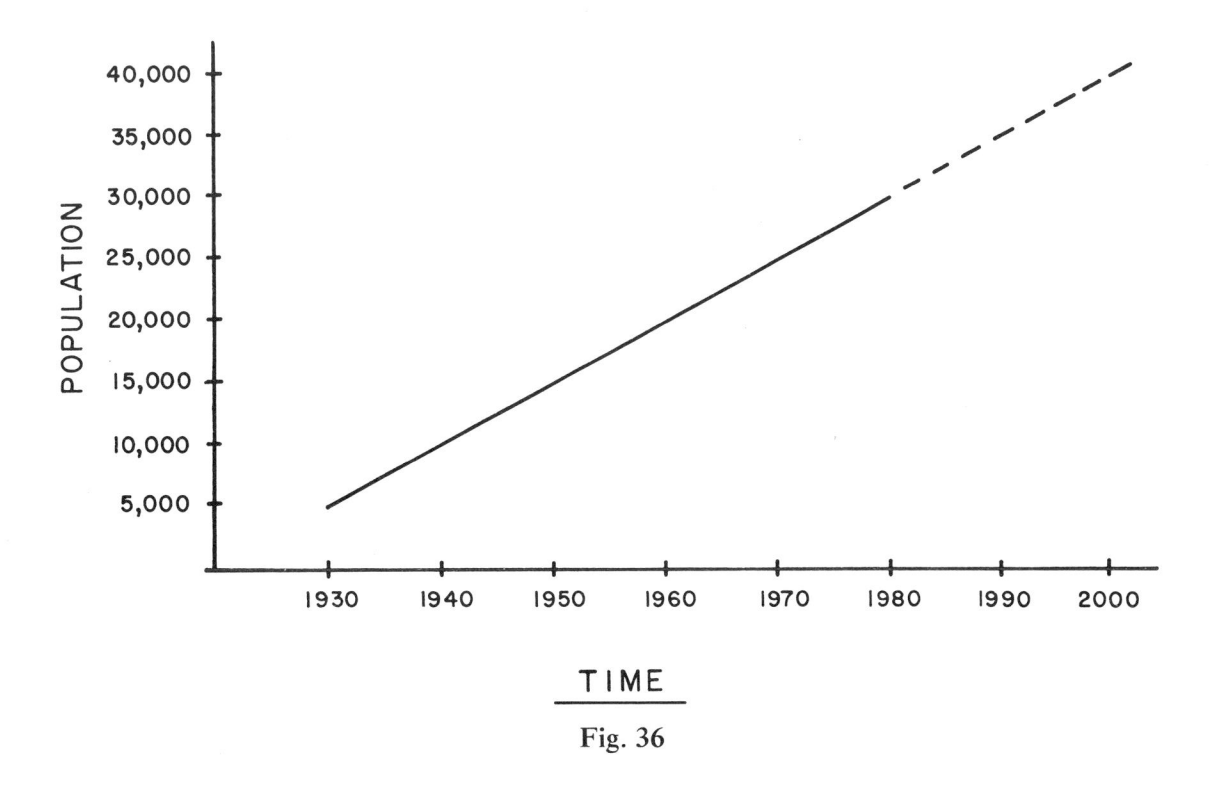

This allows us to predict the population in the year 2000. We can use the same method as for interpolating. Draw a line straight up from the year 2000 until it crosses the graph. Then draw a second straight line horizontally until it comes to the "population" axis. This gives the predicted population for the year 2000.

What population do you predict? Write your answer on this line: _____

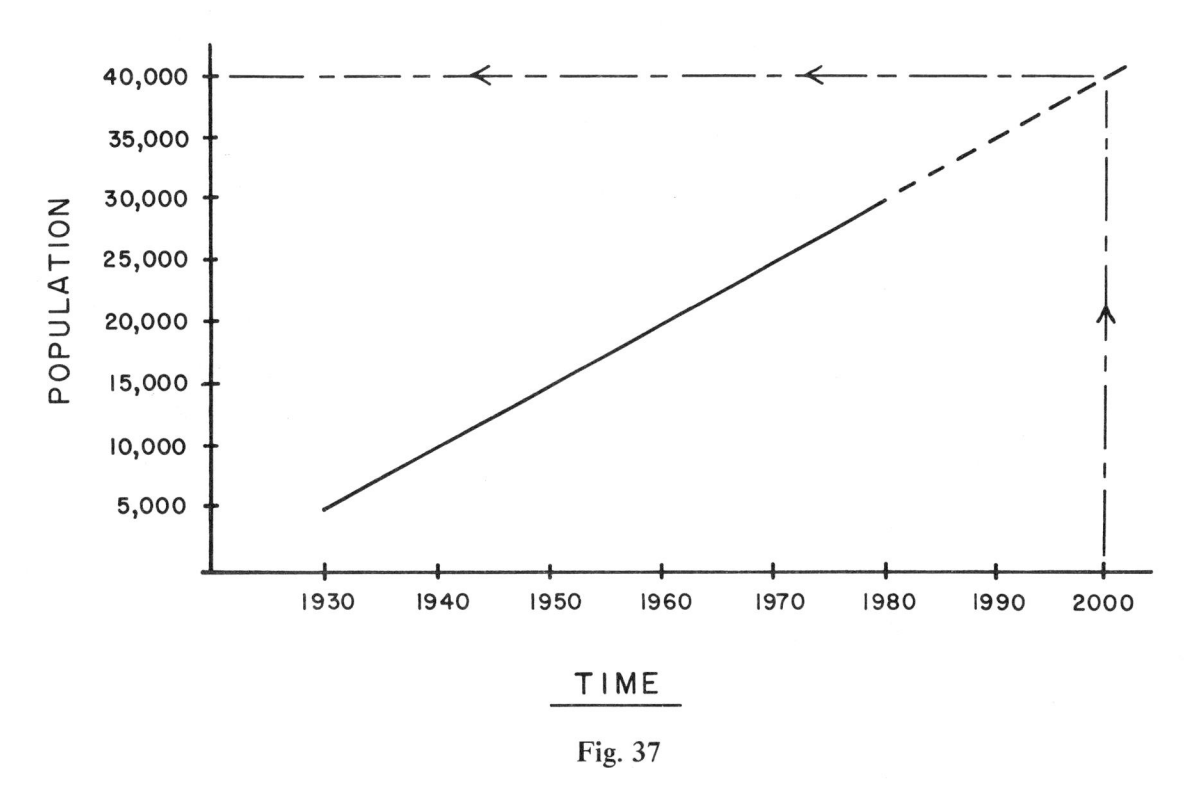

Fig. 37

Math Skills with Graphs 111

Suppose you had been asked to find the population of Yokum County in 1945. That requires **inter**polation. Write down your answer for this question here: _____

Now, how sure are you of this answer? Could you be off by 100,000? 10,000? 1,000? If you've done the interpolation carefully, you should be quite close to the correct answer, no more than a thousand or so off.

How sure can you be of the **extra**polation you did two paragraphs above? The answer is: Not very sure at all! Your answer is **a** good guess, but not **THE** only good guess possible. How do we know for sure that the population/time line will not change direction after 1980 and look something like one of the graphs in Figures 38-41?

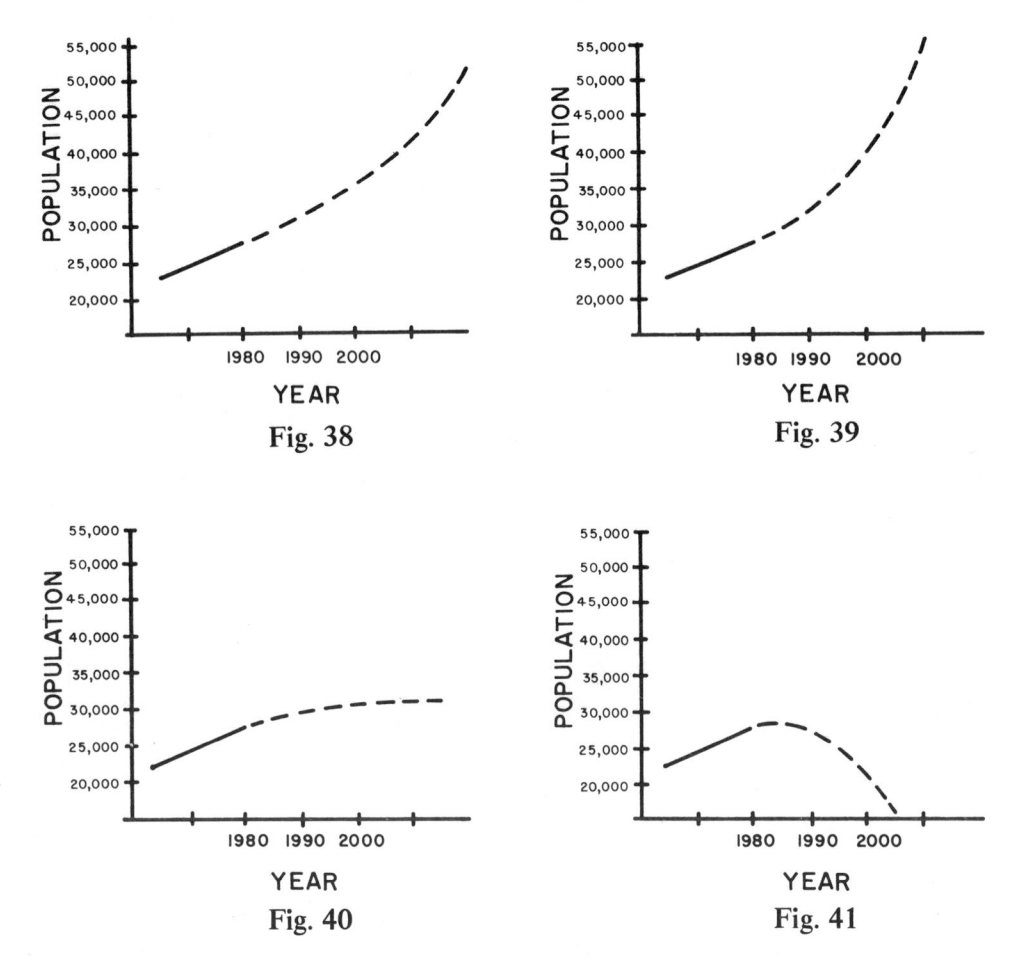

Fig. 38

Fig. 39

Fig. 40

Fig. 41

What population would you predict in 2000 according to each of these graphs? Write your answers below:

    Fig. 38. _____

    Fig. 39. _____

    Fig. 40. _____

    Fig. 41. _____

In fact, any of these five cases—the original straight line case plus the four on the opposite page—or almost **any other** pattern could develop in the future. Can you think of some reasons for each of the changes illustrated in Figures 38 through 41? Write your answers here:

1. _____
2. _____
3. _____
4. _____

As you can see, extrapolating is a much riskier job than interpolating. We never know for sure what the future will be like . . . even if we know a lot about the past.

On the other hand, extrapolating is often a much more important technique than interpolating. Anyone interested in planning for the future, for example, has to do a lot of extrapolating. Articles and reports you read are likely to include some extrapolations. When you read such reports, you always need to ask:

1. whether the extrapolation is mathematically correct, and
2. what other factors need to be considered that might affect the shape of the curve.

If you were on the Planning Board of Yokum County, what kinds of information would you want to have before extrapolating a population for the year 2000? Write down your ideas here:

1. _____
2. _____
3. _____
4. _____
5. _____

Activity Page 27, pages 116-117, has some problems on extrapolation for you to work on. Refer to the three graphs in Figures 42-44 as you answer the questions on this activity page.

Math Skills with Graphs

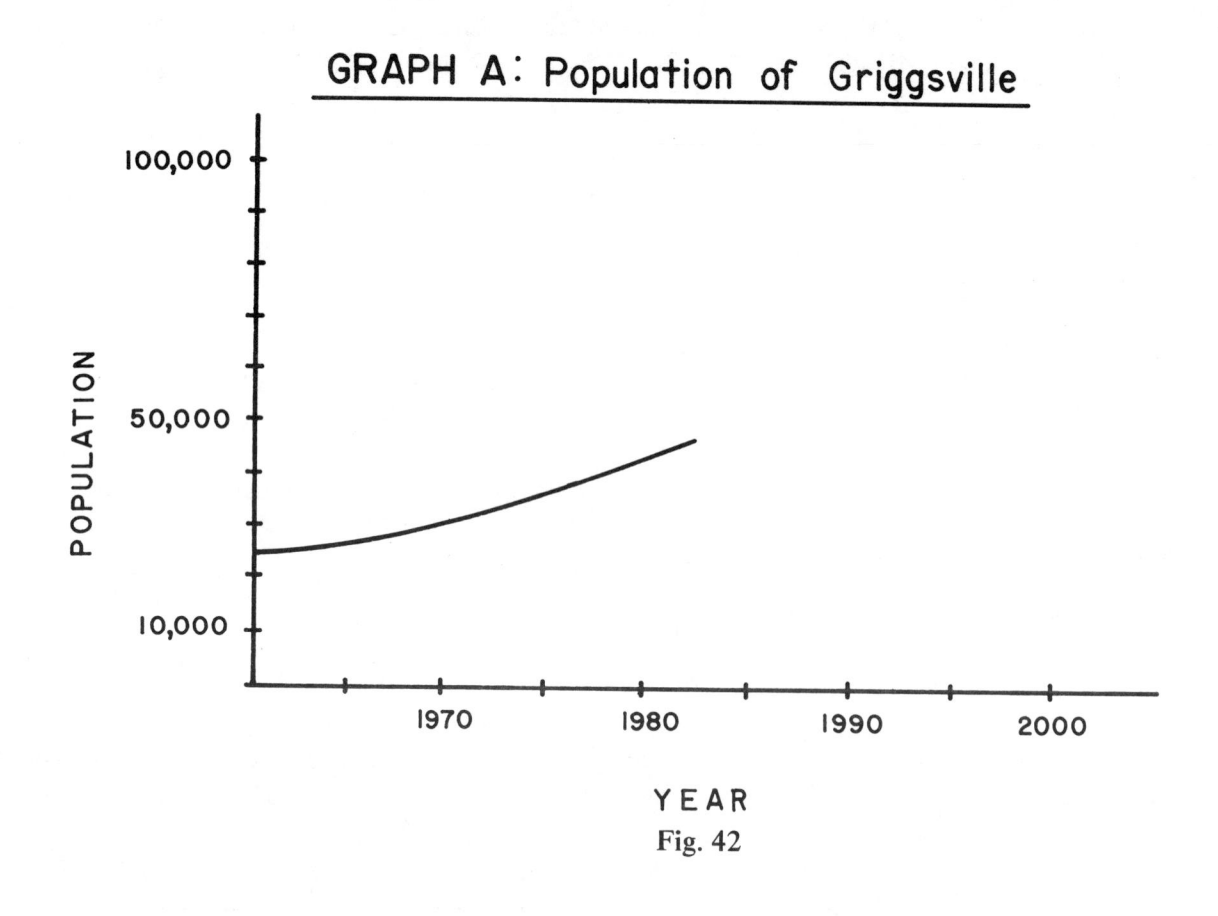

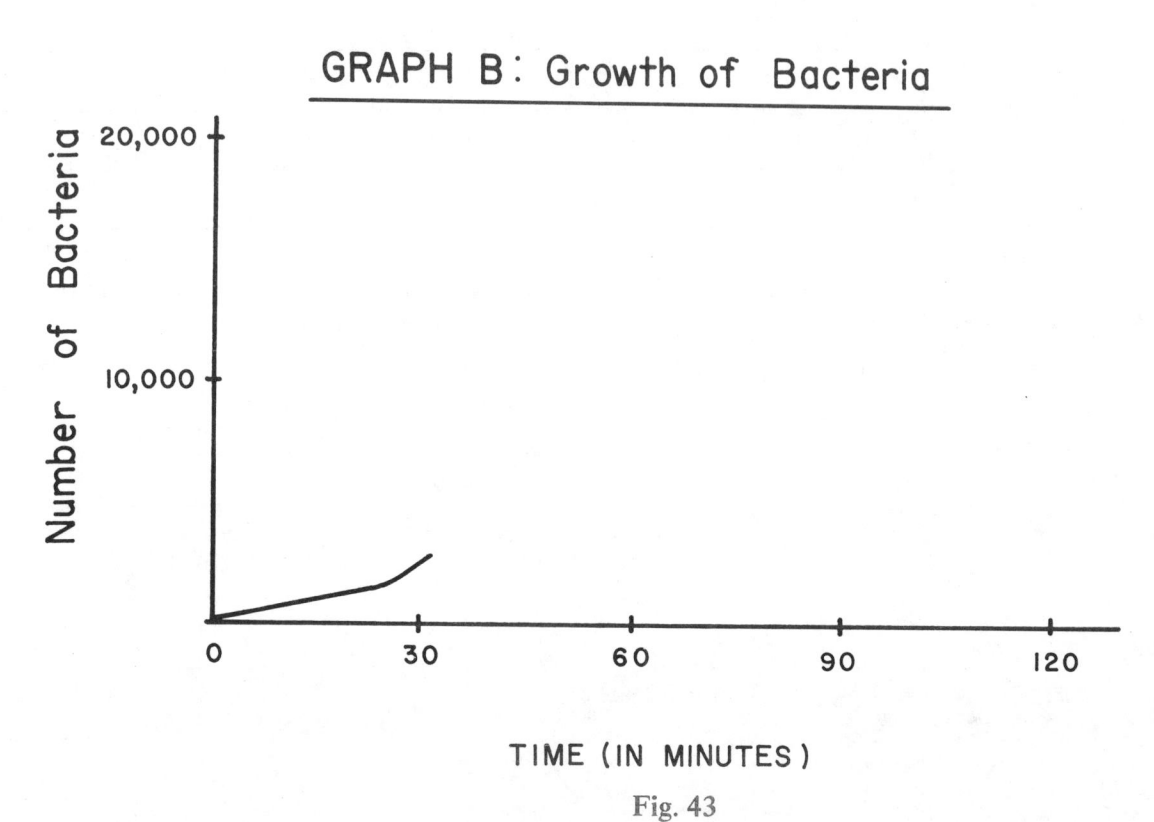

GRAPH A: Population of Griggsville

Fig. 42

GRAPH B: Growth of Bacteria

Fig. 43

114   *Section Six*

GRAPH C : Number of Deer

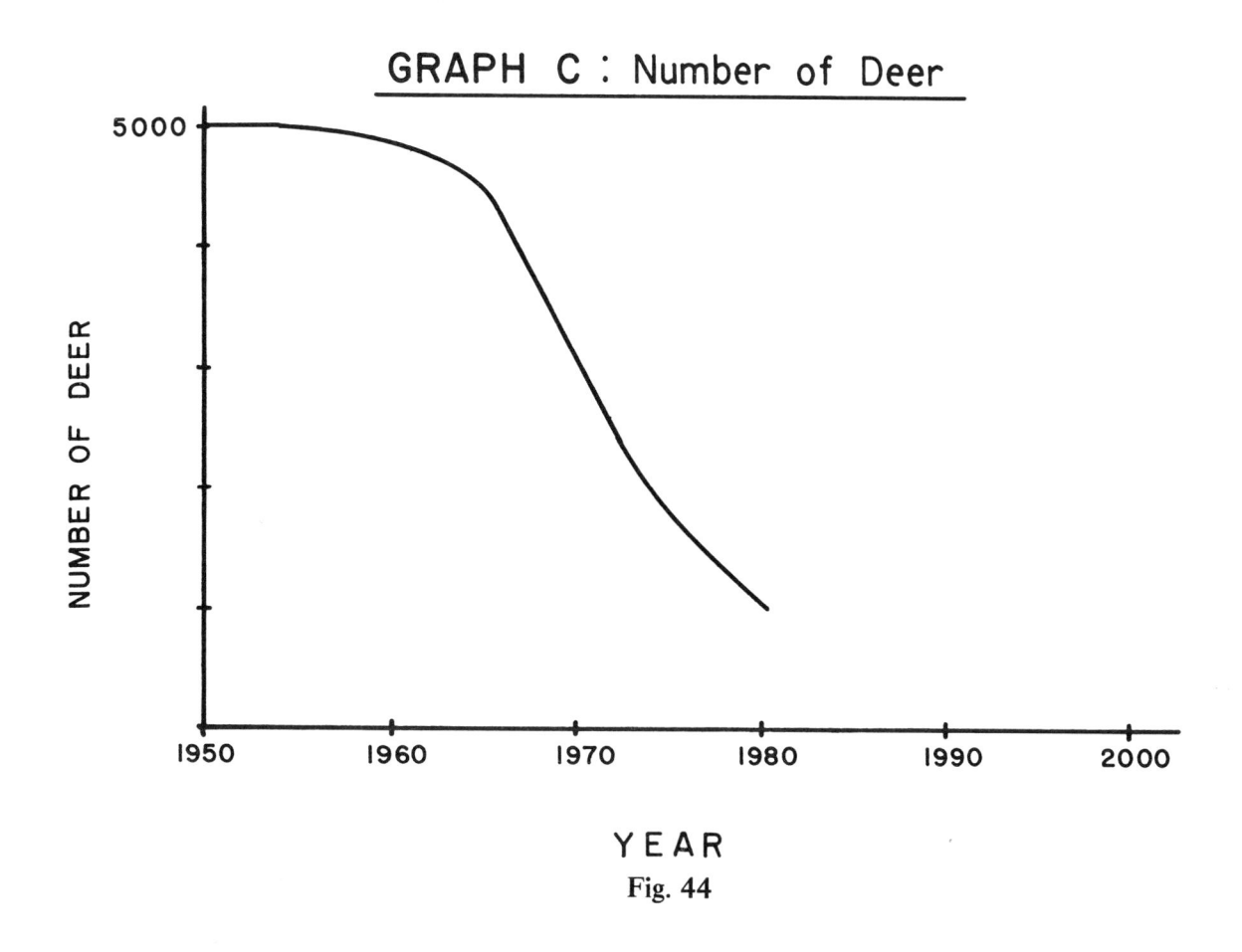

YEAR

Fig. 44

Math Skills with Graphs 115

ACTIVITY PAGE **27** EXTRAPOLATING FROM GRAPHS

DIRECTIONS: Answer the questions below by looking at the graphs on pages 114-115 of the text.

Graph A: Population of Griggsville

1. Predict the population of Griggsville for each of the following years:

   1985: _____   1990: _____   2000: _____

2. Explain how you made each of these predictions:

3. How confident are you of each prediction? Explain your answer, telling what factors might affect your prediction.

Graph B: Number of Bacteria

1. How many bacteria do you predict will be found at each of the following times:

   t = 45 min: _____   t = 60 min: _____   t = 90 min: _____

2. Explain how you made each of these predictions:

3. How confident are you of each prediction? Explain your answer, telling what factors might affect your prediction.

116   *Section Six*

Graph C: Number of Deer

1. How many deer do you think will be found in each of the following years:

    1985:_____ 1990:_____ 2000:_____

2. Explain how you made each of these predictions:

3. How confident are you of each prediction? Explain your answer, telling what factors might affect your prediction.

Math Skills with Graphs 117

Section seven
Experimenting and Related Skills

Scientists learn many things by experimenting. The skill of experimenting includes many other skills. Some of the ones that are described here include:

1. observing
2. inferring
3. classifying
4. generalizing
5. designing experiments
6. carrying out a field trip

1. The Skill of Observing

Everything we know about the world comes about by observing nature. All of the scientific knowledge we have started out from something that someone saw, heard, felt, smelled, or tasted. Notice that "observing" does not mean simply "seeing." It means using all five senses to find out about the world around you.

How does a person learn to make good observations? Probably the best answer to that question is: **practice**. The more observations you make, the better you get at observing. There are some other suggestions to keep in mind too. Here are a few:

a. Try to arrange conditions so that observations are easier to make. We'll say more about this in the section on designing an experiment. An experiment is really nothing other than an attempt to arrange things so that it is easy to observe one special characteristic: the speed with which a plant grows, the rate of a chemical reaction, or the height a ball bounces, for example.

b. Keep your eye out for unusual properties or changes. Is an animal doing something you wouldn't expect it to? Does a rock look different from others around it? Is a chemical change going more slowly than you had thought it would? We can sometimes learn about the common and ordinary parts of the world if we carefully study the unusual and different parts.

c. Compare and contrast! It often helps to look for similarities among things (comparison) or for differences (contrast).

d. Group similar things together. Are all insects in a pond alike in some ways? Do all poisons have certain properties in common? Is there something that is the same about all bridges? Learn to look for ways in which the things in a group are like each other. This process is called **classifying** and is discussed in more detail in that section.

e. Notice how things are related to each other. This is especially important when you want to remember the things you've observed. For example, suppose you want to observe the animals that live in your back yard. One way to do this would be simply to study very carefully each animal you see: worms, robins, squirrels, cats, and so on. However, a better way would be to pay attention to the way these animals are related to each other. Worms don't just have a life of their own, for example. They are the prey of robins—and robins don't just spend all of their time eating worms. They also have to watch out for cats that may be after them.

Activity Pages 28 and 29 will give you practice on observing. The first of these has to do with the optical illusions on pages 120-124. Look carefully at these optical illusions as you attempt to answer the questions on Activity Page 28, pages 125-126. Activity Page 29 tests your ability to notice details in some drawings and then to answer questions from memory about those drawings. Look carefully at the two figures shown on pages 127 and 128. Then, **without looking at these figures**, attempt to answer the questions on Activity Page 29, pages 129-130. Finally, go back and check your answers with the drawings in the text. Don't forget that the skill of observation is a very basic one. You will use it in every other exercise in this section on Experimenting and Related Skills. As you do the remaining activity pages in this section, notice how observing is used in each case.

Relative Sizes

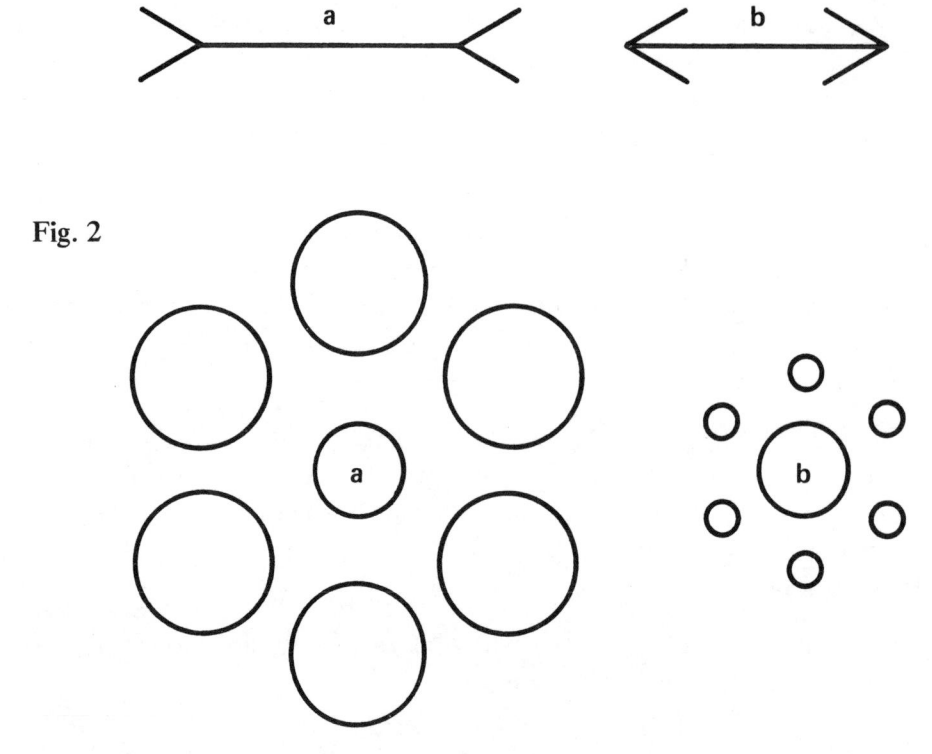

Fig. 1

Fig. 2

120 *Section Seven*

Fig. 3

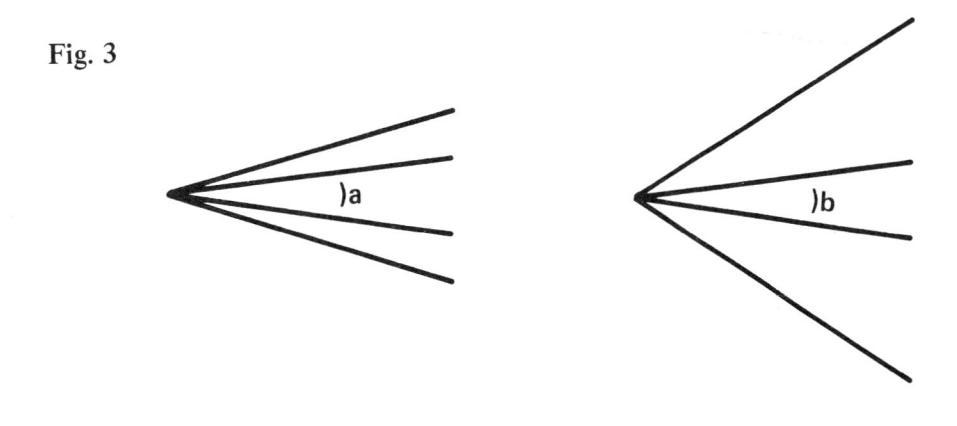

Fig. 4

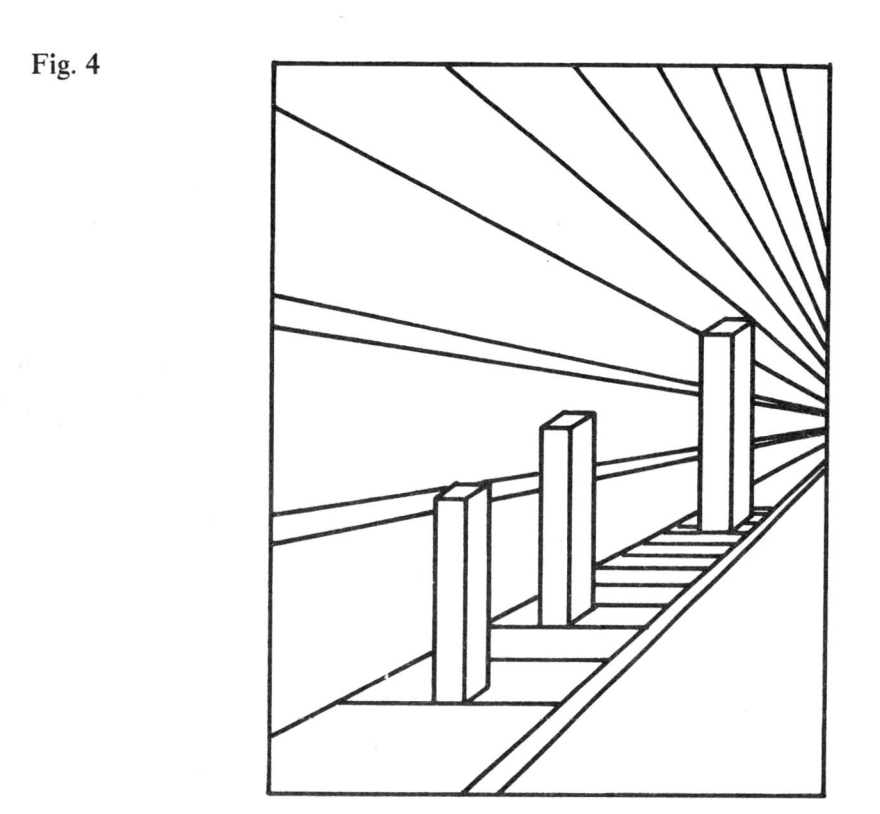

Experimenting and Related Skills **121**

Parallel and Perpendicular Lines

Fig. 5

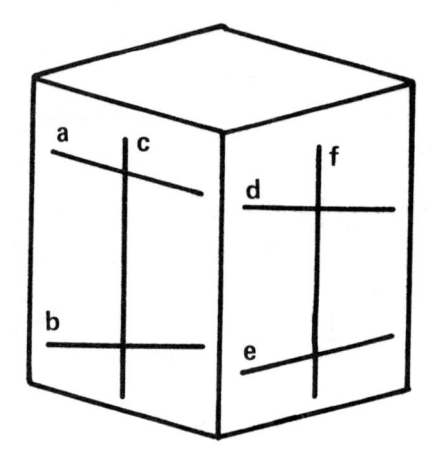

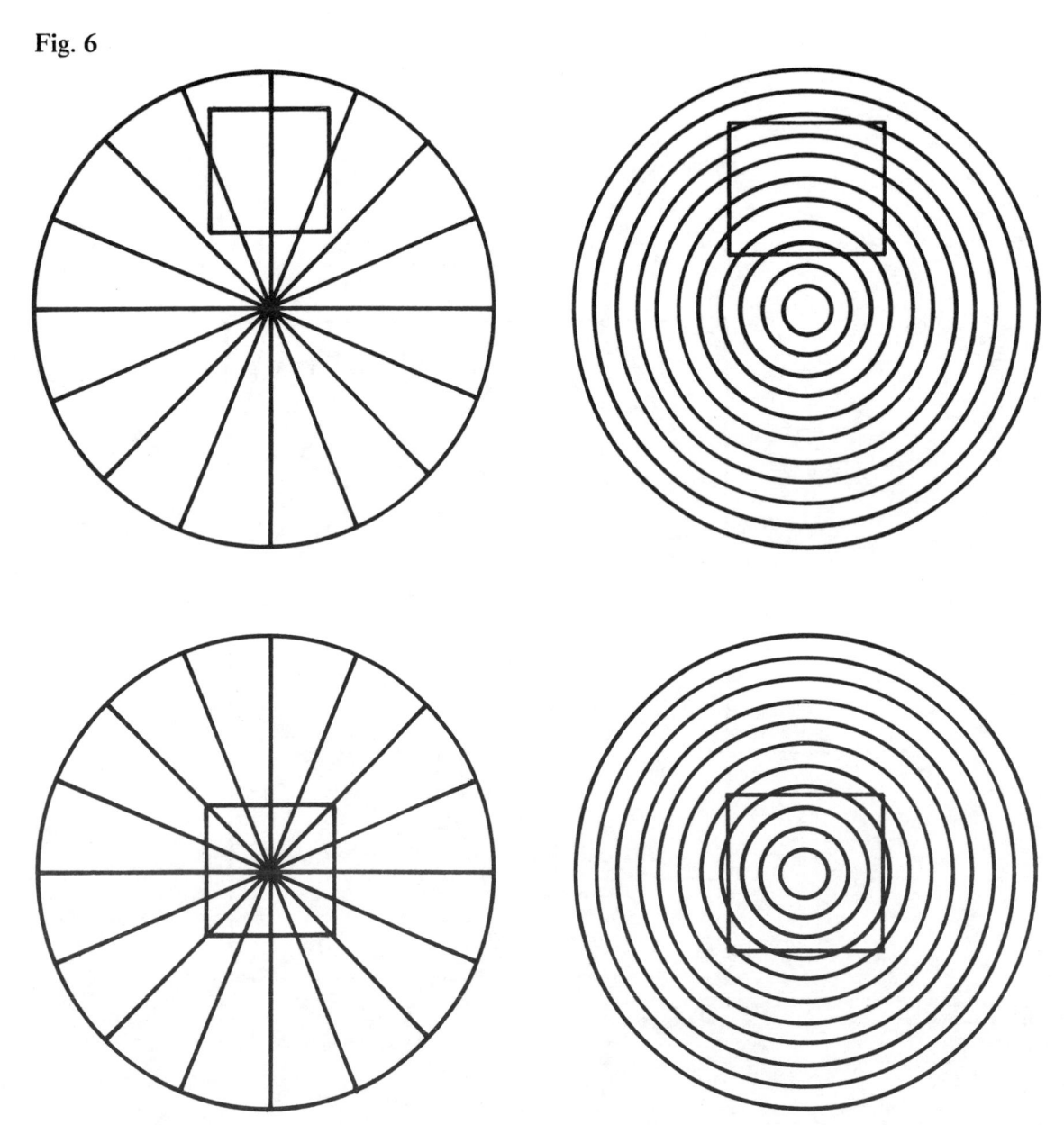

Fig. 6

122 *Section Seven*

Fig. 7

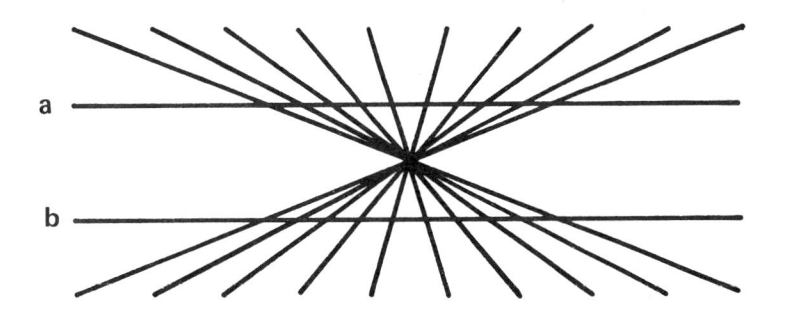

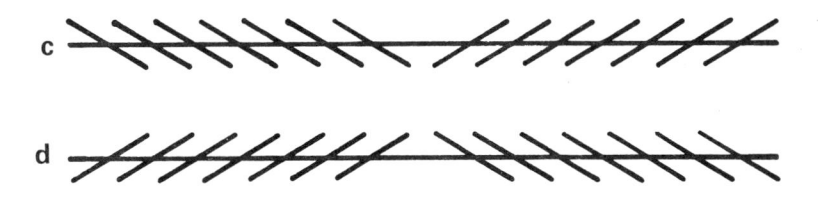

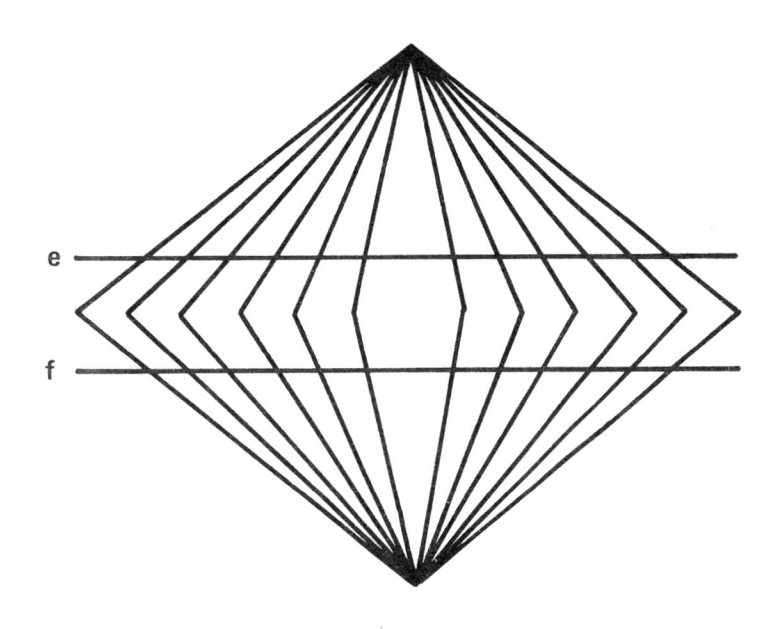

Experimenting and Related Skills 123

Ambiguous Figures

Fig. 8

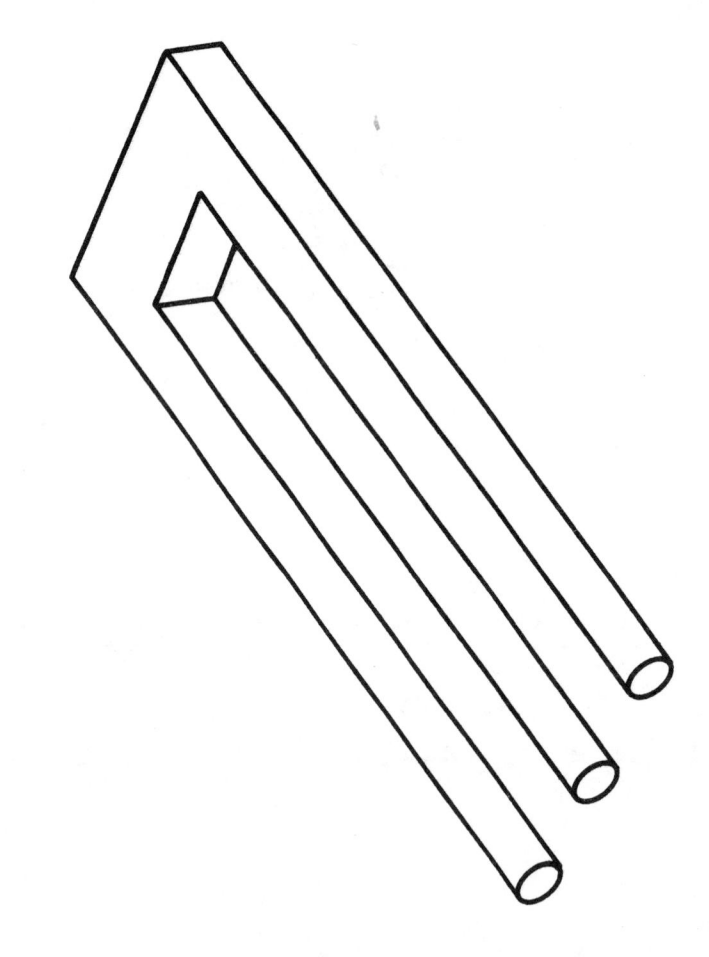

Fig. 9

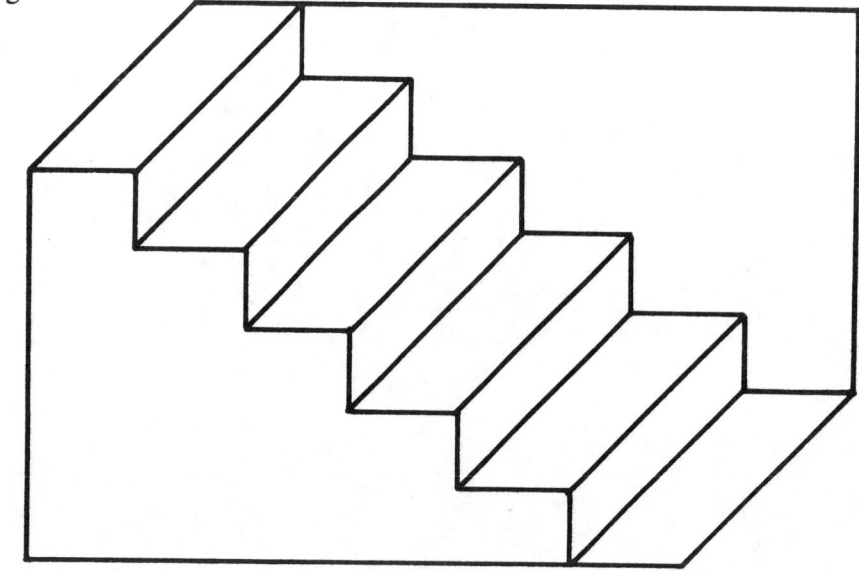

124 *Section Seven*

ACTIVITY PAGE **28** INTERPRETING OPTICAL ILLUSIONS

DIRECTIONS: Answer the following questions for each of the drawings on pages 120-124.

FIGURE	QUESTIONS	MAKE A MEASUREMENT TO FIND OUT THE CORRECT ANSWER	EXPLAIN HOW YOUR SENSES MIGHT HAVE BEEN FOOLED
1.	Which of the two horizontal lines is longer?		
2.	Which of the two circles in the center is larger?		
3.	Of the two angles in the middle of the two drawings, which is larger?		
4.	Which of the three vertical columns is tallest?		
5.	Which of the intersecting lines in this cube are parallel? Which are not?		
6.	Which of the four 4-sided figures in the circles is (are) perfect squares? Which are not?		

Experimenting and Related Skills

FIGURE	QUESTIONS	MAKE A MEASUREMENT TO FIND OUT THE CORRECT ANSWER	EXPLAIN HOW YOUR SENSES MIGHT HAVE BEEN FOOLED
7.	Are any of the labeled pairs of lines in these three drawings parallel?		
8.	How can this figure be described in two different ways?		
9.	How can this figure be described in two different ways?		

Fig. 10

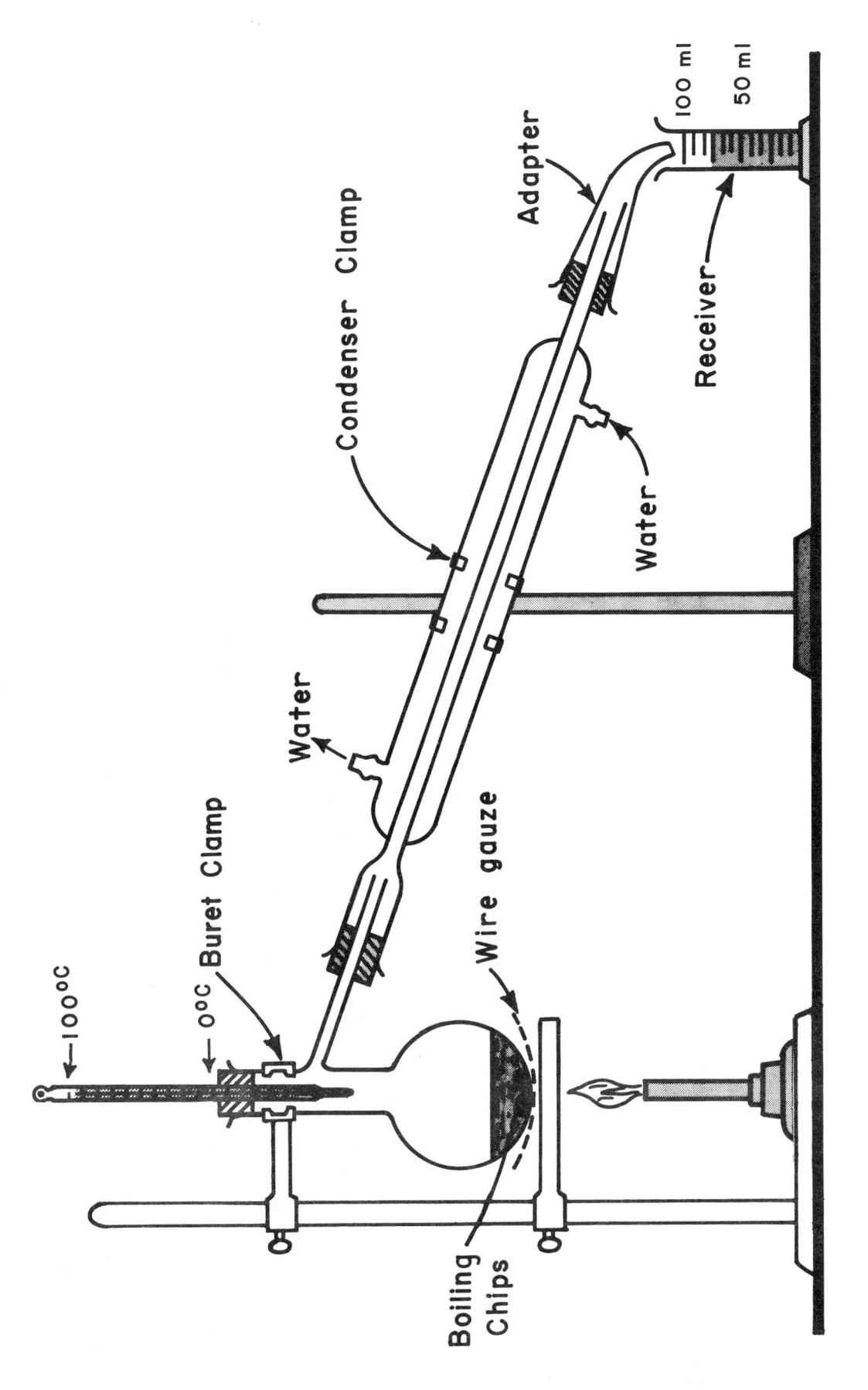

Experimenting and Related Skills 127

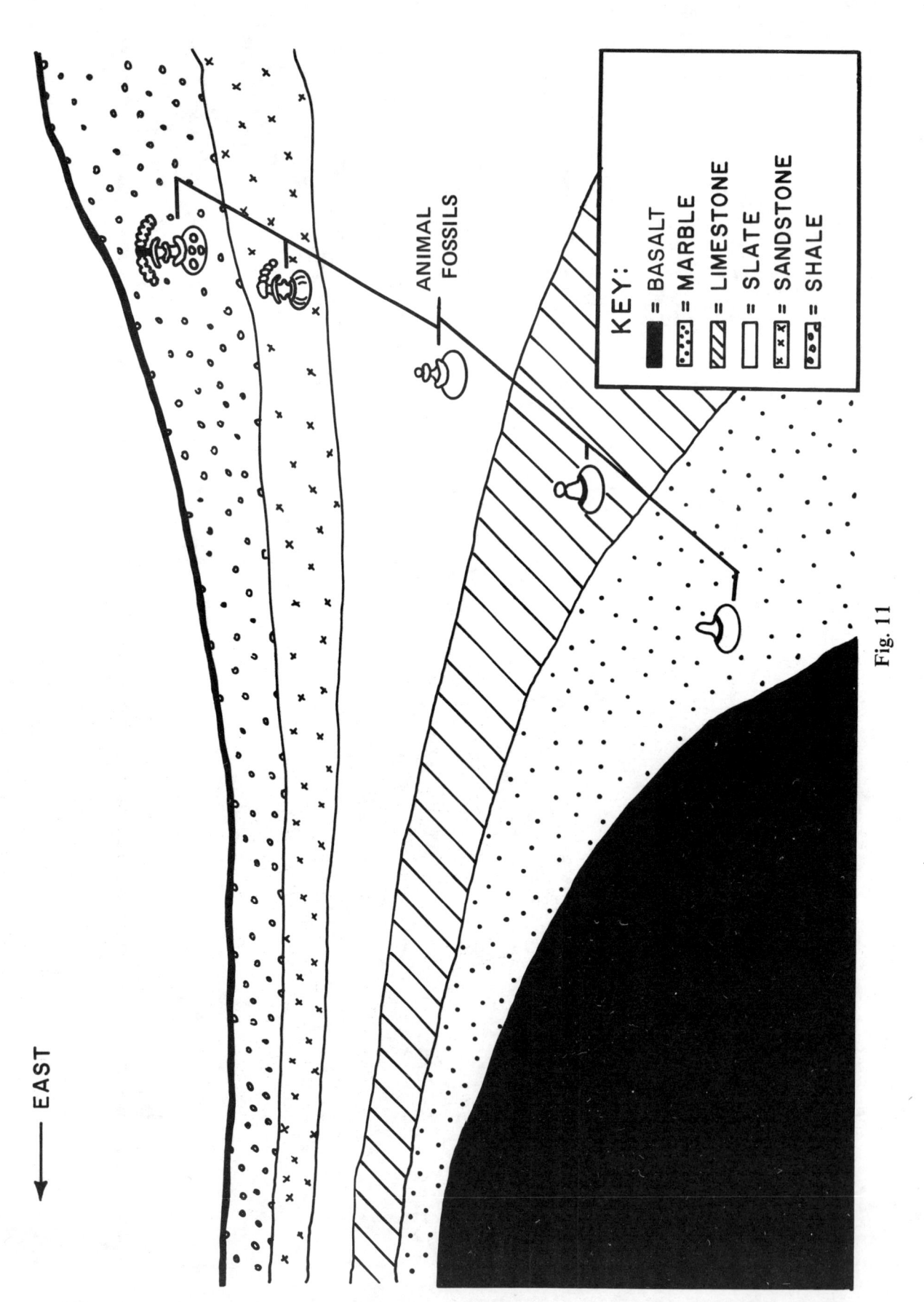

KEY:
■ = BASALT
▦ = MARBLE
▨ = LIMESTONE
☐ = SLATE
✕✕ = SANDSTONE
◦◦◦ = SHALE

ANIMAL FOSSILS

EAST

Fig. 11

128 *Section Seven*

ACTIVITY PAGE **29** THE SKILL OF OBSERVING

DIRECTIONS: Answer from memory each of the following questions about Figures 10 and 11 on pages 127-128. It is possible that the answer to one or more questions was not given in the diagrams.

Figure 10   (Distillation Apparatus)

1. Did the water used for cooling the condenser tube enter from the top or the bottom of the tube?

2. Is there anything in the boiling flask other than the liquid being distilled? If so, what is it?

3. What is the approximate temperature reading on the thermometer?

4. About how much liquid is contained in the receiving flask?

5. How is the boiling flask held in place?

6. How is the boiling flask being heated?

7. How would you describe the placement of the thermometer bulb?

8. Make a sketch of the boiling flask.

Experimenting and Related Skills

Figure 11 (Rock Outcropping)

1. How many strata are there in this section?

2. Which of the strata is thickest?

3. What type of rock makes up this stratum?

4. Do the animals become more or less complex in going from the bottom stratum to the top stratum?

5. What kind of rock is found in the top stratum?

6. Are there fossils in every stratum? If not, in which stratum or strata are they missing?

7. Do the strata become thicker towards the east or towards the west?

8. What minerals are found in this section? In what strata are they found?

2. The Skill of Inferring

The word **inferring** means trying to figure out what something means. For example, suppose you see a bluejay flying back and forth from a field to the roof of your house. Each time you see the bird, it is carrying a twig or piece of grass in its beak. Can you figure out what is happening from this description? You can probably infer that the bird is building a nest.

When you decided on your answer to this question, you were inferring, based on a set of observations. This is a second important skill in the process of experimenting. It wouldn't make much sense for a scientist simply to sit and watch (or listen to, or touch, or taste, or smell) something . . . and then not try to figure out what the observation meant!

One problem is that it is sometimes easy to confuse observations with inferences. People sometimes fail to separate what they **see** from what they think it **means**. For example, suppose you see an older man who is very, very fat. You might think, "How foolish. That person eats far too much. He is endangering his own health by not eating a proper diet." In this case, you've mixed up the observation ("the person is very, very fat") with the inference ("the person eats too much").

There are other explanations for overweight than just eating too much. For example, a person might have a disease that causes a weight problem. Perhaps the person eats no more than you do, but if the body doesn't handle food correctly, he or she gains too much weight.

You've probably heard a mistake like this called "jumping to conclusions." That phrase simply means that someone has made an inference too quickly, without thinking about other explanations for an observation. This is a bad thing to do in carrying out scientific experiments. It is also a dangerous thing to do in everyday life. Try to think of some ways in which a person might make some bad inferences (like our example of overweight above).

In the space below, write down some observations. Then write down at least two possible inferences for each observation you list. We've started you out with one example.

Observation	Possible Inferences
1. Mother shouted at me all morning.	1a. Mother is not feeling well.
	1b. I haven't behaved very well today.

This page and the following two pages contain six photographs. Each one shows a scene from the world around you. Look carefully at each one and be sure that you observe as much about it as possible. Then, try to figure out what can be inferred from what you see in each photograph. Activity Page 30, page 135, asks questions about these six photographs. Write down as much as you can infer in the spaces provided.

Photograph 1 *(Photo courtesy of Washington, D.C. Health Department)*

Photograph 2 *(Photo courtesy of National Oceanic and Atmospheric Administration)*

Photograph 3 *(Photo courtesy of USDA)*

Photograph 4 *(Photo courtesy of USDA–SOIL CONSERVATION SERVICE)*

Experimenting and Related Skills 133

Photograph 5 *(Photo courtesy of USDA–SOIL CONSERVATION SERVICE)*

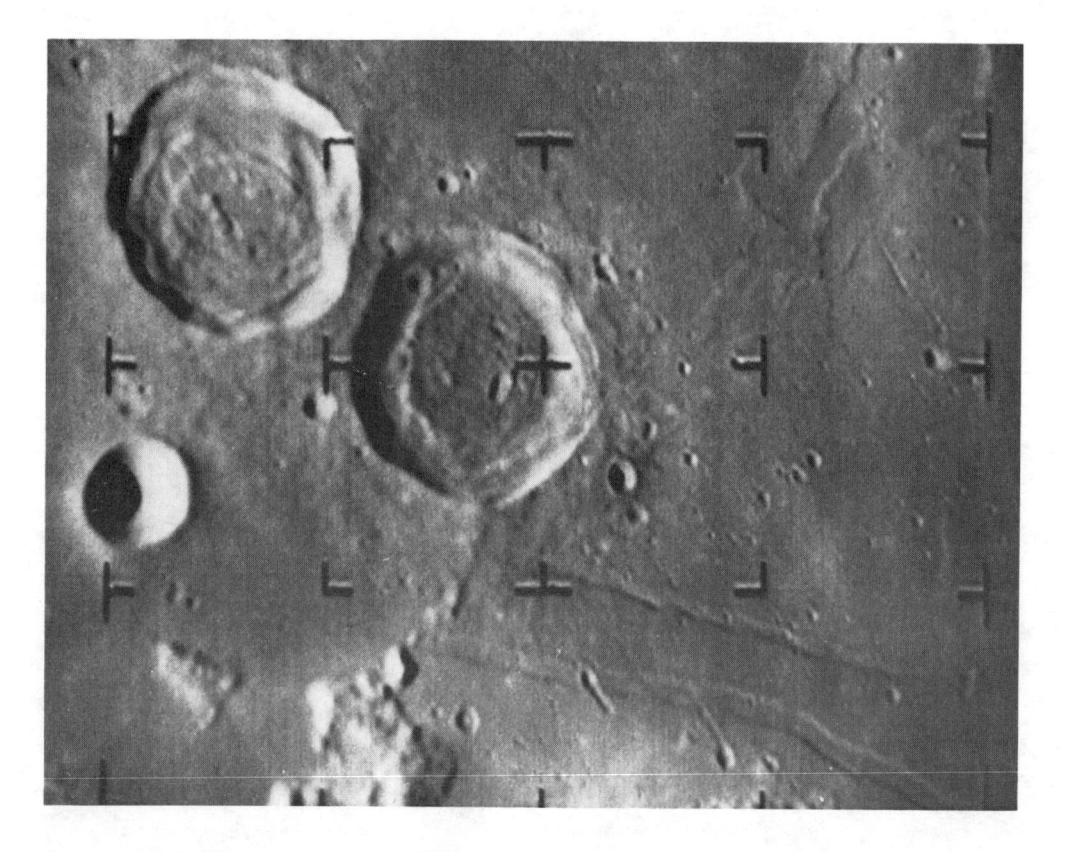

Photograph 6 *(Photo courtesy of NASA)*

ACTIVITY PAGE **30** THE SKILL OF INFERRING

DIRECTIONS: Answer the questions asked about Photographs 1-6 in the spaces provided. Then, list any other inferences you can make about each photograph.

Photograph 1

Why is this building two different shades of grey?

Photograph 2

What kind of weather is the western United States experiencing?

Photograph 3

Why do you think this farm has been deserted?

Photograph 4

What caused this roadway to collapse?

Photograph 5

Why does this region look so desolate?

Photograph 6

What do you think caused the markings on the moon you see here?

Experimenting and Related Skills 135

3. The Skill of Classifying

In some ways, the job of a scientist seems almost impossible. There are so many things to study in the natural world! Think of the astronomer's job. There are hundreds of billions of stars in the skies. Think how long it would take if an astronomer decided to study the stars one at a time. He or she could spend a whole lifetime and learn about only the very smallest fraction of stars that exist.

One way to overcome this problem is to classify things. By **classification** we mean putting together things that are related to each other. For example, one thing that astronomers do is to group stars according to their color. Every star is assigned to a class depending on whether it is white, yellow, orange, red, or blue.

How does this help? Instead of studying hundreds of billions of different stars, an astronomer only has to learn about a half dozen **classes** of stars. If all the stars in a class have similar characteristics, we can learn about many stars at once by studying the characteristics of the class as a whole. There might be 600,000,000 "yellow" stars, but we don't have to learn about each one separately. We can find out what "yellow" stars are like, and that tells us a lot (but certainly not **everything**) about those 600,000,000 individual stars.

Classification is useful in another way, too. Suppose we can find a way to classify many individual things into a single group. This could be a group of animals with six legs. Perhaps the common characteristic of the animals tells us something about the way they live. By finding a common characteristic of the animals, we may have learned more about the kind of organisms they are.

Of course, there is always more than one way to classify things. Astronomers classify stars by their brightness, as well as by their color. Sometimes it is useful to use one method of classification, and sometimes another method is more useful. You probably know a lot about classification already. In the space provided on page 137, list any systems of classification you are familiar with. We've started you out with a couple of examples. Then, examine Figures 12a, 12b, and 13, pages 138-140, and complete the practice exercises on classification on Activity Page 31, page 141.

Subject	Things Classified	Method of Classification
Your kitchen	Utensils	Drawer 1: Silverware
		Drawer 2: Plates
		Drawer 3: Pots and pans
		Drawer 4: Junk
Geology	Rocks	Igneous: "Fire rocks"
		Sedimentary: "Water rocks"
		Metamorphic: "Changed rocks"

Subject	Things Classified	Method of Classification
Biology	Animals	
Chemistry	Elements	
Physics	Kinds of energy	
Astronomy	Parts of the Solar System	
Geology	Erosional Forces	

CLOUD GENERA

Stratus ↑

Altostratus ↑

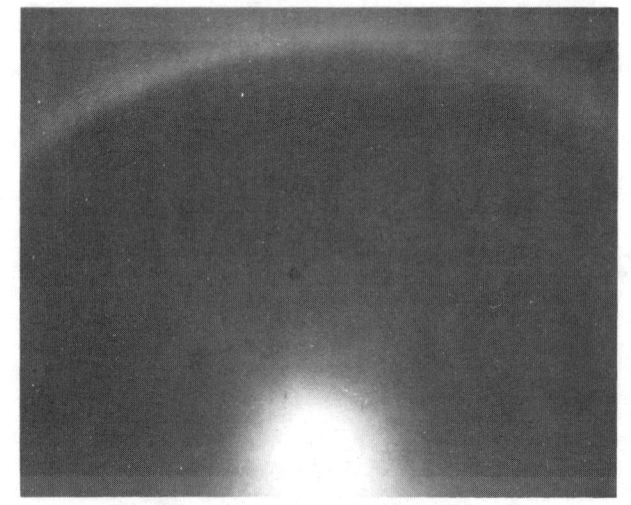

Cirrostratus ↑

Nimbostratus ↑

Cumulonimbus ↑

CLOUD GENERA

Cumulus ↑

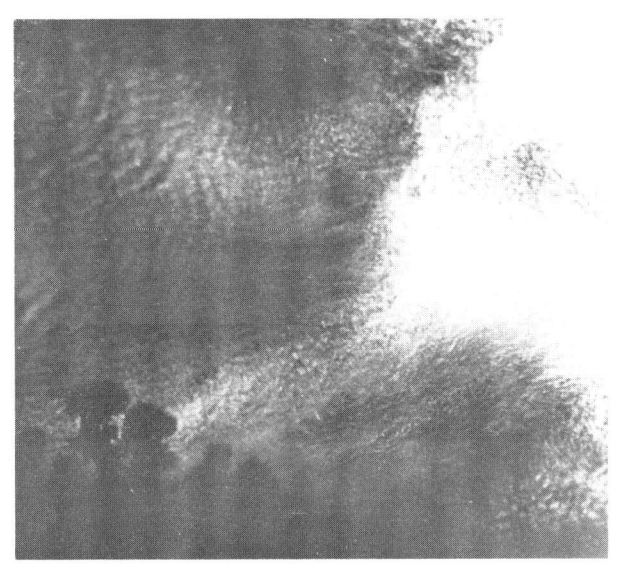

Cirrocumulus ↑

Altocumulus ↑

Cirrus ↑

Stratocumulus ↑

Figs. 12a, b

(Photos courtesy of National Oceanic and Atmospheric Administration)

Experimenting and Related Skills

Fig. 13

This photograph shows the tracks left by atomic particles as they pass through the bubble chamber. Different kinds of particles leave different kinds of paths. Classify the particles that passed through this bubble chamber.

(Photo courtesy of Lawrence Radiation Laboratory, Berkeley, California)

ACTIVITY PAGE **31** THE SKILL OF CLASSIFYING

DIRECTIONS: Classify the objects in Figures 12a, 12b, and 13 (pages 138-140) into about three groups each. At the bottom of the section, explain the basis for your classification system. Then invent a second system for classifying the same objects. Again, explain your system for classification.

Figure 12a

SYSTEM I	SYSTEM II
Group A	Group A
Group B	Group B
Group C	Group C
Explanation	Explanation

Figure 12b

SYSTEM I	SYSTEM II
Group A	Group A
Group B	Group B
Group C	Group C
Explanation	Explanation

Experimenting and Related Skills

4. The Skill of Generalizing

Hundreds of years ago, scientists learned one essential fact about doing experiments: Keep things simple! The world is a very, very complex place. If we're going to learn anything at all about the world, we have to learn it in very tiny pieces at a time. For example, suppose you want to know what conditions make dandelions grow well in your yard (with the idea that you might want to prevent them from growing well next year!). Just think of all the conditions that might be involved: amount of sun received; amount of water; other plants growing nearby; amount of mowing; length of roots. Can you think of any other factors?

How can you find out **which** of these factors is most important? Scientists believe that the way to answer this question is to study the factors one at a time. They believe that one has to ask a very, very simple and specific question to get a good answer. For example, a botanist (plant scientist) might decide to study the effect of only one element in the ground—say nitrogen—on the effect of dandelion growth. It might take many years for him or her to figure out how the amount of nitrogen in the ground affects the way dandelions grow. That might seem like a very tiny research project, but at the end of the study, the scientist would know one very exact, very small bit of information.

That's the way most scientists work. They pick very specific, very limited questions to study. Then, when they are done with their research, they end up knowing one small—but very exact—piece of information.

Is **that** all there is to scientific research? Certainly not! If it were, "science" would be nothing other than thousands of huge books containing small, specific, exact bits of information. These are the pieces of information we call **facts**. The study of dandelions, for example, might produce facts such as:

1. Dandelions in the northeast part of Illinois grew best in August of 1954, with 4.5% of nitrogen in the soil.

2. Dandelions in southern Kansas grew best in June of 1962, with soil that was 14.5% clay.

3. Dandelions in downtown Phoenix grew best in July of 1974, when they got 8.4 hours of sun a day.

4. Dandelions in suburban Boston grew best in May of 1980, when they received 0.1 cm of water a day.

You can probably see that facts like these, all by themselves, are not very useful. If you didn't live in northeast Illinois in August of 1954, for example, fact #1 would be of no value at all to you. The next important step in science, then, is to put facts together into larger groups. In a way, this is like the preceding skill since it involves **classifying** facts. The skill of finding ways that sets of facts are related to each other is sometimes called **generalizing**. It involves combining hundreds or thousands or millions of individual observations (facts) into a single grand statement that is true for all of them.

You have probably heard of a **scientific theory**. That is nothing other than a generalization such as we've just described. It is a single statement that tries to show how many different but related facts are connected with each other. This is a "thinking-and-paper-and-pencil" exercise rather than a laboratory experiment.

Of course, when a scientist first tries to put a collection of facts together, he or she isn't sure that the generalization produced is a good one. Therefore, a theory is considered to be very tentative. That means it is one person's guess about something that may or may not turn out to be a good idea. A good theory is never the final statement on a set of facts; it is a suggestion of one possible way of thinking about the facts. If it is truly a good theory, it will also suggest some experiments for testing the idea. Other scientists then have a way of checking out the new theory. New experiments are tried to see if they work out as the theory predicts. If they do, scientists become more confident in the new theory. If they don't, the theory is rejected. Then other people will think of other generalizations for the same set of facts.

You can see that science is always changing. Many times, more than one theory about the same set of facts has been suggested. At the present time, for example, there are two scientific theories about the way the universe was created. The people who invented both theories started with the same set of facts—facts about the universe—but the ideas they developed to fit those facts together are quite different. Right now, astronomers are looking for ways to test both theories, to see which is correct. They may find that one, the other, or neither one is the best explanation for the universe we see today. It is too early now to know what the result of this research will be.

Sometimes a theory has been shown to work successfully many, many times over. There seem to be no major situations in which it doesn't work quite well. Scientists become more and more confident that the theory is correct. When that happens, the theory is known as a **law**. You must be a bit careful about this word. In the non-scientific world, the term **law** refers to a statement that tells people how they **must** behave. In science, the same word is more uncertain. It tells how we **think** nature behaves, as best we can tell at the moment. One never knows for sure if a law will prove to be wrong. Many times in the history of science, a law that people had believed in was proved wrong years or centuries later. Can you think of some reasons that this might happen? Why would a generalization that people had trusted for a long time eventually turn out to be incorrect? Write down your answers before comparing them with the answers given.

Experimenting and Related Skills

Activity Pages 32 and 33 will give you some practice on making scientific generalizations. An example of the kind of task you are asked to perform is shown in Figure 14 (below). A coiled spring is hung from a tall bar and various objects are hung from the spring, one at a time. Each object causes the spring to stretch a certain amount. The weight of the object and the amount the spring stretches are recorded. What generalization can you make about these two quantities: (1) the weight of an object and (2) the amount it causes this spring to stretch?

In this example, there are many possible answers to the question. Some are quite simple, and others are more complex. For example, it should be obvious that the more an object weighs, the more it causes the spring to stretch. You can probably study this data better if you arranged it in some kind of order, such as that shown below:

Weight Added	50 g	100 g	200 g
Amount of Stretch	0.5 cm	1.0 cm	2.0 cm

Fig. 14

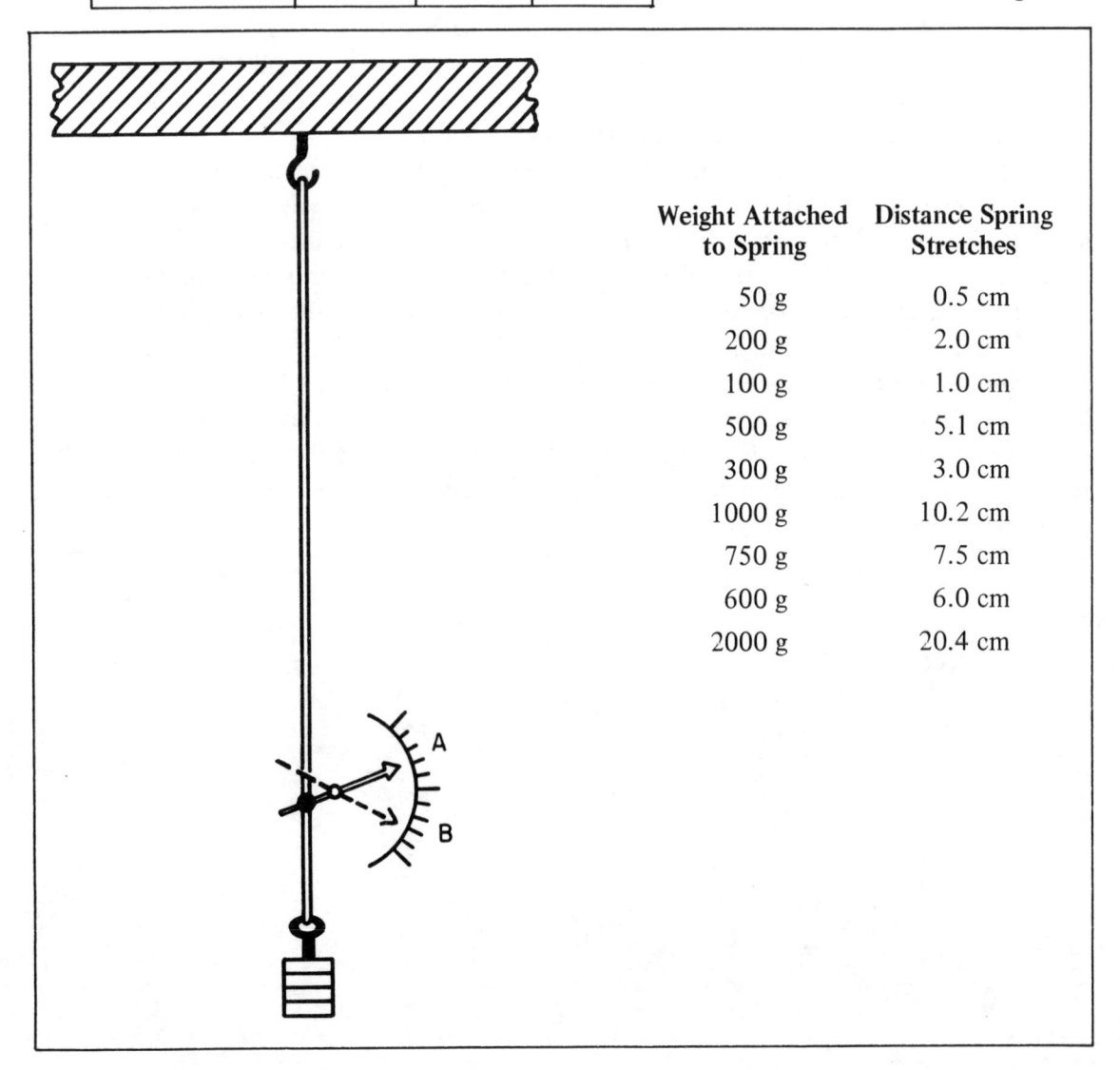

Weight Attached to Spring	Distance Spring Stretches
50 g	0.5 cm
200 g	2.0 cm
100 g	1.0 cm
500 g	5.1 cm
300 g	3.0 cm
1000 g	10.2 cm
750 g	7.5 cm
600 g	6.0 cm
2000 g	20.4 cm

One possible generalization, then, is: The heavier an object is, the more it causes a spring to stretch. Now look at the facts more carefully: we can be more exact about our generalization. Notice that an object that weighs **twice as much** causes the spring to stretch **twice as far**; one that is three times as heavy stretches the spring three times as far, and so on. We can improve our generalization, now, by saying that: The amount a spring stretches is directly proportional to the weight attached to it.

Finally, we can go one step further. You learned earlier in the text how useful it is to express ideas mathematically. The rather long English sentence above can be expressed just as well by using a mathematical formula:

$$S = f(w)$$

if we let **S** stand for the amount of stretch in the spring and **w** for the weight of the object on the spring. This is a good generalization of the facts presented here.

To see **how good** it is, we need to take one more step. We must find new experiments that are suggested by this generalization and try them out. For example, all of the facts used in this generalization came from using a single spring. Would the same kind of facts be produced using a different spring? That's an idea you could test. You can report your results in the space provided below. Can you think of other ways of testing your generalization? If so, do those experiments also and report them in the space provided below. When you've completed this practice exercise, turn to Activity Page 32 and 33, pages 146-148.

These activity pages will give you more practice in making scientific generalizations. You will not be asked to work on such huge problems as the origin of the universe. Instead, you will be given some information on some simple experiments. The activity pages contain facts collected from those experiments. Your job will be to look at those facts and make a generalization that fits them all together. Then, you may have some ideas for testing your generalization to see if it is correct or not.

ACTIVITY PAGE **32** THE SKILL OF GENERALIZING–I

1. ***DIRECTIONS:*** A ball is dropped through liquids of various densities. The speed at which the ball falls through each liquid is measured. Here are the data for this experiment. Arrange these data in some useful way. Then write a sentence, draw a graph, write a formula, or generalize about these data in some way.

DATA

Density of Liquid	Speed of Ball	Density of Liquid	Speed of Ball
2.0 g/cc	4.9 cm/sec	3.5 g/cc	3.0 cm/sec
4.0 g/cc	2.5 cm/sec	0.5 g/cc	20.0 cm/sec
3.0 g/cc	3.3 cm/sec	1.0 g/cc	10.1 cm/sec
1.5 g/cc	7.5 cm/sec	2.5 g/cc	3.9 cm/sec

GENERALIZATION

2. *DIRECTIONS:* A drug is being tested against a disease. The drug is added to a plate containing the germs that cause the disease. The number of germs killed for each dose is counted. Arrange these data in some useful way. Then write a sentence, draw a graph, write a formula, or generalize about the data in some way.

DATA

Drug Dose	Number of Germs Killed	Drug Dose	Number of Germs Killed
8 mg	128	3 mg	0
5 mg	50	11 mg	240
10 mg	200	1 mg	0
2 mg	0	9 mg	160
6 mg	72	7 mg	100
12 mg	290	4 mg	0

GENERALIZATION

ACTIVITY PAGE **33** THE SKILL OF GENERALIZING–II

1. ***DIRECTIONS:*** A piece of radioactive material is placed on a table. The amount of radiation received from this source is measured at various distances from the table. Arrange the data in some useful way. Then write a sentence, draw a graph, write a formula, or generalize about these data in some way.

DATA		GENERALIZATION(S)
distance	radiation received	
5.0 m	2.6 mCi	
4.0 m	4.0 mCi	
10.0 m	0.64 mCi	
6.0 m	1.8 mCi	
1.0 m	64.0 mCi	
20.0 m	0.16 mCi	
14.0 m	0.33 mCi	
8.0 m	1.0 mCi	

2. ***DIRECTIONS:*** From fossil remains, the size of the human brain is measured over a very long time. Here are the results of those measurements. Arrange the data in some useful way. Then write a sentence, draw a graph, write a formula, or generalize about these data in some way.

DATA		GENERALIZATION(S)
age of brain	size	
0 (modern)	1400 cc	
5,000 yr	1350 cc	
10,000 yr	1300 cc	
100,000 yr	750 cc	
500,000 yr	550 cc	
1,000,000 yr	500 cc	
250,000 yr	600 cc	
50,000 yr	1200 cc	

5. Designing Experiments

Experimenting in various fields of science can be quite different. Research on bacteria, properties of acids, volcanoes, electrical circuits, and galaxies all use special techniques and instruments. However, there are some procedures for designing experiments that are nearly the same in all fields. In this section, we'll review some of these procedures.

One must always begin with a PROBLEM or a question. A good experimenter never starts out with the attitude, "Let's see what we can discover today." He or she always has a **specific** question in mind. Where does that question come from? There are many possibilities. It may come from earlier research or reading the scientist has done. It could be an unusual event the scientist has observed. Many important discoveries in science have come about as a result of an accident. An alert man or woman has noticed that something "not quite right" has happened. He or she is puzzled about this unexpected event and sets out to figure out why it happened. In many cases, a problem is simply assigned to a researcher. Scientists who work for industrial firms, for example, may simply be told to "Go find out . . ." about something.

Once a problem has been selected, it must be STATED in very clear, precise terms. This can easily be the most difficult part of the whole research project. A researcher may know he or she wants to learn more about mushrooms, for example. But **exactly** what is it he or she wants to find out? In many cases, this may mean deciding how to limit a project. Beginning science students often choose topics that are much too broad. Finding out "how mushrooms grow," for example, may be an interesting subject. In fact, it's a topic hundreds of scientists have spent their whole lives studying. It is simply too broad a subject for any single piece of research. It is not unusual for a scientist to spend days or weeks just deciding how to state the problem he or she is going to work on. When you think about designing an experiment, then, don't be too hasty in writing down the problem you intend to study.

A scientist will often begin with some idea about the answer to a question. Suppose a meteorologist (weather scientist), for example, believes that rain can be produced artificially by dropping caramel corn on clouds. The research problem has already been decided on: How can we make rain artificially? And a possible answer is already in mind: By dropping caramel corn on clouds.

Having in mind a possible answer **before** research begins is called **framing a hypothesis**. A HYPOTHESIS is an educated guess as to what the answer to a question **might** be. Notice that it is an educated guess. It comes from a scientist's previous experience, background reading, ideas of other scientists, the results of related experiments, and so on. It is never a thoughtless "stab in the dark."

A well-stated problem and a good hypothesis have one thing in common: They help determine **what the experimenter will do**. Making decisions about the PROCEDURES is the next step in designing an experiment. Here's where various sciences differ from each other the most. The way a chemist, a biologist, a geologist, or an astronomer actually does research can be quite different—but again, there are a few common ideas in most of these fields.

For one thing, the scientist will limit research to a SINGLE VARIABLE at a time. There may be a lot of things one would like to know about carbohydrates, for example, but **only one** can be studied at a time. That one variable is **isolated** and tested while all other variables are held constant. For example, suppose a student would like to know the effect of temperature on the solubility of gases. The experiment he or she designs has two steps:

1. Find out how much carbon dioxide gas will dissolve in water at 20°C and 1.0 atmosphere of pressure.

2. Find out how much hydrogen gas will dissolve in alcohol at 40°C and 2.0 atmospheres of pressure.

Then, suppose the results of this experiment are:

1. In step 1, 25.0 ml of carbon dioxide gas dissolved.

2. In step 2, 13.5 ml of hydrogen gas dissolved.

From this information, **what factor** caused more carbon dioxide to dissolve than hydrogen? List all the answers you can think of before comparing your answers to those given.

Can you think of a way to change this experiment so that you could find the effect of temperature alone?

In order to determine the effect of temperature alone, every other factor would have to be the same ("held constant") in both parts of the experiment. For example, the student could have tried to:

1. Find out how much carbon dioxide would dissolve in water at 20°C and 1.0 atmosphere of pressure, and

2. Find out how much carbon dioxide would dissolve in water at 40°C and 2.0 atmospheres of pressure.

Suppose that these experiments were carried out and the results were:

1. In experiment 1, 25.0 ml of carbon dioxide dissolved.

2. In experiment 2, 19.8 ml of carbon dioxide dissolved.

What could you conclude from these results? Check your answer with the one given.

In most experiments, it is important to REPEAT the experiment many times. From the above example, for instance, would you be willing to say that carbon dioxide is more soluble in cold water than in warm water? Probably not? You'd probably feel better if you had three, five, ten, or a hundred examples that all turned out the same way. Your generalization would then be much more reliable.

Of course, you could go on testing the same question over and over again the rest of your life. Each time you'd be more and more sure about your answer. However, not many scientists want to spend their whole life on a single experiment! What factors do you think should be considered in deciding **how many times is enough**? Compare your answer to the one given.

In designing experiments, scientists often include a CONTROL. This is a plant, animal, chemical reaction, or other thing or event, which provides a basis to which everything else can be compared. A geologist might want to know how pressure affects the shapes of various minerals, for example. The control for this experiment, then, might be a set of crystals that are under **no pressure** at all. As pressure is applied to other crystals, the changes can be compared to the "no-pressure/control" crystals.

Now turn to Activity Page 34, pages 152-153, where you are asked to describe the control for a number of experiments.

ACTIVITY PAGE **34** CONTROLS

1. **DIRECTIONS:** In each of the following experiments, tell which variable is the control and why. Then tell what experimental factor is being tested by each of the other parts of the experiment.

Experiment A: Growth of geranium plants under various conditions.

Geranium Plant:	A	B	C	D	E	F	G	H
Light (per day)	12 hrs	24 hrs	4 hrs	12 hrs	12 hrs	12 hrs	12 hrs	12 hrs
Water (per day)	50 ml	50 ml	50 ml	100 ml	10 ml	50 ml	50 ml	50 ml
Fertilizer (per day)	none	none	none	none	none	0.1 g	1.0 g	2.5 g

In the spaces below, write CON for the plant that is the control. Next to the other plants, tell what experimental factor is being tested:

A _____ B _____ C _____ D _____

E _____ F _____ G _____ H _____

Experiment B: Reaction between two chemicals under various conditions.

	1	2	3	4	5	6	7	8
Amount of chemical A:	50 ml	50 ml	50 ml	50 ml	50 ml	50 ml	50 ml	50 ml
Amount of chemical B:	50 ml	50 ml	50 ml	25 ml	10 ml	100 ml	200 ml	150 ml
Temperature:	20°C	40°C	60°C	20°C	20°C	20°C	20°C	40°C

In the spaces below, write CON for the reaction that is the control. Next to the other reactions, tell what experimental factor is being tested:

1 _____ 2 _____ 3 _____ 4 _____

5 _____ 6 _____ 7 _____ 8 _____

2. **DIRECTIONS**: Tell what kind of control you would need in an experiment to answer each of the following questions. Then tell what experimental factors you would also use:

   a. How do changes in temperature affect growth of bacteria?

   Control: _____ Experimental factor: _____

   b. How does distance above the earth's surface affect the weight of the object?

   Control: _____ Experimental factor: _____

   c. How does the speed of a river affect the amount of erosion caused by the river?

   Control: _____ Experimental factor: _____

   d. How does the amount of salt dissolved in water affect the boiling point of water?

   Control: _____ Experimental factor: _____

Now that you know the main steps in designing an experiment, you're ready to actually begin the research itself. Many of the skills needed to perform an experiment are discussed in other sections of this book. We'll simply summarize and comment briefly on those steps here.

1. Completing an experiment in any science requires that you develop special laboratory skills for that science: filtering mixtures, weighing an object, timing an event, using a microscope, reading a rock key, making a topographic map, focusing a telescope, and so on. Some of these skills are discussed in Section Nine (Special Scientific Skills).

2. Measuring skills are especially important in every field of science. These are discussed in Section Five (Math Skills with Measurement).

3. Everything that happens in an experiment should be recorded. This includes not only **what you do** (procedures), but also **what you observe** (observations). Remember to be alert not only for those observations you are looking for and expect, but also for those that may occur unexpectedly.

4. When the experiment is over, the results may tell you a variety of things. These include:
    a. The answer to your question or the solution to your problem.
    b. Evidence that your hypothesis was **right** or **wrong.**
    c. Reasons for repeating the experiment or doing it again with some changes.
    d. Ideas for new research along similar or totally new lines.
    e. Hints that your original problem or question was **bad** or **wrong**. Sometimes people ask questions that have no answer ("Do you still beat your wife?") or make no sense ("Do you walk to school or carry your lunch?") from a scientific standpoint. It's better to recognize this **before** you begin an experiment, but that isn't always possible. Some great scientists have spent a lot of time and energy working on problems that turned out, in the end, to be the **wrong** question!

Activity Page 35, page 155, will help you put some of these ideas into practice in designing specific experiments.

ACTIVITY PAGE **35** DESIGNING EXPERIMENTS

DIRECTIONS: The topic for this experiment may come from one of two places: (1) Your teacher may assign a research question to you, or (2) you may be told to think of a question on your own. When you have the research question, write it in the first space below. Then fill in the remaining spaces.

1. The question I want to answer is: _____

2. My hypothesis about the answer is: _____

3. The steps I will follow to test this hypothesis are:

    a. _____

    b. _____

    c. _____

4. The single variable I will be testing is: _____

5. The control and experimental factors I'll use are:

    Control: _____

    Experimental factors: _____

6. The kinds of results that will tell if my hypothesis is right or wrong are:

    Right: _____

    Wrong: _____

7. Other possible results I might want to look for include: _____

8. Some possible sources of error I can think of include: _____

Experimenting and Related Skills

6. Carrying Out a Field Trip

Not all scientists do experiments in the laboratory. Think of the work that astronomers do, for example. They can't very well bring stars, comets, and galaxies into a laboratory to work on. A lot of their work has to be done "out there" in the real world. (By "real world" we mean a world that is not under human control, as it is in a laboratory.) Can you think of other kinds of research that cannot be carried out in a laboratory? Write down your ideas here before comparing them with the answers given.

Some of the skills of experimenting we've talked about apply to field research, also; others do not. For example, scientists who work in the field must also be good at inferring, classifying, and generalizing. They often do not have the chance to design experiments in a laboratory. This does NOT mean that planning is unnecessary for field work; far from it! A worthwhile field trip takes just as much work as most experiments. Before going into the field and studying wild animals, for example, a biologist would have to think about a number of questions. Some of these might be:

1. What animals will I study on this trip?

2. What characteristics will I be looking for?

3. How long will I have to be in the field?

4. How much assistance will I need to do this study?

5. What equipment will I need to bring along?

... and so on.

Below, you'll find some suggestions for planning one kind of field trip. Wetland areas (swamps, marshes, and bogs) are found nearly everywhere. Perhaps you will be able to arrange a trip to a wetland area near you. If so, you can decide how useful these suggestions are.

Some Ideas for Planning a Field Trip to a Wetland

There are two important parts to every wetland. One is the physical environment of the swamp, marsh, or bog. This includes the kind of soil found there, the characteristics of water in the wetland, and the atmospheric conditions above the wetland.

The second important part is the kind of life found in the wetland. In fact, wetlands are classified as swamps, marshes, or bogs on the basis of the kind of plants and animals that live there. In this field trip, you should find out as much as you can about both physical conditions and plant and animal life in the wetland. Here are a few things you might look for during your field trip.

1. What kind of soil is found in the wetland?

2. How deep is the water in the various parts of the area?

3. How acidic is the water?

4. How much dissolved oxygen does it contain?

5. What is the temperature of the water and the air above the wetland at various places in the area?

6. What kinds of birds do you see here?

7. What kinds of plants can you recognize?

8. What other organisms are found in the wetland?

9. What clues (such as tracks or droppings) can you find for animal life?

Activity Page 36, page 158, deals with only one part of field trips: planning the equipment you will need. Scientists who do field research usually have to carry their equipment out into nature to do their studies. When a geologist studies rocks, for example, he or she may have to take along a magnifying glass, some acid, a rock key, a rock hammer, and a measuring tape. What would each of these pieces of equipment be used for? Write down your answers before checking them against those given.

magnifying glass:

acid:

rock key:

rock hammer:

measuring tape:

Suppose you were planning a field trip to a nearby pond. You are interested in finding out what kinds of plants and animals live there. You would also like to learn more about the living conditions in the pond. What kinds of equipment would you need to take along on this trip? You can write down all the items you can think of on Activity Page 36. Then tell why each item is needed.

Experimenting and Related Skills 157

ACTIVITY PAGE **36** PLANNING A FIELD TRIP

DIRECTIONS: In the spaces below, tell the kinds of equipment you would need to take with you on a field trip to a pond and the reason(s) you would need each. (It might help to outline the field trip itself before attempting this exercise.)

Item Needed	Reason(s)

Section eight
Decision-Making Skills

People have to make decisions all the time. Sometimes the decision is simple: Should I cross the street at the corner or in the middle of the block? Others are far more complex: What career should I choose? A great thinker once said that the most important difference between humans and other animals is the number of decisions we have to make.

How are all these decisions made? There is no single skill called "decision-making" that works for every problem we face. At one level, there are simple, "snap-judgment" decisions that we make without much thought. Should you have chocolate cake or apple pie for dessert? The choice you make is hardly earth-shattering. It usually just doesn't make much difference—so you don't stop to think about all possible alternatives and then analyze the results that would follow from choosing each.

Simple decisions are not the ones we're interested in here. We're interested in more complex questions whose answers can have important influence on our lives. Actually, we can do no more than touch the surface of this question in this book. Decision-making is a complex, difficult skill that requires a whole book or a whole course all by itself!

The reason we include the skill here at all is because of the new place of science in everyday life. Until recently, most people's lives were simply not affected very much by science and technology. That may seem surprising to you. Every time you see a transistor radio, a new drug or medicine, a plastic, a dye or perfume, an automobile, truck or airplane, or any one of thousands of other items in your everyday life, you are confronted with "science at work." This was not always so. Before 1940, life was very much simpler. A person could get along very nicely without knowing very much science at all.

By the time you are an adult, you will have to make many, many decisions involving science and technology. We will mention only a very few of the possibilities:

1. Shall parents be allowed to choose the sex of their as-yet-unborn baby?

2. Shall we build more nuclear power plants to meet our energy needs?

3. Shall humans be kept alive as long as possible by artificial means, even though their body has really died?

4. What chances are we willing to take with the chemicals we add to our food?

5. Should scientists be held responsible for the uses to which society puts their discoveries and inventions?

6. Should we perform brain surgery on criminals who are convicted time after time?

How does a person go about making decisions on complicated questions like these? Again, we say that there is no simple answer to that question, but there are some guidelines that can be kept in mind. We will outline some of those guidelines here. Then, you can apply these ideas to five make-believe cases. Your analysis of each case can be written out on Activity Pages 37-41.

Some Guidelines on Decision-Making

1. Try to be very clear what the issue is in any situation. This can be difficult sometimes. There may be many issues, all related to each other. If this is the case, try to sort out the issues and deal with them one at a time. State the issue as a question or as a problem. That way, "solving the issue" will mean finding an answer to the question or the problem.

2. List the options that are available. This means finding out what answers or solutions may be possible to the problem you've stated. You should be very careful at this point. It may seem that there is only one answer to the dilemma—or you may think there is NO answer! Neither of these is likely to be true. Most issues in real life have some kind of an answer, one way or another. Even not doing something is one answer to a problem. People who think that a question is too difficult or has no solution are really allowing someone else to make the decision for them.

3. Read as much about the problem as you can. On controversial issues there is usually a great deal of information to be found. It will appear in magazines, newspapers, on television and radio, in books, and in publicity handed out by people on all sides of the problem. Do NOT worry that the information is biased on one side or another. Nearly everyone has an opinion on any social issue of importance. The important skill is to **be aware** that everyone has his or her own "ax to grind" and to **be able to recognize** prejudice in arguments. Of course, if you can find information without any bias, that's very good—but it may be difficult to do.

The term **bias** is an important one to understand. It means that a person is not willing to be completely open, impartial, and objective to all sides of an argument. The person definitely would like to see a question answered in one special way. How does bias show up in a speech, an article, or a piece of publicity? Sometimes, a person will simply give false information; he or she will lie. Most of us find it hard to believe that anyone speaking in public will purposely say things that are not true. However, this does happen, and it's good reason for always trying to get more than one view on a subject.

Another way to show bias is to select only certain facts on a topic and to ignore others. For almost any subject you pick, there will be dozens of facts. Usually, some facts will support one opinion and other facts will support another opinion. A biased writer or speaker will choose to mention only those facts that fit into his or her own beliefs; the others will simply be ignored. That's the reason for reading and listening to many sources. The facts that one person "forgets" may be mentioned by another.

At other times, a speaker or writer may want you to believe that certain **opinions** are **facts**. The statement that "smoking makes a person more attractive" may sound like a fact. It might give you the idea that some group of scientists had studied people and found that, in general, smokers are more attractive than non-smokers. That isn't true. No research exists to support the idea that if you smoke, people will find you more attractive than if you don't smoke. Of course, some people may have the **opinion** that smokers are more attractive than non-smokers. That opinion is just that: someone's belief. It is **not** a fact.

4. List the arguments on all sides of an issue. In some cases, these may be the arguments **for** and **against** an idea or an action. There are usually more than two choices on an issue, so you will have to figure out what the good and bad things are about each possible option. Remember that someone with a bias on an issue can help you to see arguments both for and against his or her own case.

5. Be able to distinguish facts from opinions. In some ways, this may be the most important decision-making skill of all. Remember that **facts** are statements about the world that can be tested and agreed to by any reasonable person. A statement that boiling water is hot is one that most people can agree with. **Opinions** are the personal attitudes we have about facts. Some people may think it is a good idea to pour boiling water over others with whom they disagree. That **belief**, however, is not a **fact**—it is a personal **opinion**. It is completely all right for people to have opinions—that's what it means to live in a free country—but a person's opinions about something mean something very different from a fact about that thing. The facts are something we can probably all agree upon. The opinions are legitimate bases for debate, argument, and discussion.

6. Decide what additional information is needed on this issue. After reading and listening to arguments on all sides, you may decide that there are more facts you need to learn. You might want to have some additional opinions about the issue. Be sure that you know all you need to know before starting to make up your own mind.

7. Find out where to get the information you need. Since you have already done some reading and listening, you will probably have some ideas about where to go next. If not, ask or write the people whose opinions you have already heard.

8. Think about what to do when experts disagree with each other. The fact that scientists often argue for different sides of the same issue may confuse people. Some great physicists, for example, have spoken out **for** the use of nuclear weapons; others have opposed them. How can scientists disagree, people ask, on the same scientific question? The answer is that they usually **don't** disagree on the **science** that's involved. They usually agree on the factual part of the argument. It's questions of economics, religion, philosophy, social priorities, and the like that cause scientists to disagree. Again, the best thing to do is to separate the factual part of a scientist's argument from the opinions and values that are included along with the facts.

It also helps to keep an eye open to the connections a scientist has. A physicist who works for a nuclear power company or the Department of Defense is likely to have quite different ideas on the use of nuclear power than someone who does not. If possible, when you read someone's arguments on a question, try to find out who they work for. Then assess their arguments with that in mind.

9. Try to make up your own mind about the issue. We repeat that this is often hard to do. Sometimes it seems as though there **are** no answers at all. You are probably in the best

possible position to make up your mind, at least for the moment. You probably are not old enough to vote, to own property, or to pay taxes. You really can be an objective outsider. This gives you an opportunity to give a fair hearing to all sides and make up your own mind without bias... perhaps for the last time in your life!

Of course, you should be very aware that any decisions you make are almost certainly temporary ones. Conditions change, new information becomes available, and our attitudes and values grow. What we thought we knew for sure last year or last week may no longer make any sense next year or next week.

Introduction to Case Studies

Your teacher will explain the way these five cases are to be handled. You may be asked simply to write out your ideas on Activity Pages 37-41 (one follows each case study). You could be asked to meet with other students and discuss the case together. Some of you could play the role of people mentioned in the case, or you could have a debate with some class members on each side of the argument. For any of these activities, you should begin with a completed activity page for the case in front of you. The five case studies used here are all adapted from David E. Newton's *Social Issues in Science* (Portland, Maine: J. Weston Walch, Publisher, 1982).

Case Study #1: Prolonging Human Life: The Case of Clinton John Broderick IV

Clinton John Broderick IV suffers from acute iliatory laminitis (AIL). Mr. Broderick, 72 years of age, has been confined to the hospital for eighteen months, during which time his condition has become increasingly worse. There is no known cure for AIL, and patients tend to deteriorate slowly after its onset, usually late in life. Life expectancy ranges from two to about twenty years after appearance of the disease, which is characterized by gradual weakening of the limbs, loss of strength in the muscles, loss of eyesight and coordination, impaired mental function, and general disability.

Mr. Broderick's case has been somewhat unusual in that it has been characterized by alternate periods of rapid deterioration and temporary remission. Although there appears to be no hope of Mr. Broderick's recovery, the medical staff is making every effort to sustain his life and make him as comfortable as possible. Frequent minor surgery has been performed, and occasional sessions on the artificial kidney have become necessary. Mr. Broderick has been comatose for the last two months and has not spoken coherently for almost four months.

Mr. Broderick's three children have recently been discussing the advisability of maintaining their father's life in his present condition. The eldest son is especially concerned about the enormous expense of his father's medical care (hospital bills have been mounting at about $3,000 per month), which will bankrupt the family business within two years.

The only daughter insists on the maintenance of her father's life, at whatever cost and by whatever means, in the hope that a cure will be found. Research has produced some promising leads, and some scientists predict the finding of a complete cure within two years.

The third child points out the "uselessness" and misery of their father's present life. For all practical purposes, he has been dead for at least eighteen months. While there remains a chance that Mr. Broderick will recover, there is no reason to believe that he will ever again be able to function in any "human" way.

What decision should be made regarding the maintenance of Clinton John Broderick IV's life?

ACTIVITY PAGE 37 ANALYZING CASE STUDY #1

1. In a single sentence, state what the issue is in this case study: _____
   _____

2. List the possible solutions, answers, or options that are possible: _____
   _____

3. What arguments are there **for** and **against** each of the options you listed?

	For	**Against**
Option 1:	_____	_____
Option 2:	_____	_____
Option 3:	_____	_____

4. List all of the facts and all the opinions given in this selection:

	Facts	**Opinions**
1.	_____	_____
2.	_____	_____
3.	_____	_____
4.	_____	_____

5. What additional information would you like to have on this issue? _____
   _____

6. What is your **present opinion** about the correct option to choose? (Explain your choice briefly.)
   _____
   _____
   _____

Section Eight

Case Study #2: Controlling Human Behavior with Chemicals

Fillmore Junior High School is located at the edge of the inner core of Wildwood City. As in many large cities, Wildwood's downtown area is populated by families with low income, more than half of whom are nonwhite. The suburbs, on the other hand, tend to be made up of middle-class white families. The children of both groups attend Fillmore Junior High.

Recently, there have been a number of "incidents" in which students have attacked other students and teachers. There is a high level of disobedience and misbehavior in many classrooms. Some people blame the tension on racial problems, but a number of fights have been among members of the same race. Attempts to explain the problem on the basis of class conflict (lower class vs. middle class) are also not very convincing. Some authorities complain that pressures in the community are so great that kids are just "keyed up" most of the time. Whatever the cause, conditions have become so bad that police patrol the school halls, and two school board members have actually called for closing the school a month early this year.

A professor of educational psychology at a nearby university suggests that students with a disciplinary record be screened by a board of three physicians. This board would then recommend drug therapy (either tranquilizers or stimulants) for those whom it diagnosed as hyperkinetic. The permission of parents would be necessary, but for those who agreed, the city would pay 75% of drug costs and parents, 25%. While this plan might not eliminate Fillmore's problems, the professor claims, it should help to reduce them significantly.

ACTIVITY PAGE **38** ANALYZING CASE STUDY #2

1. In a single sentence, state what the issue is in this case study: _____

2. List the possible solutions, answers, or options that are possible: _____

3. What arguments are there **for** and **against** each of the options you listed?

	For	**Against**
Option 1:	_____	_____
Option 2:	_____	_____
Option 3:	_____	_____

4. List all of the facts and all the opinions given in this selection:

	Facts	**Opinions**
1.	_____	_____
2.	_____	_____
3.	_____	_____
4.	_____	_____

5. What additional information would you like to have on this issue? _____

6. What is your **present opinion** about the correct option to choose? (Explain your choice briefly.)

_____

_____

_____

Section Eight

Case Study #3: Using Genetic Engineering to Improve Humans

Professor Augustus Worthy has been engaged in genetic research for almost thirty years. His recent interest in deciphering the DNA code for "handedness" leads him to believe that a person becomes either right- or left-handed because of two factors, one genetic and the other environmental. The genetic factor produces only a **tendency**, which can be definitely established through biochemical analysis of DNA structure.

However, if the environment is right, **any** person can be brought up to be **either** right- **or** left-handed. That is, parents can force a child who shows tendencies toward being right-handed to become left-handed. Of course, this may cause psychological damage.

Dr. Worthy's research has convinced him that he is capable of performing genetic surgery that would allow parents to choose right- or left-handedness for their prospective offspring. Essentially, this involves removing a sample of bodily fluids from the fetus in the mother's womb, "correcting" the DNA structure by chemical means, and then returning the fluids to the fetus. There is no reason to expect any harmful effects from this type of operation.

ACTIVITY PAGE **39** ANALYZING CASE STUDY #3

1. In a single sentence, state what the issue is in this case study: _____

2. List the possible solutions, answers, or options that are possible: _____

3. What arguments are there **for** and **against** each of the options you listed?

	For	Against
Option 1:	_____	_____
Option 2:	_____	_____
Option 3:	_____	_____

4. List all of the facts and all the opinions given in this selection:

	Facts	Opinions
1.	_____	_____
2.	_____	_____
3.	_____	_____
4.	_____	_____

5. What additional information would you like to have on this issue? _____

6. What is your **present opinion** about the correct option to choose? (Explain your choice briefly.)

Case Study #4: Food Additives: How Much Protection Do We Need?

Dr. Vivian Stark has been studying the effects of potassium phenoxylated bromide (PPB) for almost two years in an attempt to determine its long-range effects on human health. Hamsters, who are fed 0.001 grams of PPB in their daily meals, show retinal cancer about five percent above that normally observed. The quantity of PPB used in her research is about 100,000 times as great as that normally eaten by an individual in a whole week, and smaller amounts have not been shown to produce any serious damage to the hamsters' health. The data so far is just not clear-cut enough for Dr. Stark to say that PPB definitely causes cancer.

On the other hand, PPB is widely used in the preparation of white bread and millions of men, women, and children are exposed to the compound each day. The long-term effects and the answers to other questions about PPB may not be known for years. It's possible that hundreds or thousands of people will be doomed because of the PPB they ate this year.

A strict interpretation of the law would probably require that PPB be banned immediately. This may not occur, however, because PPB is the cheapest and most widely used agent for producing smaller holes and better consistency in bread. Restrictions on its use would cost the baking industry millions of dollars annually. Simon J. Bunn, President of the Amalgamated Bakeries, has said, "Dr. Stark's studies at this point tell us nothing at all about the dangers of PPB to human health. We vigorously support all additional research efforts aimed at clarifying the role of PPB in human nutrition. In fact, we have awarded Dr. Stark a grant of $1,000 to continue her important work. But until more substantial evidence is obtained, we feel that the use of PPB by the baking industry should not be curtailed."

Reaction to that statement has come from Representative Hollard F. X. Dimmley:

> The continued use of PPB represents an immediate and serious threat to the health of the American public. Research evidence suggests strongly that the rate of cancer increased in certain animals fed PPB. In view of the nature of cancer itself, we can reasonably expect to find an increasing rate of the disease with longer use of the chemical in future studies. In any case, we can hardly afford to gamble with the lives of millions of children by allowing continued use of this dangerous drug.

ACTIVITY PAGE **40** ANALYZING CASE STUDY #4

1. In a single sentence, state what the issue is in this case study: _____

2. List the possible solutions, answers, or options that are possible: _____

3. What arguments are there **for** and **against** each of the options you listed?

	For	Against
Option 1:	_____	_____
Option 2:	_____	_____
Option 3:	_____	_____

4. List all of the facts and all the opinions given in this selection:

	Facts	Opinions
1.	_____	_____
2.	_____	_____
3.	_____	_____
4.	_____	_____

5. What additional information would you like to have on this issue? _____

6. What is your **present opinion** about the correct option to choose? (Explain your choice briefly.)

Case Study #5: Water Pollution: Are We Our Brothers' Keepers?

Donald's Creek, located on the Wahatapouchee River (a tributary of the Missouri), had a population around four thousand until the founding of a new branch of the state university three miles from town in 1965. Population boomed to more than nine thousand in 1968, more than twelve thousand in 1972, and twenty thousand were projected by 1980.

This increase in population has occurred so quickly that the town has been unable to construct a new sewage treatment plant, so the previous practice of dumping untreated wastes directly into the river continues.

The citizens of Donald's Creek have not experienced any serious water pollution problems, but the residents of Buffalo Bend (population 2,500) ten miles downstream have begun to complain about the fouling of the river. The river is still essentially clean in Donald's Creek itself, and there is reason to believe that the Buffalo Bend problem is largely due to wastes discharged from the Penanpensel Paper Company factory, four miles downstream from Donald's Creek. In any case, the citizens of Donald's Creek can't understand the anger and concern of the citizens of Buffalo Bend.

Although its field analysis of the Wahatapouchee is not complete, the state water commission has announced that **at least part** of the pollution of the river in Buffalo Bend is due to untreated sewage being dumped at Donald's Creek. They have, therefore, ordered the town to construct a sewage treatment plant within the next year. Failure to comply with the order will result in a fine of $5000 per week.

Complaints about the state's action have arisen in various segments of the Donald's Creek community. Members of the chemistry department of the state university say that the water commission acted before it had definite data on the extent to which Donald's Creek was causing the problem at Buffalo Bend. A number of citizens are appalled at the estimate of $4-$5 million for the construction of the new plant, and many are suggesting that they would rather pay the fine. Finally, State Representative Glackinski's office indicates the governor will appoint a new water commission next year, and the present decision may be set aside. All in all, the town has unified itself in opposition to the construction of the new sewage plant.

Decision-Making Skills

ACTIVITY PAGE **41** ANALYZING CASE STUDY #5

1. In a single sentence, state what the issue is in this case study: _____

2. List the possible solutions, answers, or options that are possible: _____

3. What arguments are there **for** and **against** each of the options you listed?

	For	**Against**
Option 1:	_____	_____
Option 2:	_____	_____
Option 3:	_____	_____

4. List all of the facts and all the opinions given in this selection:

	Facts	**Opinions**
1.	_____	_____
2.	_____	_____
3.	_____	_____
4.	_____	_____

5. What additional information would you like to have on this issue? _____

6. What is your **present opinion** about the correct option to choose? (Explain your choice briefly.)

Section nine

Special Scientific Skills

In each science, there are certain special skills that have to be mastered. For example, a geologist has to know how to read topographic maps. A chemist has to know how to write chemical equations. A biologist has to know how to use a "key." In many cases, a particular skill is used in many sciences. Chemists, biologists, physicists, astronomers, and geologists all need to know how to write chemical formulas and equations, for example. Drawing flow charts is no longer a skill required just by computer experts, but is something that scientists in all fields should know something about.

In this introductory text, we cannot cover **all** of the basic skills in **all** of the major sciences. What we can do is to give you a brief introduction to the kinds of skills needed in chemistry, physics, biology, and the earth sciences. Then, when you begin to specialize in certain sciences, you will go on and learn more about the skills of that specific science. For each of the skills discussed in following sections there is an activity page that will allow you to practice the skill you have just learned.

1. Chemical Formulas

In chemistry, the 105 known elements are represented by **symbols**. These are one- or two-letter codes that represent **one atom** of an element. The symbol **O**, for example, stands for one atom of oxygen. The symbol **Fe** stands for one atom of iron. The symbols of some of the elements are given in Table 1 on page 174.

Chemical formulas are combinations of symbols that represent molecules. For example, the formula H_2O represents one molecule of water. The number written to the right and slightly below the symbol tells **how many** atoms there are of that kind. If there is no number there, it means that there is just **one** atom of that kind. The formula tells us that one molecule of water contains two atoms of hydrogen and one atom of oxygen. The formula for baking soda is $NaHCO_3$. That formula tells us that one molecule of baking soda consists of one atom of sodium (Na), one atom of hydrogen (H), one atom of carbon (C), and three atoms of oxygen (O). To see if you understand the meaning of formulas, write down the meaning of each of the following before comparing your answers with those given.

Special Scientific Skills 173

TABLE 1

Symbols and Valences of Some Common Elements

ELEMENT	SYMBOL	VALENCE(S)*
aluminum	Al	+3
bromine	Br	-1
calcium	Ca	+2
chlorine	Cl	-1
copper	Cu	+1, +2
hydrogen	H	+1
iodine	I	-1
iron	Fe	+2, +3
lead	Pb	+2
lithium	Li	+1
magnesium	Mg	+2
mercury	Hg	+1, +2
nickel	Ni	+2
oxygen	O	-2
potassium	K	+1
silver	Ag	+1
sodium	Na	+1
sulfur	S	+4, +6, -2
zinc	Zn	+2

*Some elements may have more than one valence.

What is the meaning of:

K _____ CH$_4$ _____

Ca _____ H$_3$PO$_4$ _____

HCl _____ NaNO$_2$ _____

Chemists learn how to write formulas by using **valences**. The term **valence** refers to the way that an atom will combine with other atoms. Valences can be positive (+) or negative (–). Atoms with positive valences combine with atoms with negative valences. Some atoms can have both positive and negative valences, which allows them to combine with almost any other kind of atom. The valences of some common elements are given in Table 1 on page 174.

In writing chemical formulas, the total positive valence must always be equal to the total negative valence. An example will illustrate this point. Suppose we want to write the formula for the compound formed between sodium and bromine. If we look at Table 1, we find:

$$\text{sodium: Na}^{+1} \qquad\qquad \text{bromine: Br}^{-1}$$

Since sodium has a positive valence, and bromine a negative valence, these two can combine with each other. If we take one atom of each, we will have the same positive and negative valences:

$$\text{NaBr}$$
$$+1 \text{ valence} = -1 \text{ valence}$$

What formula would represent the compound made from potassium and oxygen? Check Table 1 for the valences of these two elements. We find that:

$$\text{potassium: K}^{+1} \qquad\qquad \text{oxygen: O}^{-2}$$

If we just put these two together, the way we did with the last example, we would have:

$$\text{K O}$$
$$+1 \text{ valence} \quad -2 \text{ valence}$$

Notice that the total positive valence is NOT the same as the total negative valence. What should we do?

The way to solve this problem is to use more than one atom of one or the other. Notice that if we take two atoms of potassium, we would then have the formula:

$$\text{K}_2\text{O}$$

Now, how do the positive and negative valences compare?

$$2 \times (+1) \quad\quad -2$$
$$+2 \quad = \quad -2$$

In order to balance a chemical formula, then, we must always take as many atoms of each kind as necessary to make the TOTAL POSITIVE VALENCE EQUAL THE TOTAL NEGATIVE VALENCE.

There's only one more thing you need to know about formula writing. There are some groups of atoms that often stay together and act like a single atom. They are something like groups of kids who spend so much time together, you think of them as a single unit. These groups of atoms are called **polyatomic ions**. Some of the more common ones are listed in Table 2.

TABLE 2

Some Common Polyatomic Ions

POLYATOMIC ION	FORMULA	VALENCE
ammonium	NH_4	+1
carbonate	CO_3	−2
hydroxide	OH	−1
nitrate	NO_3	−1
phosphate	PO_4	−3
sulfate	SO_4	−2

You won't have to worry about these if you keep in mind that they **act** like single atoms. You can treat them that way in writing formulas. For example, what would be the formula for a compound made of calcium and hydroxide? Looking at Tables 1 and 2, we see that:

calcium: Ca^{+2} \quad\quad\quad hydroxide: OH^{-1}

Our first try at a formula would give us:

$$Ca \quad OH$$

You can see that this won't work! Check the total positive and total negative valences:

$$Ca \quad OH$$
$$+2 \text{ valence} \quad -1 \text{ valence}$$

Can you see what to do to make the valences equal? Try correcting this formula before going on.

The solution is to take two of the hydroxides in the formula. Then we would have:

$$Ca(OH)_2$$

Notice that we put parentheses around the hydroxide to show that it is a polyatomic ion; the "2" written next to it applies to the **whole** group, not just the "H." Now what are the total positive and negative valences? Write down your answer before comparing it with the answer given.

You should now be ready to try the problems on Activity Page 42, page 178.

ACTIVITY PAGE **42** WRITING CHEMICAL FORMULAS

DIRECTIONS: Write formulas for each of the following compounds. Refer to Tables 1 and 2 (pages 174 and 176) for valences of elements and polyatomic ions. Show your work in the space under each name.

1. potassium chloride: _____

2. sodium hydroxide: _____

3. calcium bromide: _____

4. magnesium sulfate: _____

5. hydrogen phosphate: _____

6. aluminum chloride: _____

7. lithium iodide: _____

8. iron (III)* hydroxide: _____

9. potassium sulfate: _____

10. sodium oxide: _____

11. hydrogen sulfide: _____

12. magnesium oxide: _____

13. aluminum phosphate: _____

14. iron (III)* sulfate: _____

15. calcium phosphate: _____

16. aluminum sulfide: _____

---

*"(III)" indicates an iron atom with a valence of +3.

178   *Section Nine*

2. Writing Chemical Equations

A chemical equation is a set of symbols and formulas that tells what happens in a chemical reaction. Here is a simple example:

$$2H_2O \xrightarrow{\sim\sim\sim} 2H_2\uparrow + O_2\uparrow$$

What this equation says is:

    Two molecules of water   ($2H_2O$)

        will produce   ($\rightarrow$)

        two molecules of hydrogen   ($2H_2$)

        which is a gas   ($\uparrow$)

        and one molecule of oxygen   (O_2)

        which is a gas   ($\uparrow$)

        when electricity is passed through the water   ($\sim\sim\sim$)

We have to pause for just a moment and tell you an interesting thing about certain elements like oxygen and hydrogen. The atoms of these elements almost never exist by themselves. That is, when it is an element, hydrogen almost never occurs in single atoms, as **H**. Every atom pairs up with another atom to form a molecule: $H + H \rightarrow H_2$. Notice this is a different kind of molecule than we studied in the last section.

All the atoms in this molecule (all two of them) are exactly alike. The elements that act this way are:

    hydrogen: H_2 oxygen: O_2

    nitrogen: N_2 fluorine: F_2

    chlorine: Cl_2 bromine: Br_2

                  iodine: I_2

That is an important point to keep in mind in writing equations.

The problem a chemist usually has is this: He or she knows what happens in a chemical reaction, **in words**. What needs to be done is to write a chemical equation that represents that. For example, suppose you know the following information:

    When heated, iron combines with sulfur to make iron (II) sulfide.

Let's try to write a chemical equation for this reaction. First, write down the symbols and formulas for everything in the reaction:

        iron: Fe

        sulfur: S

        iron (II) sulfide: FeS

Special Scientific Skills   **179**

Now balance the valences to get a formula before checking your answer.

Then, combine the symbols and formulas as shown in the word equation:

iron combines with sulfur to make iron (II) sulfide
Fe + S → FeS

Finally, look at the equation to see that it "balances." This means that there must be the same number of atoms on both sides of the equation. Why is that necessary?

Suppose you write something like the following:

$$H_2 + O_2 \rightarrow H_2O$$

Something doesn't make sense here! This equation says there are two atoms of oxygen to begin with (O_2), but only one at the end of the reaction (H_2O). What happened to the other atom of oxygen? It can't just disappear into empty space. That may seem obvious to you, but it is also a basic rule of chemistry: you can't just make atoms appear or disappear in a chemical reaction. Every atom you begin with has to be accounted for; every one you end up with must have been there to start.

The example we're working with really presents no problems. Notice that there is one atom of iron (Fe) at the beginning, and one at the end (FeS). Also, there is one atom of sulfur (S) to begin with, and one at the end (FeS). All we need to do is to add a symbol that stands for the "when heated" part of the statement, and our equation is complete:

$$Fe + S \xrightarrow{\Delta} FeS$$

That was a simple example. Let's do one that is a bit more complicated. Try writing the chemical equation for the reaction:

When sodium is added to water, sodium hydroxide and hydrogen gas are produced.

Again, start by writing down the symbols and formulas of everything involved:

sodium: Na

water: H_2O

sodium hydroxide: NaOH

hydrogen gas: H_2 (Remember that hydrogen is one of those "special" elements!)

Then, arrange the symbols and formulas to fit the word description of the reaction:

sodium   is added to   water   (produces)   sodium hydroxide
Na   + H_2O →   NaOH

and   hydrogen gas
+ H_2 ↑

If you count up atoms, everything seems all right at first:

RIGHT SIDE OF EQUATION		LEFT SIDE OF EQUATION
sodium atoms (Na)	1	1
oxygen atoms (O)	1	1
hydrogen atoms (H)	2	3 Oh, Oh! A PROBLEM

It isn't possible to end up with **three** atoms of hydrogen if you begin with only **two**. What can be done?

You will probably be tempted to do the WRONG thing—that would be to change the formula for one of the compounds. For example, if you wrote "H_3O" for water, everything would work—check it to see—but you can't do that. You've already learned that the positive and negative valences must ALWAYS be equal in a formula, and that wouldn't be true of the formula H_3O. Check the balance of the valences in that formula before comparing with the answer given.

The only choice we have, then, is to change around the numbers of molecules in the equation. For example, suppose we were to start with **two** molecules of water (2 H_2O) and end with **two** molecules of sodium hydroxide (2 NaOH). Then, the number of hydrogen atoms **would** balance. Check this out to be sure you see it's true:

Na + 2 H_2O ⟶ 2 NaOH + H_2 ↑

(2 x 2H = 4H)   (2 x 1H + 2 x 1H = 4H)

However, this causes problems with the number of sodium atoms. There are now two sodium atoms on the right (2 NaOH) and only one on the left (Na). You can probably guess how to solve this: Taking two sodium atoms to begin with (2Na) will make the sodiums balance:

2 Na + 2 H_2O → 2 NaOH + H_2 ↑

... and so does everything else.

Special Scientific Skills 181

We have now written a chemical equation that describes what happens in a chemical reaction and does not violate any rules about atoms appearing or disappearing mysteriously!

Let's summarize the steps we just went through in balancing this chemical equation:

1. Write the symbols and formulas for all atoms and molecules involved in the reaction.

2. Join these symbols and formulas by + and → signs to show what happens in the reaction.

3. Balance the equation by taking the right number of atoms and molecules so that nothing mysteriously appears or disappears in the reaction.

4. Add any abbreviations that are needed to represent the formation of gases, the use of heat or electricity, or any other special conditions that need to be mentioned.

Activity Page 43, page 183, gives some chemical reactions for which you should try to write correctly balanced chemical equations.

ACTIVITY PAGE **43** BALANCING CHEMICAL EQUATIONS

DIRECTIONS: Refer to Tables 1 and 2 (pages 174 and 176) to write and balance chemical equations for each of the following reactions:

1. Lead plus sulfur (with heat) yields lead (II) sulfide.

2. Calcium plus water (hot) yields calcium hydroxide and hydrogen gas.

3. Sodium chloride breaks down to give sodium and chlorine gas when an electric current is passed through it.

4. Sodium oxide added to water gives sodium hydroxide.

5. Chlorine gas added to calcium bromide yields bromine and calcium chloride.

6. When magnesium carbonate is heated, it produces magnesium oxide and carbon dioxide gas.

7. Potassium bromide added to lithium iodide makes lithium bromide and potassium iodide.

8. When silver nitrate is added to calcium chloride, calcium nitrate and silver chloride (a precipitate) are formed.

9. Potassium sulfate plus magnesium chloride makes a precipitate of magnesium sulfate and potassium chloride.

10. When iron (III) nitrate is added to sodium hydroxide, the result is a precipitate, iron (III) hydroxide and sodium nitrate.

Special Scientific Skills **183**

3. Using a Key for Identification

In Section Seven on Experimenting and Related Skills, you learned about the value of placing similar objects together into a single class. This makes it easier to study the objects **as a group**, rather than individually. However, it may also be necessary to distinguish the members of a group from each other. One way of doing that is to use an **identification key**.

For example, it is useful to place all cat-like animals together into a single biological group known as "the cat family." The technical name for this group is **Felidae**. It contains animals such as the lion, lynx, cheetah, leopard, puma, jaguar, and domestic house cat. We know a lot about these animals simply by recognizing that they are all members of the same biological family.

Suppose we would like to be able to identify a **specific** cat-like animal that we know belongs to this family, but whose name we don't know. For example, you might see a picture of a wild cat and want to know exactly which one it is. Could it be a jaguar, a puma, a cheetah, or a leopard? You think it may be one of these, but you're not sure which one. An identification key will help you decide **which** member of the family you're looking at.

This lesson will not teach you how to identify members of the cat family, since it would be hard for you to work with lions, tigers, and cheetahs. Instead, the key we'll describe here is for the identification of trees. You shouldn't have any difficulty finding trees to work with for this exercise!

There are various ways to identify a tree. One is simply by its **shape**. Perhaps you can look at the pictures on pages 185-192 and decide which is a willow, which an elm, and which a poplar simply by looking at their shapes. Trees also have distinctive **barks**. The photographs on pages 193-198 show some barks that are easiest to recognize. The kind of buds produced by trees is still a third way of identifying a tree.

Photos courtesy of U.S. Forest Service

Special Scientific Skills **185**

Weeping Willow

Elm

Lombardy Poplar

Eastern White Pine

White Fir

Giant Joshua

Photos courtesy of U.S. Forest Service

Special Scientific Skills 187

Bristlecone Pine

Tamarack — Eastern Larch

Swamp White Oak

Honey Locust

Deodar Cedar

White Bark Pine

Photos courtesy of U.S. Forest Service

Special Scientific Skills **189**

Black Cherry

Quaking Aspen

Camphor

Sugar Maple

Palmetto Cabbage

Cork Oak

Photos courtesy of U.S. Forest Service

California Black Oak

Oil Palm

Large Live Oak

Engelmann Spruce

Ponderosa Pine

Utah Juniper

Photos courtesy of U.S. Forest Service

Special Scientific Skills   193

Guava

Hercules-Club

Mango

Nuttall Oak

New Mexican Locust

Papaya

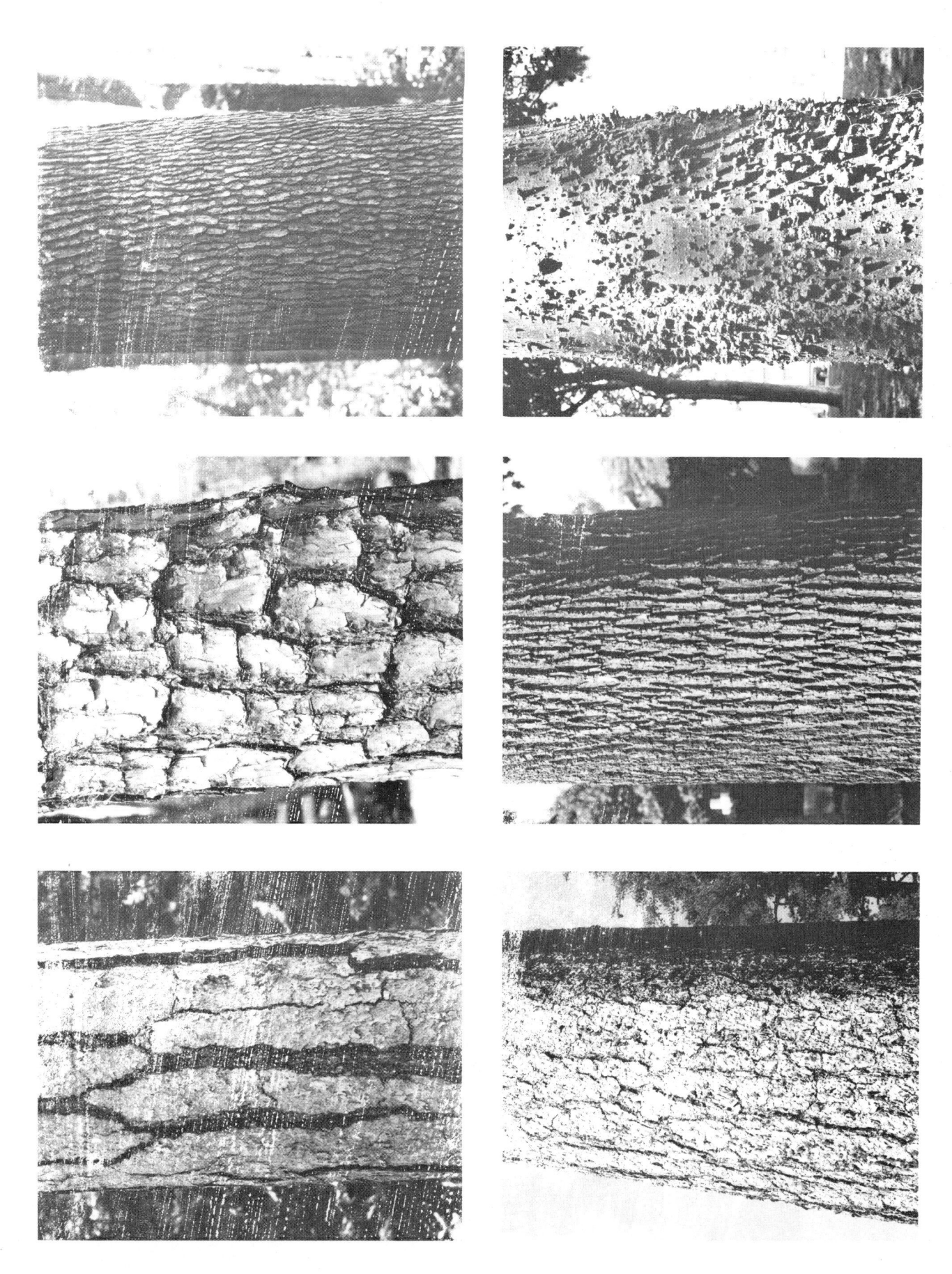

Photos courtesy of U.S. Forest Service

Special Scientific Skills 195

Sugarberry

Sweetgum

Norway Maple

Sand Pine

Sugar Pine

Ponderosa Pine

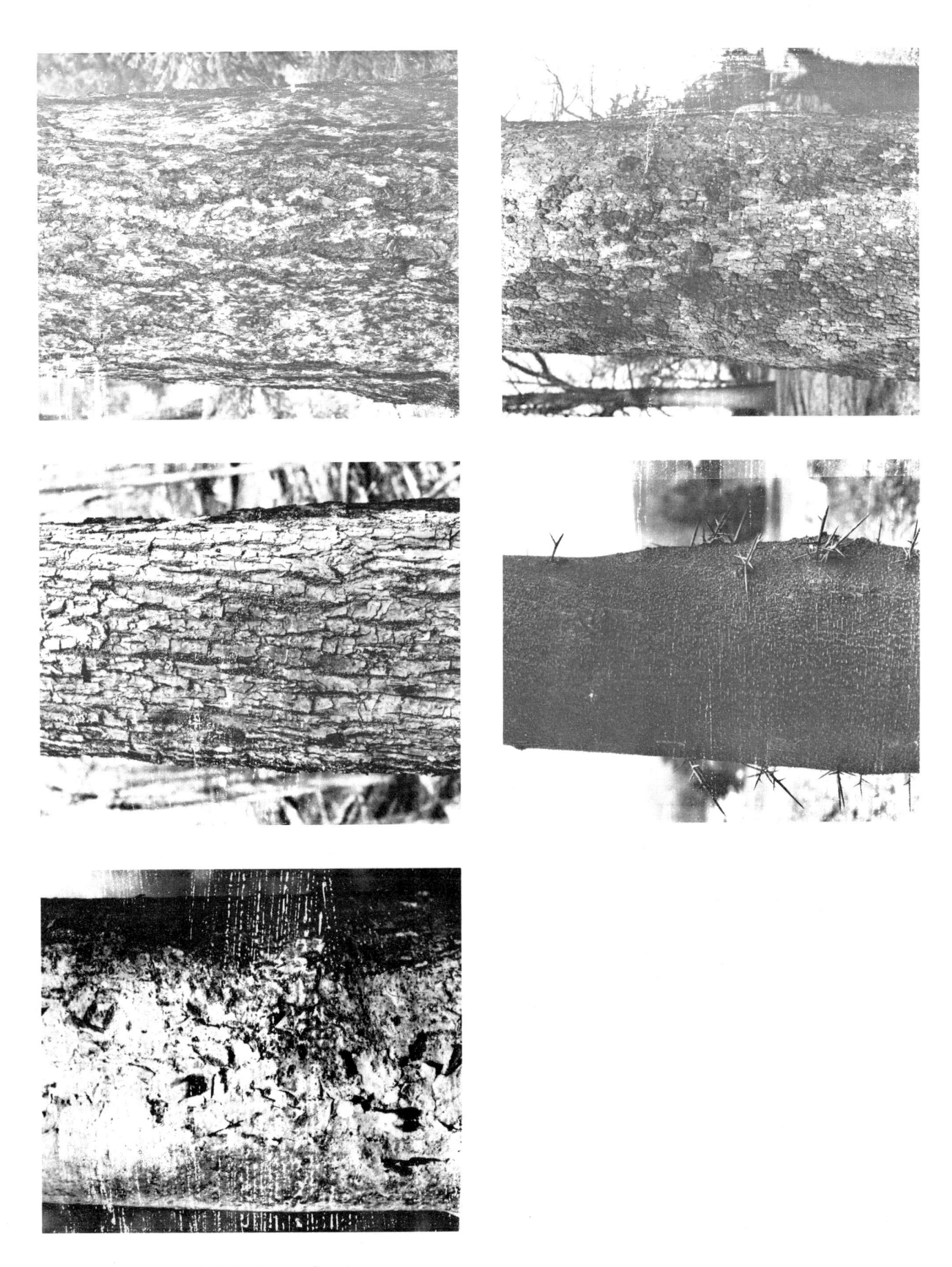

Photos courtesy of U.S. Forest Service

Special Scientific Skills 197

American Sycamore

Western Larch

Waterlocust

White Basswood

Gumbo-Limbo

A LEAF KEY

In this exercise, we will make use of a fourth, and perhaps most common, method of identifying trees: by the leaves they produce. As you go through this identification exercise, you could use shape of tree, bark, bud type, and other characteristics to **confirm** your decisions made with the leaf key. However, the appearance of a tree's leaves will be your major clue in recognizing a tree.

How does a key work? The key used here is called a **dichotomous** key. That means that at every step along the way, you have one of two choices. You will look at a leaf and decide that it is EITHER one thing OR another. Depending on the choice you make, you will go to EITHER one new statement OR another. Let's look at a very simple example to begin with.

Suppose we are interested in the family of **geometric figures with two dimensions**. Some of the members of this family include the circle, square, triangle, pentagon, and trapezoid. These figures are shown in Figure 1 on page 200. Here is the key we might use to identify members of this family:

Step 1:   Figure has corners: Go to step 2

            Figure has no corners; is curved at all points: CIRCLE

Step 2:   Figure has four sides: Go to step 3

            Figure has more or less than four sides: Go to step 4

Step 3:   All sides are equal in length: SQUARE

            All sides are not equal in length: TRAPEZOID

Step 4:   Figure has three sides: TRIANGLE

            Figure has five sides: PENTAGON

Special Scientific Skills

CIRCLE

SQUARE

TRIANGLE

PENTAGON

TRAPEZOID

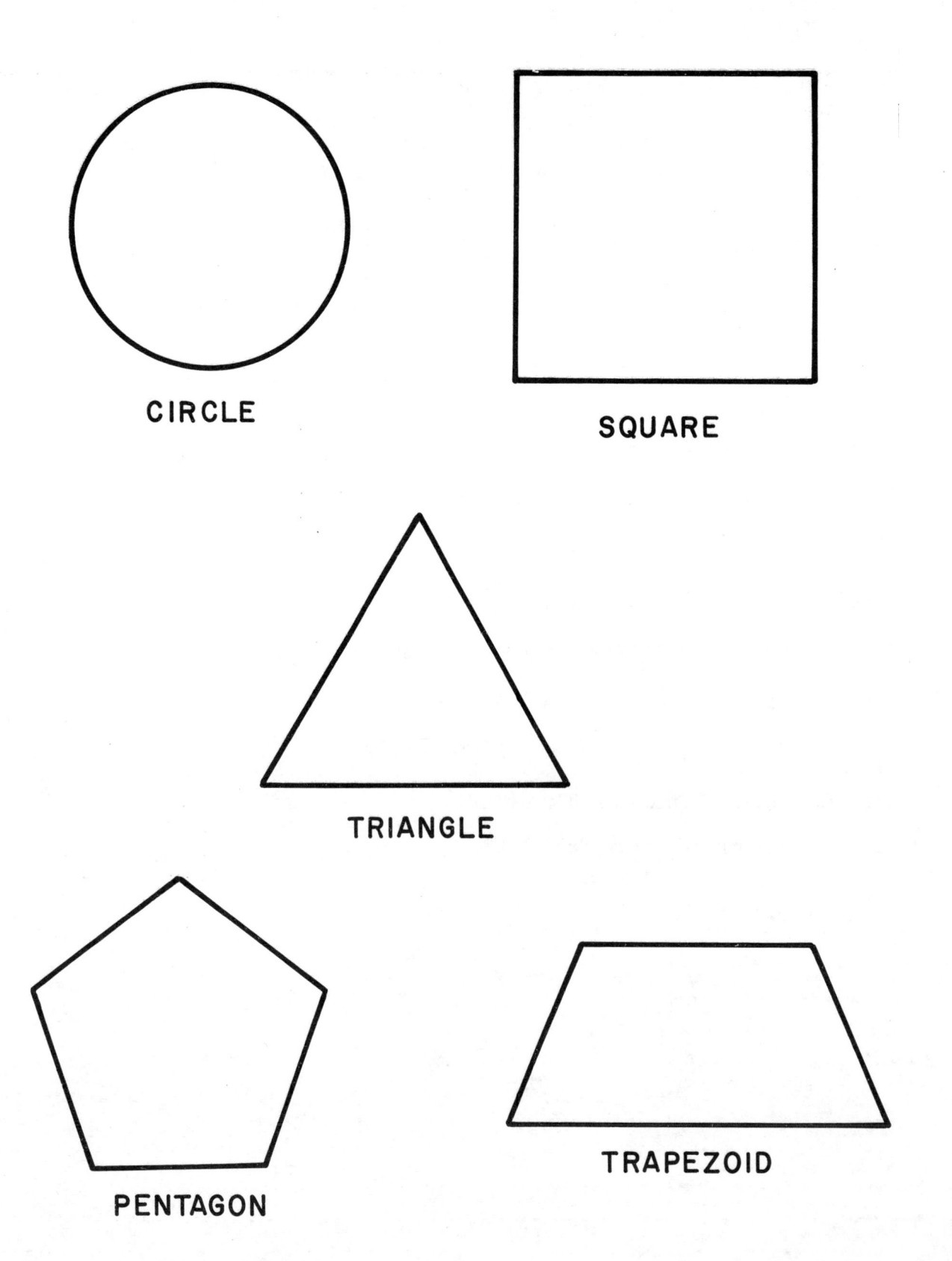

Fig. 1

Now, look at Figure 2 below. Try to decide what it is by using the key on page 199. Write down your answer before going on with the rest of this explanation. The answer may be obvious to you, but try working it out with the key anyway. That will give you practice in using a key.

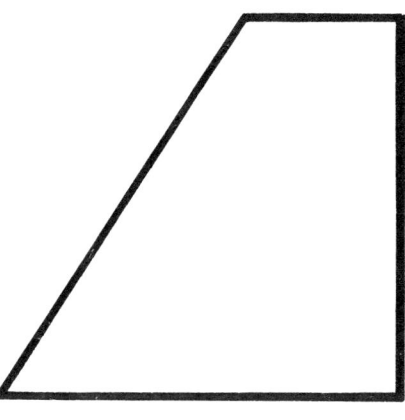

Answer: _____

Fig. 2

The first step in this process is to decide whether the figure has any corners or not. It does, so, according to step 1, you should go to step 2.

In step 2 you are told to count the number of sides. This figure has four, so you are to go to step 3.

In step 3, you are told to see if all sides are equal or not equal. In this figure, it is obvious that they are not equal: the figure you are looking at is a TRAPEZOID.

This example is overly simple, of course, but it teaches the fundamental ideas behind using a key. Let's go now to a more complicated key that uses leaf characteristics as a means of identifying trees. Before you can use this key you have to understand the meaning of a number of terms. The diagram on page 202 will explain those terms. Pages 202-205 are reprinted from David E. Newton's *Science Skills* (Portland, Maine: J. Weston Walch, Publisher, 1961), pages 17-21.

Activity Page 44 provides an opportunity to identify trees by looking at their leaves. Choose at least two trees from your area whose names you don't know. Collect a good leaf from each one. Use the information in the Leaf Key on pages 203-205 to identify the trees from the leaves you collected. The steps you go through should be recorded on Activity Page 44, page 206. Your teacher may want to give you instructions on ways of preserving your leaf.

PARTS OF A LEAF

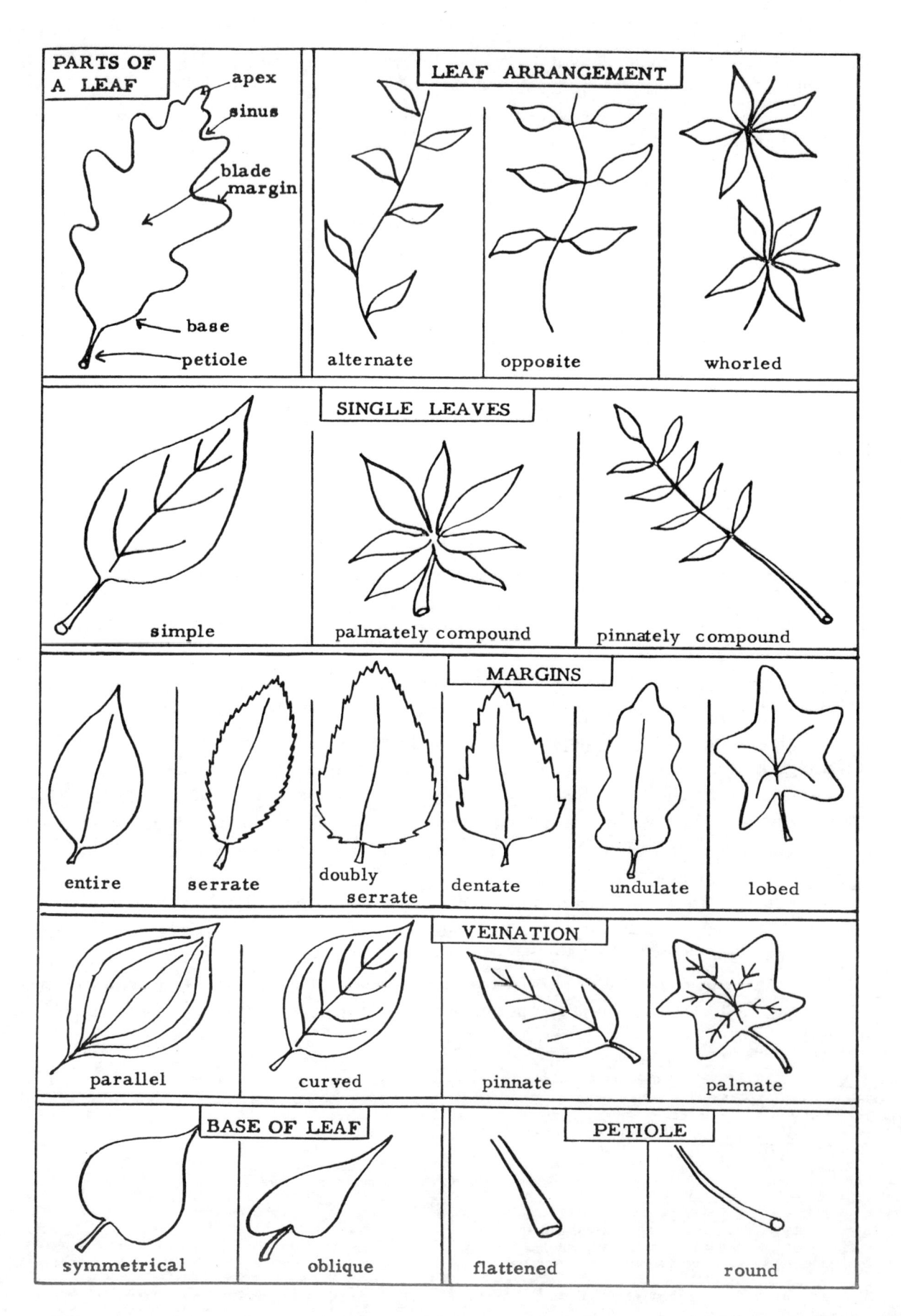

apex, sinus, blade, margin, base, petiole

LEAF ARRANGEMENT

alternate, opposite, whorled

SINGLE LEAVES

simple, palmately compound, pinnately compound

MARGINS

entire, serrate, doubly serrate, dentate, undulate, lobed

VEINATION

parallel, curved, pinnate, palmate

BASE OF LEAF

symmetrical, oblique

PETIOLE

flattened, round

LEAF KEY

1. Leaves are needles or scale-like—go to 2
1. Leaves are broad and flat—go to 14
    2. Leaves are needles—go to 3
    2. Leaves are scale-like—go to 13
3. Needles are in bundles—go to 4
3. Needles are not in bundles—go to 9
    4. Needles are in bundles of 5 or more—go to 5
    4. Needles are in bundles of 2 or 3—go to 6
5. Needles are in tufts—TAMARACK OR LARCH
5. Needles are in bundles of five—WHITE PINE
    6. Needles are in bundles of three—PITCH PINE
    6. Needles are in bundles of two—go to 7
7. Needles are thick and 1 to 1½ inches long—JACK PINE
7. Needles are flat, slightly twisted, 2 to 3 inches long—SCOTCH PINE
7. Needles are flexible, 4 to 6 inches long—go to 8
    8. Sheaf around bundle is short—AUSTRIAN PINE
    8. Sheaf around bundle is long—NORWAY (RED) PINE
9. Needles are plain, green on both sides—go to 10
9. Needles have white lines on under side—go to 11
    10. Needles are stiff and sharp—SPRUCE
    10. Needles are flexible and flattened—YEW
11. Needles are flat, sessile—BALSAM FIR
    12. Needles are flat, have petioles—HEMLOCK
13. All needles are flattened—ARBOR VITAE (WHITE CEDAR)
13. Some needles are flattened, some are sharp—JUNIPER (RED CEDAR)
    14. Leaves are arranged opposite on branches—go to 15
    14. Leaves are arranged alternate on branches—go to 27
15. Leaves simple—go to 16
15. Leaves compound—go to 23
    16. Leaves pinnately veined, margin smooth—FLOWERING DOGWOOD
    16. Leaves palmately veined—go to 17
17. Margin entire, leaf very large—CATALPA
17. Margin lobed, fruit a samara—go to 18
    18. Sinuses pointed—go to 19
    18. Sinuses rounded—go to 20
19. Sinuses are deep—SILVER MAPLE
19. Sinuses are shallow—RED MAPLE
    20. Drop of "milk" appears at end of petiole if broken—go to 21
    20. No drop of "milk" appears at end when petiole is broken—go to 22
21. Leaves are green in spring—NORWAY MAPLE
21. Leaves are deep purple in spring—SCHWEDLER MAPLE
    22. Leaves are deep green and longer than wide—SUGAR MAPLE
    22. Leaves are deep green and wider than long—BLACK MAPLE
23. Leaflets pinnately arranged—go to 24
23. Leaflets palmately arranged—go to 26

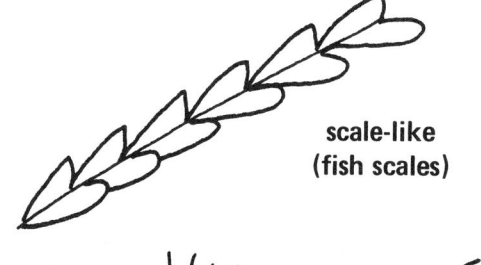

24. 3 to 5 irregularly shaped leaflets—BOX ELDER (COMPOUND LEAFED MAPLE)
24. 5 to 11 leaflets—go to 25
25. Leaflets are sessile—BLACK ASH
25. Leaflets have petioles—WHITE ASH
    26. 5 leaflets to a leaf—OHIO BUCKEYE
    26. 7 leaflets to a leaf—HORSE CHESTNUT
27. Leaves simple—go to 28
27. Leaves compound—go to 51
    28. Margin entire or nearly so—go to 29
    28. Margin serrate—go to 30
    28. Margin undulate, base of leaf oblique—WITCH HAZEL
    28. Margin dentate—go to 46
    28. Margin lobed—go to 47
29. Leaf heart-shaped, fruit a pod—RED BUD
29. Leaves "mitten-shaped," fruit a drupe—SASSAFRAS
    30. Stems of twigs with thorns—HAWTHORN
    30. Stems of twigs without thorns—go to 31
31. Base a leaf oblique—go to 32
31. Base a leaf symmetrical—go to 34
    32. Leaf as wide or wider than long—BASS
    32. Leaf 1½ times as long as wide—go to 33
33. Teeth completely around margin—AMERICAN ELM
33. No teeth near base—HACKBERRY
    34. Veins are straight and evenly spaced—go to 35
    34. Veins are not straight and evenly spaced—go to 38
35. Bark of tree peels horizontally—go to 36
35. Bark does not peel horizontally, base of leaf is heart-shaped—IRONWOOD
    36. Leaves in pairs—go to 37
    36. Leaves single, base of leaf straight across, bark is white—WHITE BIRCH
37. Bark is brown—BLACK BIRCH
37. Bark is bronze—YELLOW BIRCH
    38. Leaves have pungent odor, there are lenticles in bark—go to 39
    38. Leaves without odor, no lenticles in bark—go to 41
39. Leaf is long and tapering—go to 40
39. Leaf is obovate—CHOKE CHERRY
    40. White dots on twigs—BLACK CHERRY
    40. Brown dots on twigs—PIN CHERRY
41. Leaf linear—WILLOW
41. Leaf triangular—go to 42
    42. Petiole flattened—go to 43
    42. Petiole round—BALM OF GILEAD
43. Base of leaf straight across—go to 44
43. Base of leaf not straight across—go to 45
    44. Leaf longer than wide—COTTONWOOD
    44. Leaf wider than long—LOMBARDY POPLAR
45. Teeth very large—LARGE-TOOTH ASPEN
45. Teeth very tiny—QUAKING ASPEN

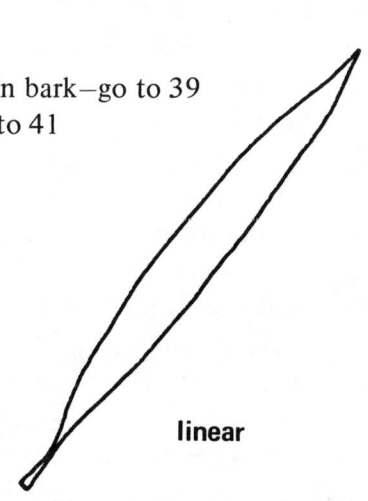

46. Leaf thin and shiny smooth on both sides with one tooth for every vein—BEECH
46. Leaf large, teeth curved toward apex of leaf—CHESTNUT
47. Fruit not an acorn—go to 48
47. Fruit an acorn—go to 50
    48. Leaf pinnately veined—go to 49
    48. Leaf parallel-veined, leaf fan-shaped, with two equal lobes—GINGKO
49. Leaf looks as though tip were cut off—TULIP TREE
49. Leaf very large and coarse, bark on tree peels naturally—SYCAMORE
    50. Lobes bristle-pointed—BLACK OAK FAMILY
    50. Lobes rounded—WHITE OAK FAMILY
51. Leaflets with entire margin—go to 52
51. Leaflets with serrate margin—go to 53
    52. Leaves once compound, branches armed with short, sharp thorns—BLACK LOCUST
    52. Leaves once or twice compound, branches with long thorns—HONEY LOCUST
53. Leaflets rounded with abrupt apex—MOUNTAIN ASH
53. Leaflets elongate—go to 54
    54. Leaves with 13 to 41 leaflets, leaflets with 1 or 2 coarse teeth at base—AILANTHUS
    54. Leaves with 5 to 23 leaflets, leaflets complete serrate—go to 55
55. Leaves with 5 to 7 leaflets—go to 56
55. Leaves with 7 to 23 leaflets—go to 57
    56. Leaflets smooth, bark separates in loose, shaggy strips—SHAGBARK HICKORY
    56. Leaflets downy beneath—BUTTERNUT
57. Brown pith in twigs—BUTTERNUT
57. Cream pith in twigs—BLACK WALNUT

bristle-pointed

ACTIVITY PAGE **44** USING A LEAF KEY

DIRECTIONS: In the spaces provided below, record the steps you follow from the Leaf Key on pages 203-205 to identify the trees from which your leaves came.

LEAF ONE

Step 1: Leaf one is _____ or _____ . (Circle the term that applies to your leaf.)

Step 2: Go to _____ because _____ .

Step 3: Go to _____ because _____ .

Step 4: Go to _____ because _____ .

Step 5: Go to _____ because _____ .

Step 6: Go to _____ because _____ .

LEAF TWO

Step 1: Leaf two is _____ or _____ . (Circle the term that applies to your leaf.)

Step 2: Go to _____ because _____ .

Step 3: Go to _____ because _____ .

Step 4: Go to _____ because _____ .

Step 5: Go to _____ because _____ .

Step 6: Go to _____ because _____ .

A MINERAL KEY

Not all keys work in exactly the same way. The Mineral Key on pages 210-211 is not a dichotomous key; sometimes you have more than two choices to make. The general idea about its use is not very different from the Leaf Key on pages 203-205, however—you should be able to use it without any further directions. The meaning of terms used in the key are defined below. When you have read through these explanations, you will use the key to identify several minerals.

Characteristics of Minerals

The following terms are used in the Mineral Key on pages 210 and 211:

COLOR and STREAK: Color is usually not a good property to use in identifying minerals. The pure mineral itself might be a distinctive color, but very small amounts of impurities can change that color. In a few cases, the color of a mineral is so distinctive, it may be the only property you need for a good identification. Malachite, for example, has a very characteristic green color, and azurite is as blue as the "azure" in its name would lead you to suspect.

Many minerals show one color when they occur as a compact lump, and another color when they are ground to a fine powder. This can be a good way of identifying a mineral. The problem is that you usually don't want to take the time to grind up a mineral to see what its "other" color might be. The easy way around this is to use a **streak plate**. This is simply a small piece of unglazed porcelain on which the unknown mineral is rubbed. When the mineral is rubbed on the plate, a streak is left behind that is the color of the mineral in its powder form. A good example of this property is pyrite, often called "fool's gold." In its lump form, this mineral is a beautiful brass yellow, almost gold. However, its streak is a very dark green or black.

The term LUSTER refers to the appearance of a mineral's surface in its lump form. The luster is determined by the amount of light that is reflected from the mineral's surface and the way that light is reflected. Most of the terms used to describe luster are fairly self-explanatory:

vitreous	=	glassy	metallic	=	bright and shiny
pearly	=	like a pearl	waxy	=	like a piece of wax
satiny	=	like a satin cloth			
fibrous	=	"stringy" like a rough piece of cloth			
irridescent dull	=	earthy, no noticeable luster			

HARDNESS in minerals varies a great deal. Some are so soft they can be scratched with a fingernail; talc and graphite are examples. Others are the hardest naturally occurring objects in the world; diamond is at the top of this list. In order to have an exact measure of a mineral's hardness, the following scale of minerals was developed many years ago. It is known as Moh's scale, after the man who invented it.

10	diamond		5	apatite
9	corundum		4	fluorite
8	topaz		3	calcite
7	quartz		2	gypsum
6	feldspar		1	talc

Any mineral on this list will scratch all of the minerals below it. It will not scratch any of the minerals above it; it will be scratched by them. (Note, however, that you have to use a sharp point on the mineral to test its scratching ability.)

For example, apatite is harder than fluorite. Therefore, apatite will scratch fluorite. Apatite will also scratch calcite, gypsum, and talc. It will not scratch feldspar, quartz, topaz, corundum, or diamond. What minerals would feldspar scratch? Which ones would it not scratch? Write down your answers before comparing them with those given.

Let's use Moh's scale to find the hardness of an unknown mineral, X. We use a piece of talc to see if talc will scratch X. If it does, we know that talc is harder than X (or X is softer than talc), so the hardness of X must be less than 1.

If talc does **not** scratch X, then we see if a piece of gypsum will scratch X. If it does, then X is softer than gypsum. That means its hardness is more than 1 (harder than talc) but less than 2 (softer than gypsum).

If gypsum does **not** scratch X, then we try calcite. We repeat this process, always trying the next mineral up the scale, until we come to a mineral that **will** scratch X. That mineral, then, is harder than X, which is harder than the mineral next in line on Moh's scale. This allows us to assign a value between two numbers on the scale to mineral X.

In actual practice, it is clumsy to carry all ten of these minerals around with you in order to test for hardness. Instead, three or four handy substitutes are used. These are: (1) your fingernail, with a hardness of a little over 2; (2) a copper penny, hardness about 3; (3) an iron nail, hardness about 5; (4) a knife blade of high-grade steel, hardness about 5.5 or 6; and (5) a piece of window glass, hardness about 6.

The terms CLEAVAGE and FRACTURE describe what happens to a mineral when it breaks. In some cases we find that the mineral breaks evenly and smoothly in one, two, or three directions. This is known as **cleavage**. In other cases the mineral does not break in any particular direction, but crumbles or falls apart in some irregular way. This is called **fracture**.

Cleavage in a mineral is often easy to identify since the places where the mineral cleaves (breaks apart) are always smooth and flat. Some minerals cleave in only one direction. Mica, for example, breaks very smoothly into wide, flat sheets. The surfaces of these sheets show the bright, shiny, smooth appearance of "cleavage faces." Each time you find a cleavage face on a mineral, there is another cleavage face on the opposite side of the mineral. Therefore, cleavage faces always occur in pairs, and mica really has **one pair** of cleavage faces.

Feldspar shows cleavage in two directions. If you look at a piece of feldspar you will note that two pairs of sides on it are smooth and mirror-like. Grasp a piece of feldspar with the thumb and first finger of your right hand on one pair of cleavage faces. With the thumb and first finger of your left hand, grasp a second pair of cleavage faces. Notice how the parts of the mineral not between your fingers are rough and uneven. These are places of fracture and not of cleavage.

Also observe the angle at which the cleavage faces come together. These angles between cleavage faces are often useful in identifying minerals that are otherwise very much alike. Calcite is an example of a mineral that shows cleavage in three directions. If you break a piece of calcite, you will notice that it does not fall apart in just any way; it breaks regularly in three different directions. The three pairs of cleavage faces in calcite give it the appearance of a tilted box.

If a mineral does not break regularly (if it has no cleavage), we try to describe its fracture. The terms uneven, rough, hackly, splintery, and fibrous all describe a particular type of fracture that you can easily picture from the names. The term **conchoidal fracture** refers to the smooth curved surfaces, like those on a clam shell, which are produced when glass is broken.

The CRYSTAL FORM of a mineral is the shape it takes when it has a chance to grow slowly from the liquid state. For a number of reasons some minerals are almost never found in their original crystal shape, while others are almost always found in this appearance. Special names are given to the various possible crystal forms that a mineral may have. However, these are so highly technical that we will mention only three here: cubic, rhombohedral, and hexagonal.

A box that has six sides of equal size is called a cube; a mineral with a shape like this is said to have a cubic crystal form. Both galena and pyrite occur frequently as cubic crystals. The "tilted box" appearance of calcite that we mentioned previously is technically called a rhombohedral crystal form. A hexagonal crystal is one that resembles a long box with six sides and two ends. Quartz often occurs as a crystal that looks much like a six-sided pencil. Generally, crystal form is difficult for beginners to use in identifying minerals.

A few minerals have some SPECIAL PROPERTIES not very common to other minerals. Three that you will probably meet are (1) attraction by a magnet, (2) taste, and (3) feel. Magnetite is one of the very few minerals that can be attracted by a magnet. This test, along with a few other simple ones, is enough to identify magnetite. Halite (rock salt) is easily identified by its bitter, salty taste. (Tasting anything in the laboratory **can** be very dangerous. **Never** try it unless your teacher tells you it's safe!) Graphite can easily be picked out because it has a slippery feeling that leaves a black smudge on your fingers. Graphite is the "lead" in lead pencils. Special properties will be mentioned in the key wherever they are important.

Use the information in this key to identify several minerals. Record the steps you go through on Activity Page 45, page 212.

MINERAL IDENTIFICATION*

```
A
Non-metallic L
Light colored
│
├── Hard, scratches glass and knife (H more than 6)
│   ├── Clearly shows cleavage
│   │   ├── Gray, gray-green, green-white or white (rarely pink); C, 2 faces at nearly right angles; cleavage faces show "pin scratches" H, 6   PLAGIOCLASE (feldspar)
│   │   └── Flesh-colored or white; C, 2 faces at nearly right angles; no "pin scratches" on cleavage faces; H, 6   ORTHOCLASE (feldspar)
│   └── Cleavage poor or absent
│       ├── L, vitreous; often transparent; CF, hexagonal; H, 7; F, conchoidal   QUARTZ
│       ├── Same as quartz, only milky-white in color   MILKY QUARTZ
│       ├── Same as quartz, only pink in color   ROSE QUARTZ
│       ├── L, dull, light gray, yellow, light brown, white; H, 7; F, conchoidal   FLINT
│       └── L, vitreous; olive-green or green-brown; often transparent; F, smooth; H, 6.5   OLIVINE
│
└── Soft, does not scratch glass; knife will scratch (H less than 6)
    ├── Shows cleavage
    │   ├── Colorless to white; salty taste; C, cubic; H, 2.5   HALITE
    │   ├── White, yellow, to colorless; H, 3; C, rhombohedral   CALCITE
    │   ├── White to transparent; H, 2; occurs as flexible plates, earthy masses, etc.   GYPSUM
    │   ├── Green to white; soapy feel; H, 1   TALC
    │   ├── Colorless to light yellow; transparent in thin sheets; C, 1 good direction; occurs as elastic plates; H, 2.5   MUSCOVITE (mica)
    │   ├── C, fibrous; green to white color   ASBESTOS
    │   └── White, yellow, purple, green; C, very good, 4 pairs of cleavage faces; H, 4   FLUORITE
    └── No cleavage
        ├── White; earthy odor when damp; F, earthy; H, 2   KAOLINITE
        └── Green to white; soapy feel; H, 1   TALC
```

*KEY

H	hardness	L	luster	F	fracture
C	cleavage	S	streak	CF	crystal form

From *Science Skills*, by David E. Newton (Portland, Maine: J. Weston Walch, Publisher, 1961), pp. 26-27.

B — Non-metallic Luster, dark colored

Hard, scratches glass and knife

- **Shows cleavage**
  - Black, greenish-brown, greenish-black; H, 5-7; C, 2 planes at nearly right angles; short thick crystals — **AUGITE** (pyroxene)
  - Black, greenish-black, greenish-brown; H, 5-7; C, 2 planes at about 60° and 120°; long, slender crystals — **HORNBLENDE** (amphibole)
  - Gray to blue-gray; H, 6; C, 2 planes at nearly right angles; "pin scratches" on cleavage faces — **PLAGIOCLASE** (feldspar)
- **No cleavage**
  - Red to red-brown; H, 6.5 to 7.5; fracture resembles poor cleavage; brittle — **GARNET**
  - Gray to gray-black; L, vitreous; H, 7; F, conchoidal — **SMOKY QUARTZ**
  - Red to red-brown, dark gray or black; L, dull; H, 7; F, conchoidal — **JASPER** (red), **FLINT** (brown or black)

Soft, does not scratch glass; knife will scratch

- **Shows cleavage**
  - Brown to black; C, 1 very good plane, thin plates; H, 2.5 — **BIOTITE** (mica)
  - Dark green to greenish-black; H, 2 to 2.5; S, white; slippery feel, C, platy — **CHLORITE**
  - Blue; S, blue; H, 3.5 to 4 — **AZURITE**
  - Bright green; S, pale green; H, 3.5 to 4 — **MALACHITE**
- **No cleavage**
  - Green, brown, blue, purple; H, 5; S, white; L, vitreous — **APATITE**

C — Metallic Luster

- **Black, green-black, or dark green streak**
  - Black, strongly magnetic; H, 6 — **MAGNETITE**
  - Lead-pencil black; smudges fingers when handled; H, 1 — **GRAPHITE**
  - Pale brass yellow; H, 6 to 6.5; often occurs as cubic crystals — **PYRITE**
  - Dark brass yellow; H, 3.5 to 4; tarnishes purple — **CHALCOPYRITE**
  - Shiny gray; very heavy; C, perfect cubic; H, 2.5 — **GALENA**
- **Red streak**
  - Red-brown to nearly black; may appear to be quite soft — **HEMATITE**
- **Yellow or brown streak**
  - Yellow-brown to dark brown; may be almost black; H, 6 (varies) — **LIMONITE**

From *Science Skills*, by David E. Newton (Portland, Maine: J. Weston Walch, Publisher, 1961), pp. 26-27.

ACTIVITY PAGE **45** USING A MINERAL KEY

DIRECTIONS: In the spaces provided below, record the steps you follow from the Mineral Key on pages 210-211 to identify your minerals.

MINERAL ONE

Step 1:   Mineral one is _____ or _____ . (Circle the term that applies to your mineral.)

Step 2:   Go to _____ because _____ .

Step 3:   Go to _____ because _____ .

Step 4:   Go to _____ because _____ .

Step 5:   Go to _____ because _____ .

Step 6:   Go to _____ because _____ .

MINERAL TWO

Step 1:   Mineral two is _____ or _____ . (Circle the term that applies to your mineral.)

Step 2:   Go to _____ because _____ .

Step 3:   Go to _____ because _____ .

Step 4:   Go to _____ because _____ .

Step 5:   Go to _____ because _____ .

Step 6:   Go to _____ because _____ .

4. Making and Reading Circuit Diagrams

Do you know how the doorbell in your home works? You probably realize that it runs on electricity. When someone pushes the doorbell button, an electrical current passes through the doorbell circuit. This causes a bell to ring. Suppose you would like to take this circuit apart and work on it. What are the parts that make up the circuit? Where are they located? How are they connected to each other?

Questions like these are very common today. There are many, many devices in your home that run on electricity. A repair person needs to know how they are put together. What method could be used to provide this information? For one thing, we could take a picture of the circuit, showing where each part is found and how they are all connected to each other. Or we could make a drawing, sketching in a bell, a transformer, wires, and other parts of the circuit. Either of these would be time-consuming and clumsy, however. As we go to more complex electrical equipment (like your television set), they would really be impossible methods.

Long ago, physicists invented a simplified system of representing electrical circuits. Most people today have seen a **schematic diagram** like the one in Figure 3. This one happens to be for a transistor radio. You probably have no idea what these symbols mean. You would have to take an advanced course in physics to understand a schematic this complicated, but it's fairly easy to learn the basic ideas of making and reading circuit diagrams. That's the purpose of this exercise.

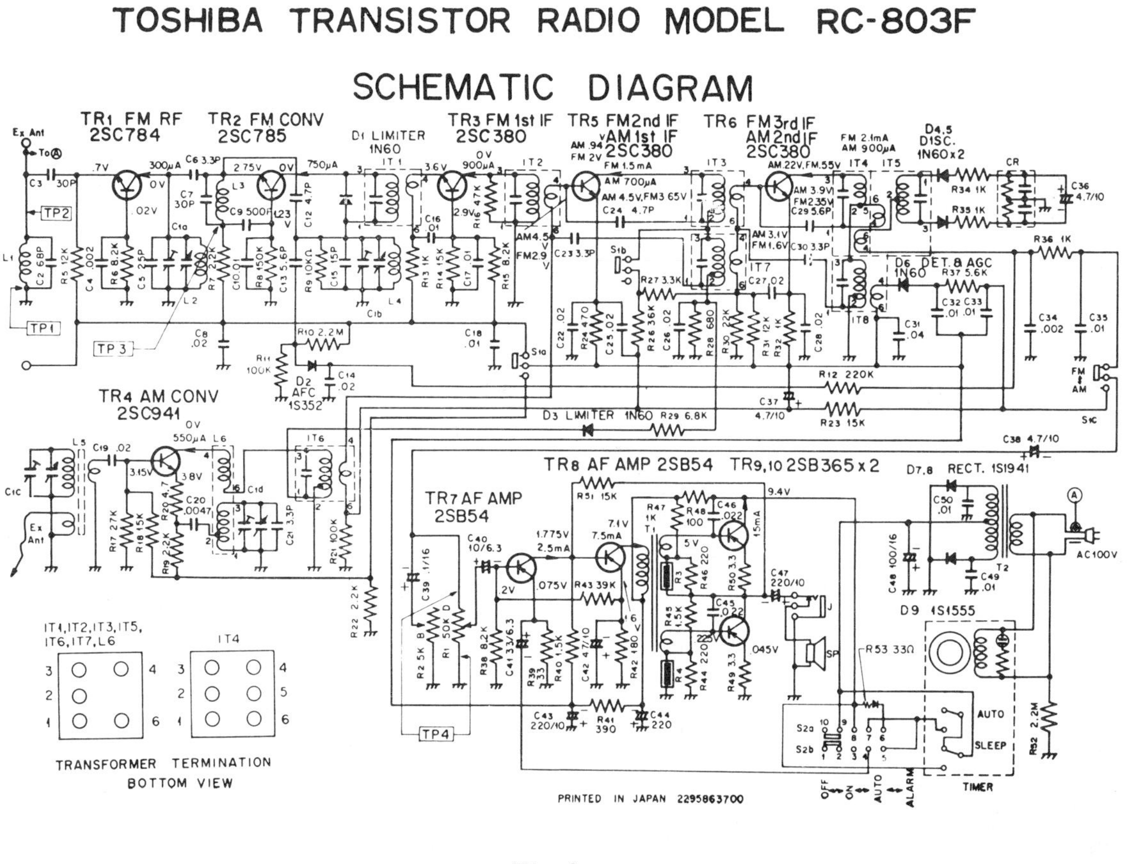

Fig. 3

Special Scientific Skills

You should begin by reviewing a little information about electrical circuits. You know that every circuit must have (or usually has):

1. A source of electricity
2. A pathway on which the electricity will travel
3. A switch to open and close the circuit
4. An appliance that is operated by the flow of electricity
5. A meter to measure the amount of electrical current (or some other property of the circuit.)

Figures 4 and 5 below and on page 215 show symbols used in circuit diagrams.

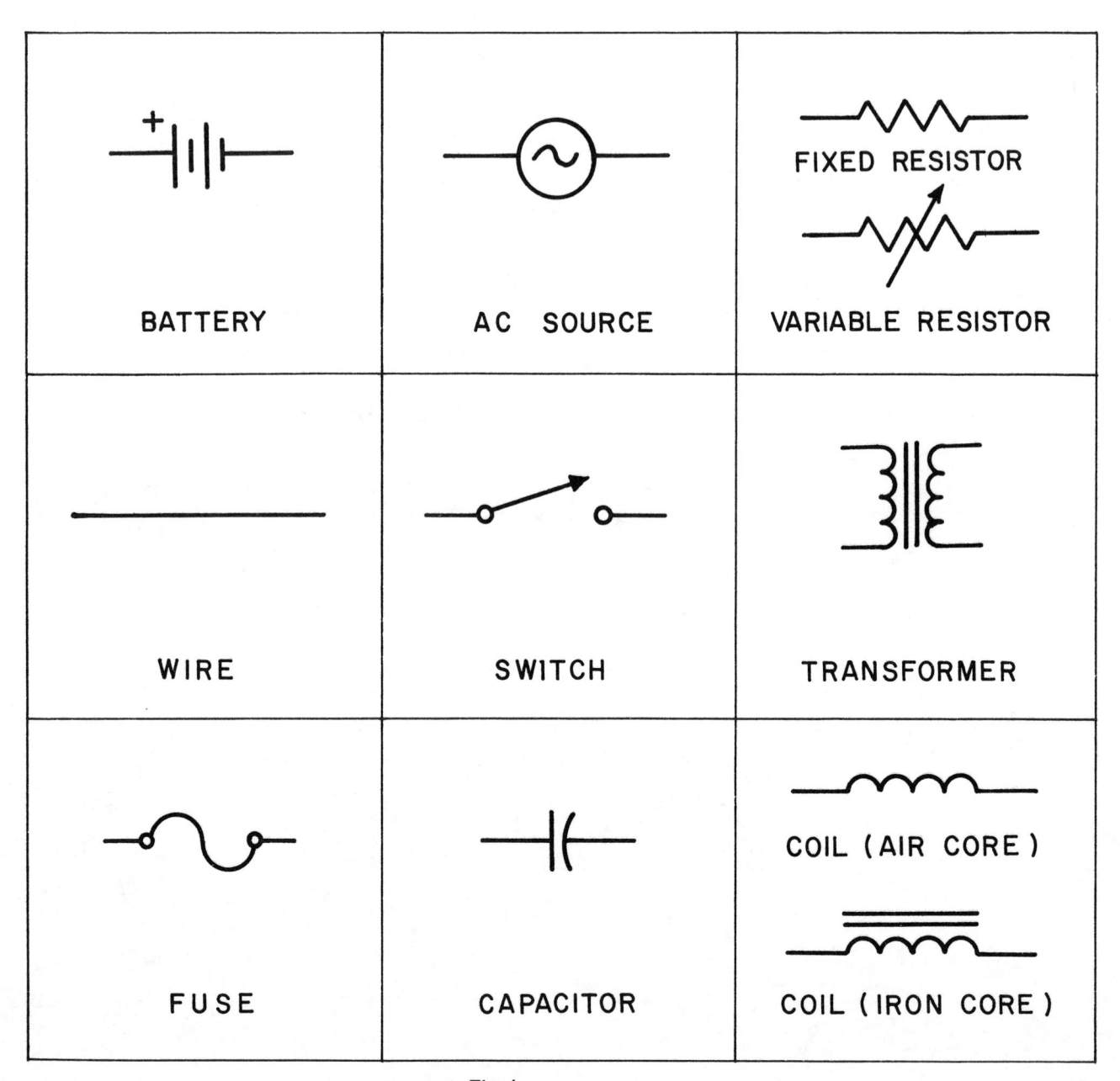

BATTERY	AC SOURCE	FIXED RESISTOR / VARIABLE RESISTOR
WIRE	SWITCH	TRANSFORMER
FUSE	CAPACITOR	COIL (AIR CORE) / COIL (IRON CORE)

Fig. 4

214 *Section Nine*

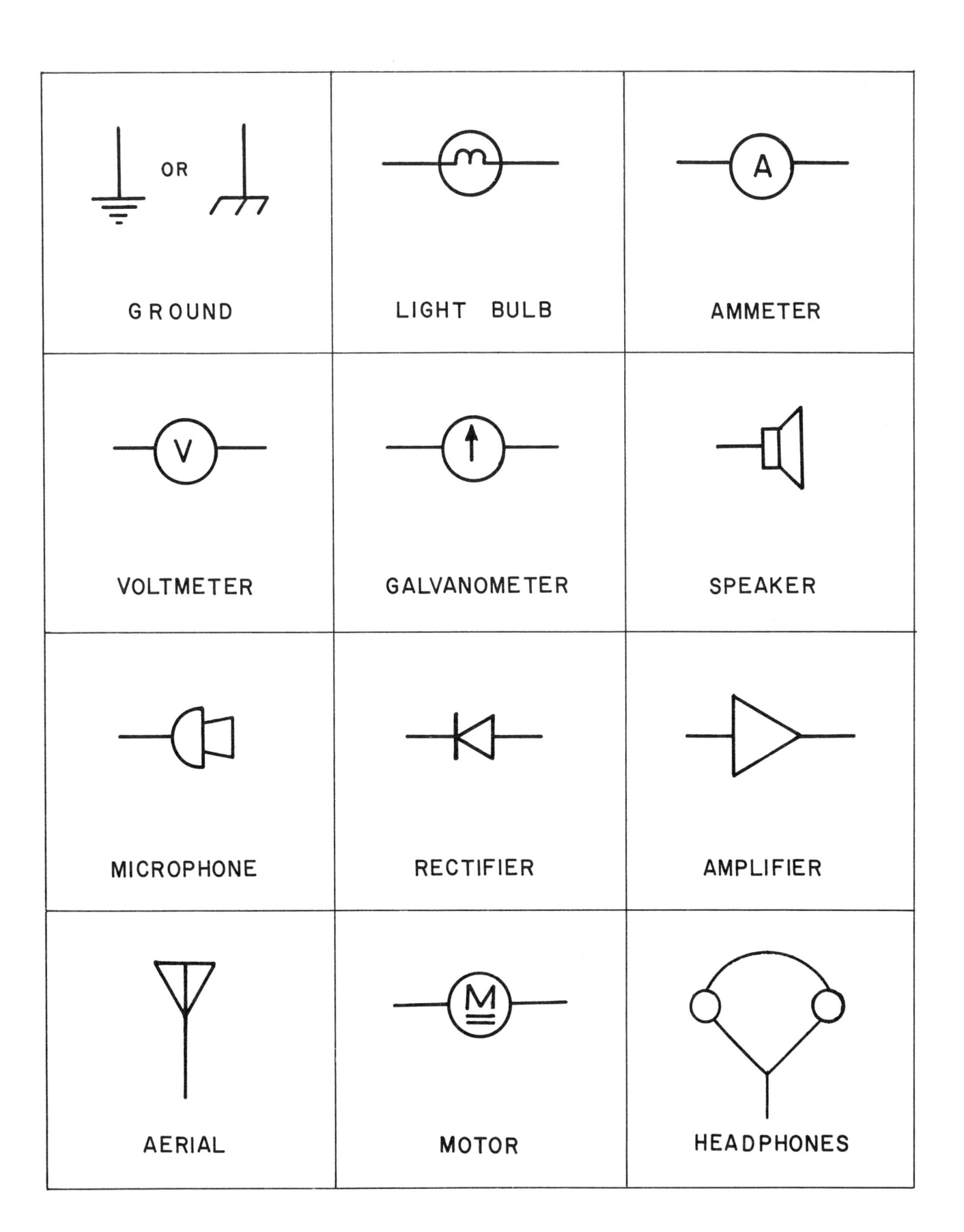

GROUND	LIGHT BULB	AMMETER
VOLTMETER	GALVANOMETER	SPEAKER
MICROPHONE	RECTIFIER	AMPLIFIER
AERIAL	MOTOR	HEADPHONES

Fig. 5

Photographs 1 and 2 on page 217 show the kind of electrical circuits you could set up in your own classroom. Figure 6 below is a schematic diagram of the circuit in Photograph 1:

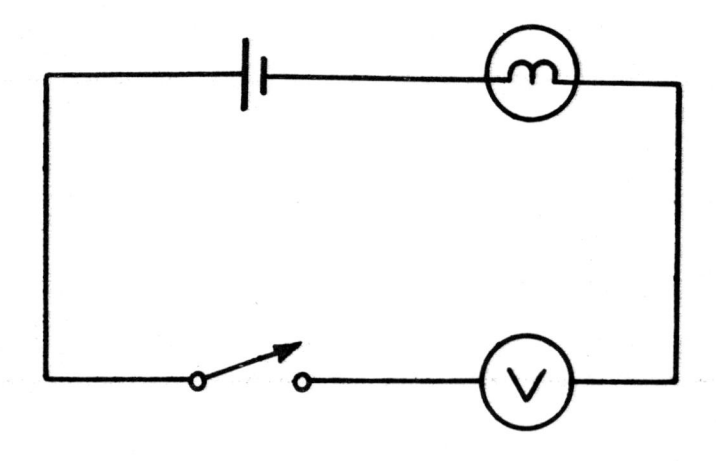

Fig. 6

Be sure that you see how each part of the schematic goes with each part of the circuit shown in Photograph 1. Ask your teacher if there are any parts you do not understand. Then look at Photograph 2 and draw a schematic that will represent the parts of this electrical circuit (refer to the symbols on 214-215) before comparing with the schematic in Figure 7.

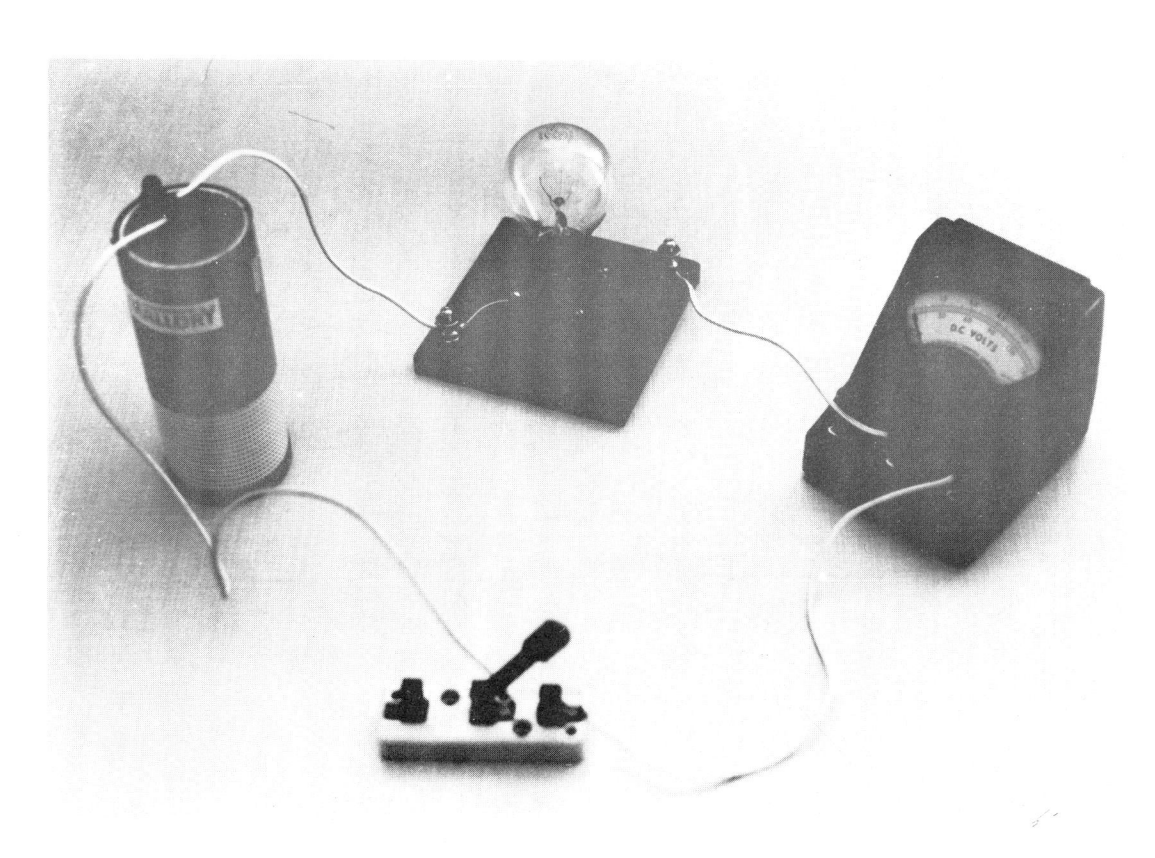

Photograph 1

Photograph 2

Special Scientific Skills 217

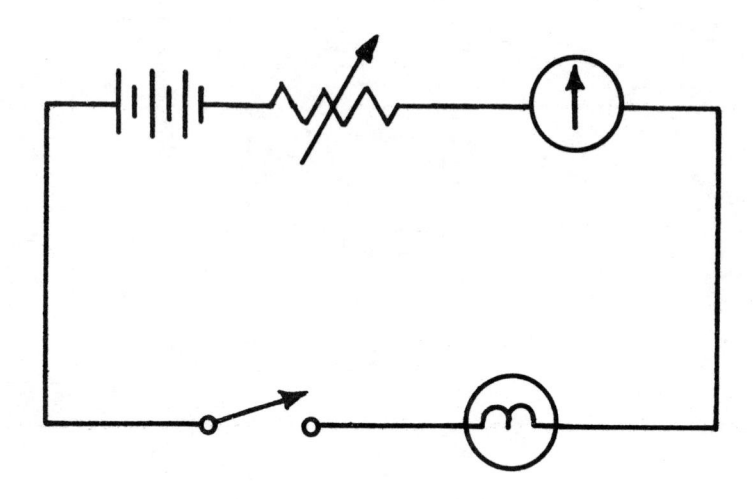

Fig. 7

When you have completed this practice exercise, draw schematics for each photograph in the space provided on Activity Pages 46, 47, 48, and 49, pages, 219-222.

ACTIVITY PAGE **46** DRAWING SCHEMATICS FOR ELECTRICAL CIRCUITS—I

DIRECTIONS: In the space provided, draw a schematic diagram of the electric circuit shown in Photograph 3 below.

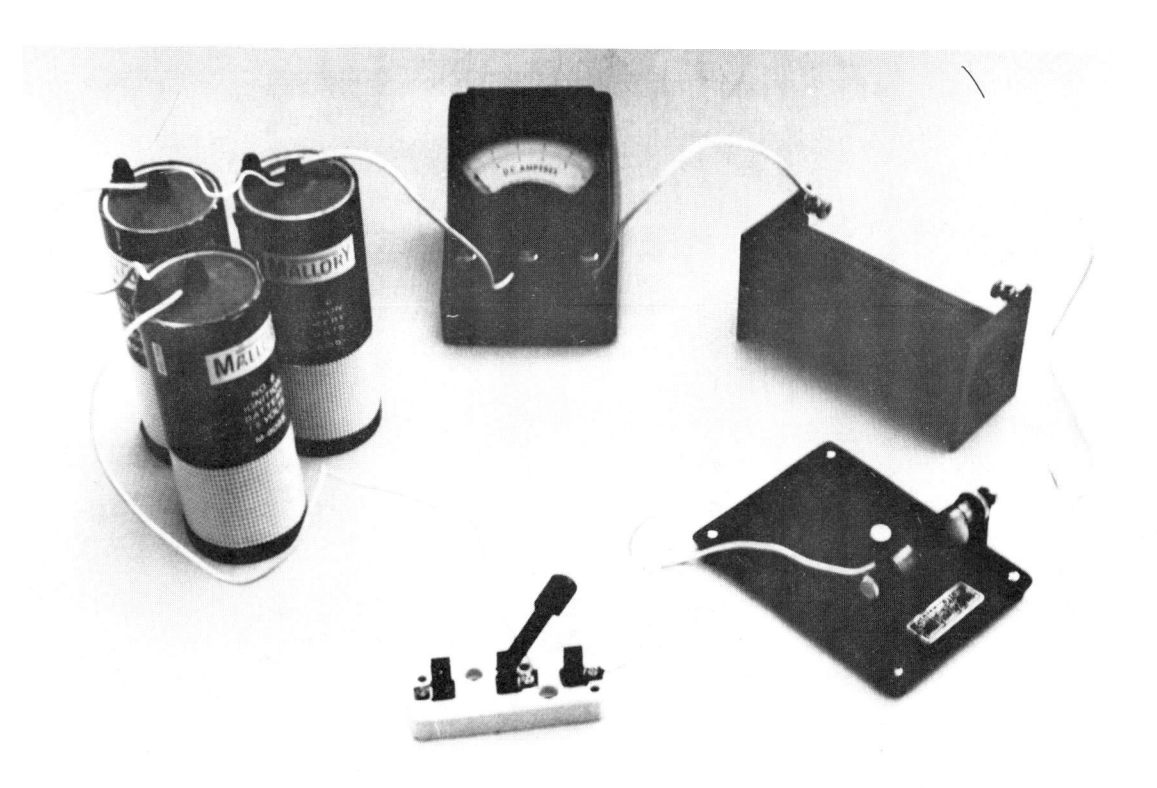

Special Scientific Skills 219

ACTIVITY PAGE **47** DRAWING SCHEMATICS FOR ELECTRICAL CIRCUITS—D

DIRECTIONS: In the space provided, draw a schematic diagram of the electric circuit shown in Photograph 4 below.

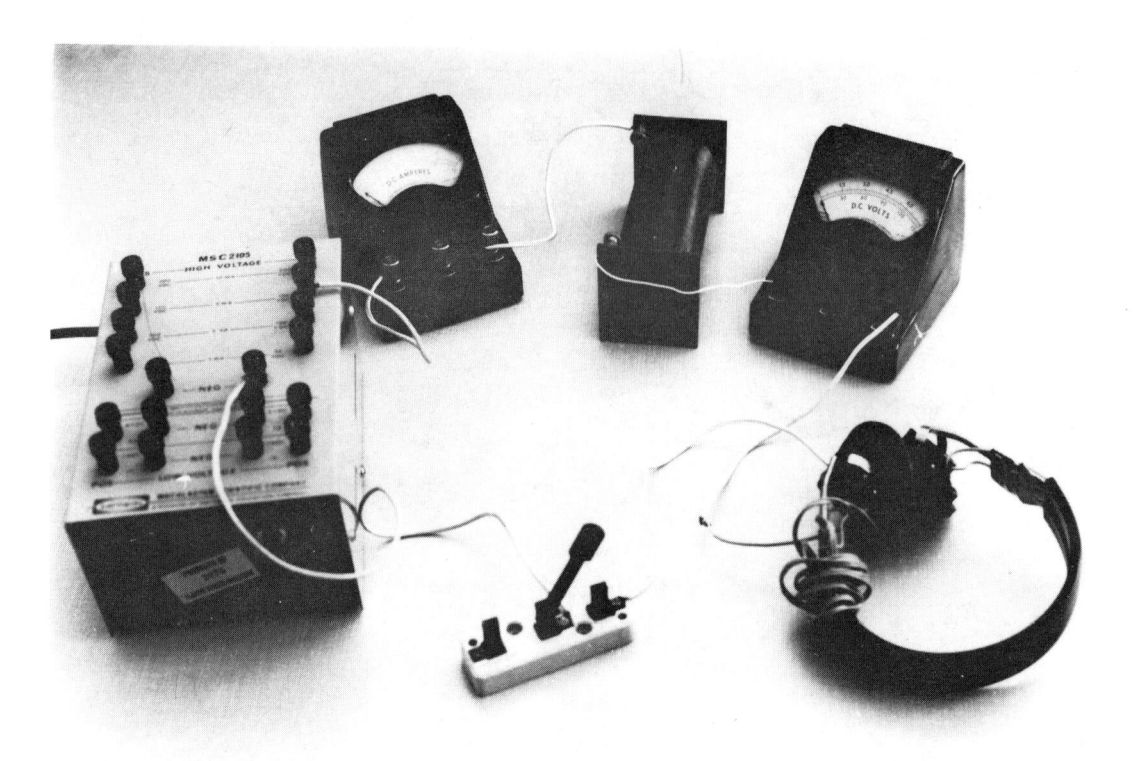

220 *Section Nine*

ACTIVITY PAGE **48** DRAWING SCHEMATICS FOR ELECTRICAL CIRCUITS—III

DIRECTIONS: In the space provided, draw a schematic diagram of the electric circuit shown in Photograph 5 below.

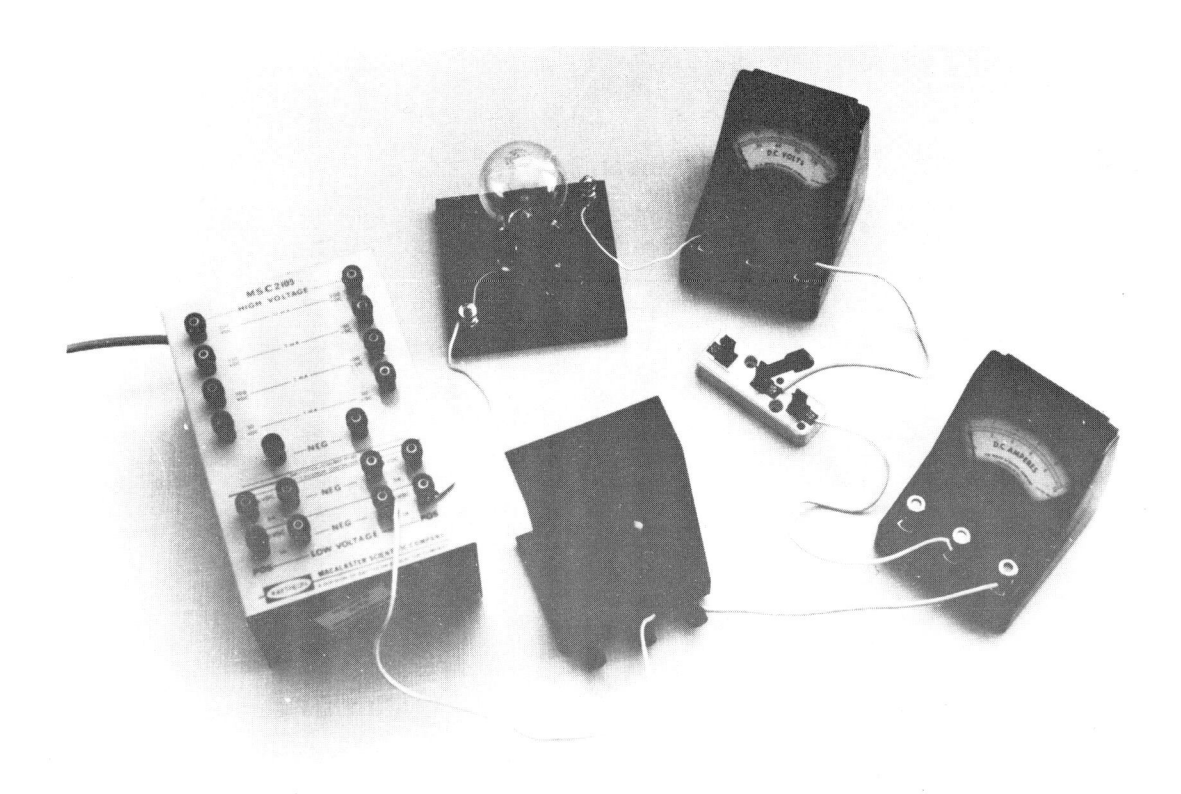

Special Scientific Skills 221

ACTIVITY PAGE **49** DRAWING SCHEMATICS FOR ELECTRICAL CIRCUITS—IV

DIRECTIONS: In the space provided, draw a schematic diagram of the electric circuit shown in Photograph 6 below.

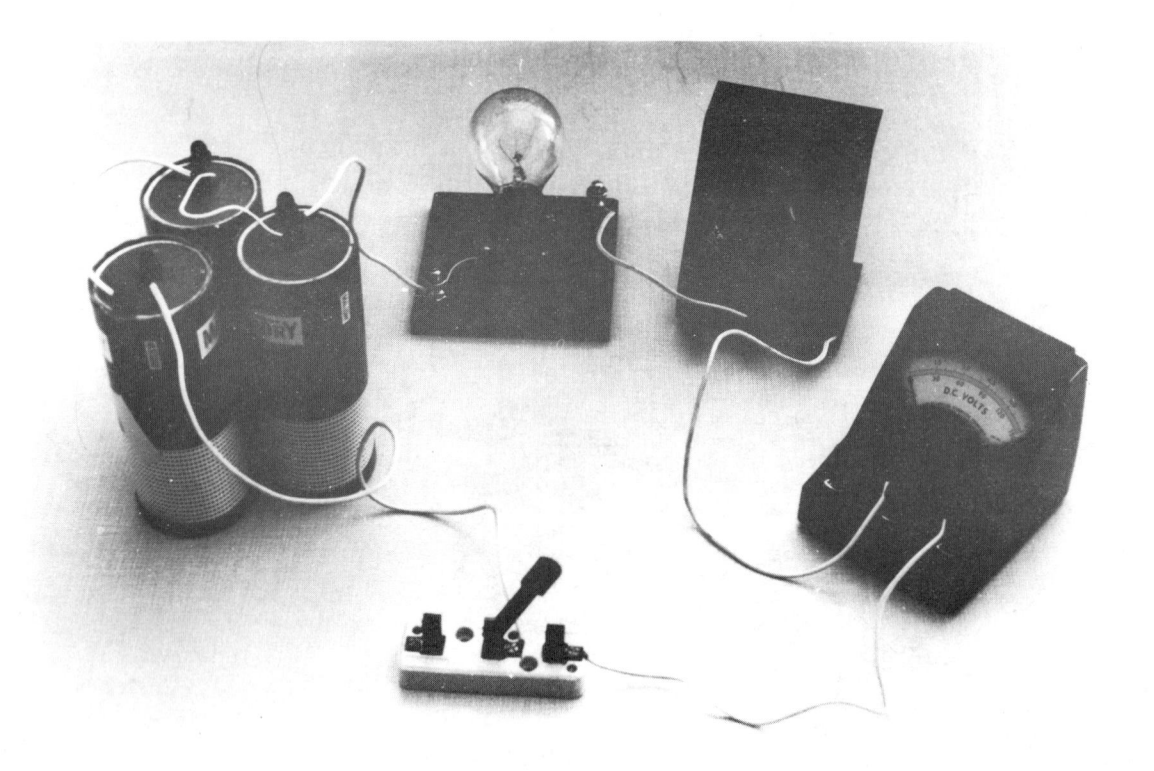

222 *Section Nine*

5. Reading Maps

Nearly everyone has had some experience in reading a map. Perhaps you have traveled across the state by car. Being able to read a map would be important in such a case. You may be used to traveling by bus or subway. Going to a new part of the city means that you might have to read a route map. What are some other ways you may have used a map in the past?

1. _____

2. _____

3. _____

4. _____

Maps are important in geography, geology, meteorology, and other earth sciences. The maps used in scientific research are often similar to the ones you may have used. They show the locations of various points on the earth's surface. On some maps, it may be highways and cities that are most important. Other maps might pay special attention to mountains, rivers, and deserts. Still others might show where mines, factories, and railroads are to be found. Under what conditions might each of these kinds of maps be useful? Write your answers before comparing with the ones given.

Map of highways and cities: _____

Map of mountains, rivers, etc.: _____

Map of mines, factories, etc.: _____

Some maps can be fairly easy to make. Suppose, for example, that you wanted to show someone how to get from your house to your schoolroom. Make a sketch in the space below that shows how this map would look. Then show the map to someone else in the class. See if that person understands what you have drawn.

Special Scientific Skills 223

What things did you have to think about when you made the map on the previous page? Write down as many of these things as you can think of in the space below:

1. _____

2. _____

3. _____

4. _____

The larger your map gets, the more difficult it is to draw. In the space below, try drawing a map of one part of your town. Choose a section that is about five blocks long and five blocks wide.

What new problems did you run into in making this map? How was it more difficult than the first map you drew? Write down your answers to these questions in the space below.

New Problems:

1. _____

2. _____

3. _____

4. _____

5. _____

Now suppose you wanted to make a map of your whole city. What kinds of information would you need to have before you could make this map? What new problems do you think you would run into in making this map? Write down your answers to these two questions in the space below.

Information you need for map:

1. _____

2. _____

3. _____

4. _____

5. _____

Problems you might have in making the map:

1. _____

2. _____

3. _____

4. _____

5. _____

There is one kind of map that you may not have seen before. It is called a topographic map. An example of a topographic map is shown on page 226. Notice, first of all, that most of the information you are used to seeing on a map is in this map too. You know what the relative position is of various places compared to each other. Answer the following questions about this map before comparing with the answers given.

Special Scientific Skills 225

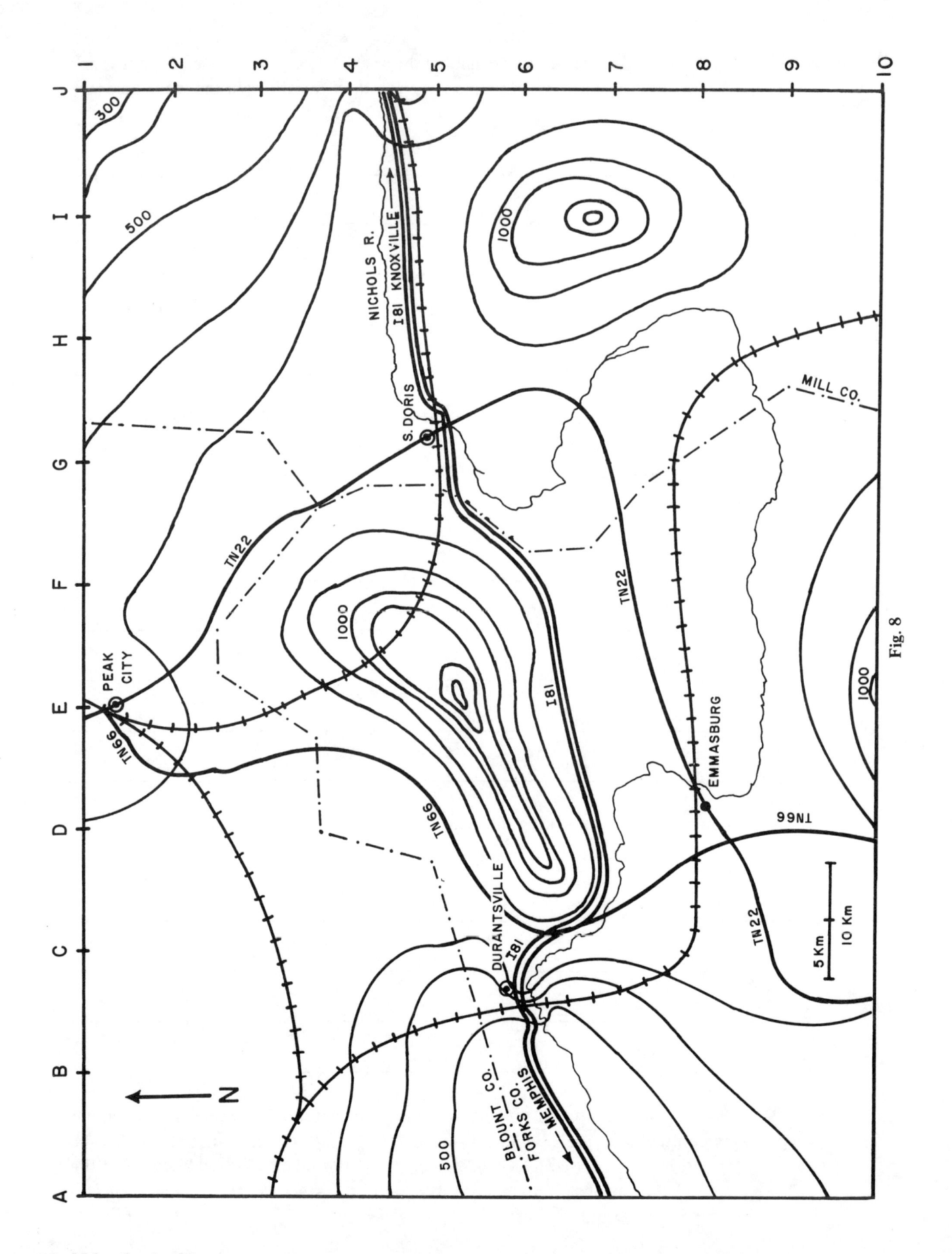

Fig. 8

226 *Section Nine*

1. What direction would you have to go to get from Durantsville to South Doris?

2. How far is it from Durantsville to South Doris?

3. Could you get from Durantsville to South Doris by train? If so, describe the route.

4. Could you get from Durantsville to South Doris by water? If so, describe the route.

5. What state is Durantsville in? What county is it in?

6. Name at least two major highways in the area.

You may have noticed one major difference on the topographic map on page 226 that you don't see on ordinary road maps. These are the long, nearly parallel lines in the upper right hand corner of the map. They are called **contour lines**. Each contour line connects all points on the map that have the same elevation. For example, the contour line marked "500" connects all points on the map that are 500 meters above sea level. The line marked "1000" connects all points that are 1000 meters above sea level.

You can see that contour lines tell you something about the vertical shape of the land, just as ordinary road maps tell you about the horizontal appearance of the land. For example, suppose that a set of contour lines are very close to each other on the map. Find a point on the map where that is true and circle it. This means that the land is rising or falling quite rapidly. The points that are 500, 600, 700, and 800 meters high are not very far apart. In the area that you have circled, tell how fast the land rises in the distance of ten kilometers.

The map we have been using shows what this region looks like from above. You could imagine that you are flying in an airplane over this piece of land. What would the area look like if you were on the ground, at the edge of the map, looking across the region? That's a question you could not answer with an ordinary road map. Such a map usually doesn't tell you about the rise and fall of the land, but a topographic map does. Looking at a topographic map will give you an idea about the vertical dimensions of the area. In fact, you can make a simple sketch of a part of this area simply by looking at the topographic map. Let's see how that can be done. For this exercise, use the topographic map on page 226.

Special Scientific Skills 227

Place a strip of paper along any portion of the map you choose. The edge of the paper represents the line of sight as you stand at point A on the map and look toward point B. Make a dot on the strip of paper for each contour line underneath the paper (Figure 9, page 229). Make sure that you know the vertical distance represented by each contour line. Mark some of the dots on your paper strip so that you will know what these elevations are. Regular distances such as 100 meters, 200 meters, 300 meters, and so on would be a good idea.

Now transfer your strip of paper to the lined chart in Figure 10 on page 230. Make a graph on this lined chart paper that corresponds to the elevations recorded on your strip of paper. For example, for the dot on your strip that stands for "100 meters," make a point on your lined chart at a height of 100 meters. For a dot on the strip that stands for "500 meters," make a point on the lined chart at the height of 500 meters. When each dot on the strip has been recorded on the lined chart or graph paper, connect all points with a smooth curve. This curve should represent the vertical profile across the line of sight you selected.

When you have completed this exercise, turn to Activity Page 50, page 231. This activity page asks you questions about the topographic map on page 226.

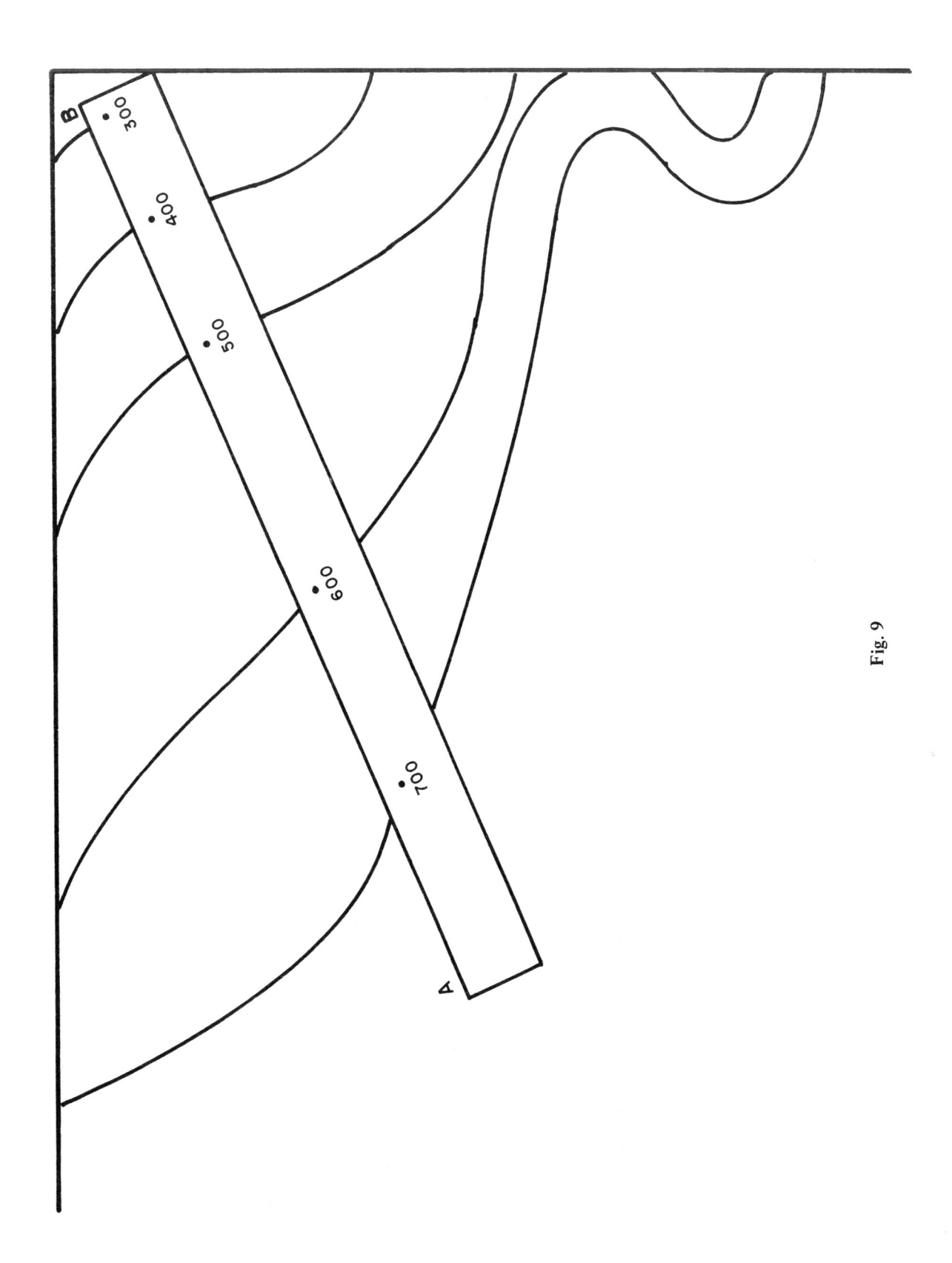

Fig. 9

HEIGHT (IN METERS)

100, 200, 300, 400, 500, 600, 700, 800, 900, 1000

POINT A

PLACE YOUR STRIP OF PAPER ALONG THIS LINE.

POINT B

Fig. 10

230 *Section Nine*

ACTIVITY PAGE **50** UNDERSTANDING TOPOGRAPHIC MAPS

DIRECTIONS: Refer to the topographic map on page 226 of the text in order to answer the following questions.

1. A section called Chalk Cliffs is located in the area shown by this map. It is not labeled on the map, but what do you think the coordinates of this section are?

2. In traveling from Durantsville to South Doris, would you be going uphill or downhill? How do you know?

3. What is the approximate vertical drop of the Nichols River from one side of the map to the other? In which direction is the river flowing?

4. Where do you think Nolet Hill is located? Give the coordinates of this hill.

5. Is Emmasburg in a valley or on a plateau? How do you know?

6. What vertical distance would you travel in going from Emmasburg to South Doris?

7. Is Peak City higher or lower than South Doris? How do you know?

8. Standing in South Doris, in which direction would you look to see the highest spot on the map? How do you know?

9. In the space below, construct a vertical section of the land along a line from Emmasburg to Peak City.

Special Scientific Skills 231

6. Reading Weather Maps

The science of meteorology—the study of weather—changed dramatically during World War II. It was then, for the first time, that we learned some basic ideas about predicting weather. We found out that an important factor in determining weather is the presence of huge masses of warm or cool air in the atmosphere. When these masses move over the earth's surface, they encounter other masses that are colder or warmer than they are. The interaction of these air masses of different temperatures is a major cause of the weather produced in a region.

Two of the most common occurrences are illustrated in Figures 11 and 12 on page 233-234. In Figure 11, a moving mass of warm air has encountered a mass of air cooler than itself. The warm air is less dense, so it slides up over the cool air forming a boundary known as a **warm front**. Certain kinds of weather conditions are commonly associated with the arrival of a warm front. Find out what these conditions are and list them in the space provided below under "Warm Front."

Figure 12 illustrates what happens when a moving mass of cool air encounters a mass of warm air. The cool air forces its way under the existing warmer air and produces a boundary known as a **cold front**. Find out the weather conditions usually associated with a cold front. List these in the space provided below under "Cold Front."

Weather conditions associated with:

Warm Front	**Cold Front**
1. High clouds (cirrus, cirrocumulus, and cirrostratus) form ahead of front.	1. Move faster than warm fronts.
2.	2.
3.	3.
4.	4.
5.	5.

If we know about the movement of warm and cold fronts, we can often predict the weather for an area twenty-four or forty-eight hours in advance . . . and with good accuracy. We can make longer-range forecasts also, but with less accuracy. Who would be interested in having such forecasts? Why would they be interested? Write down your answers to those questions in the space on page 235.

Section Nine

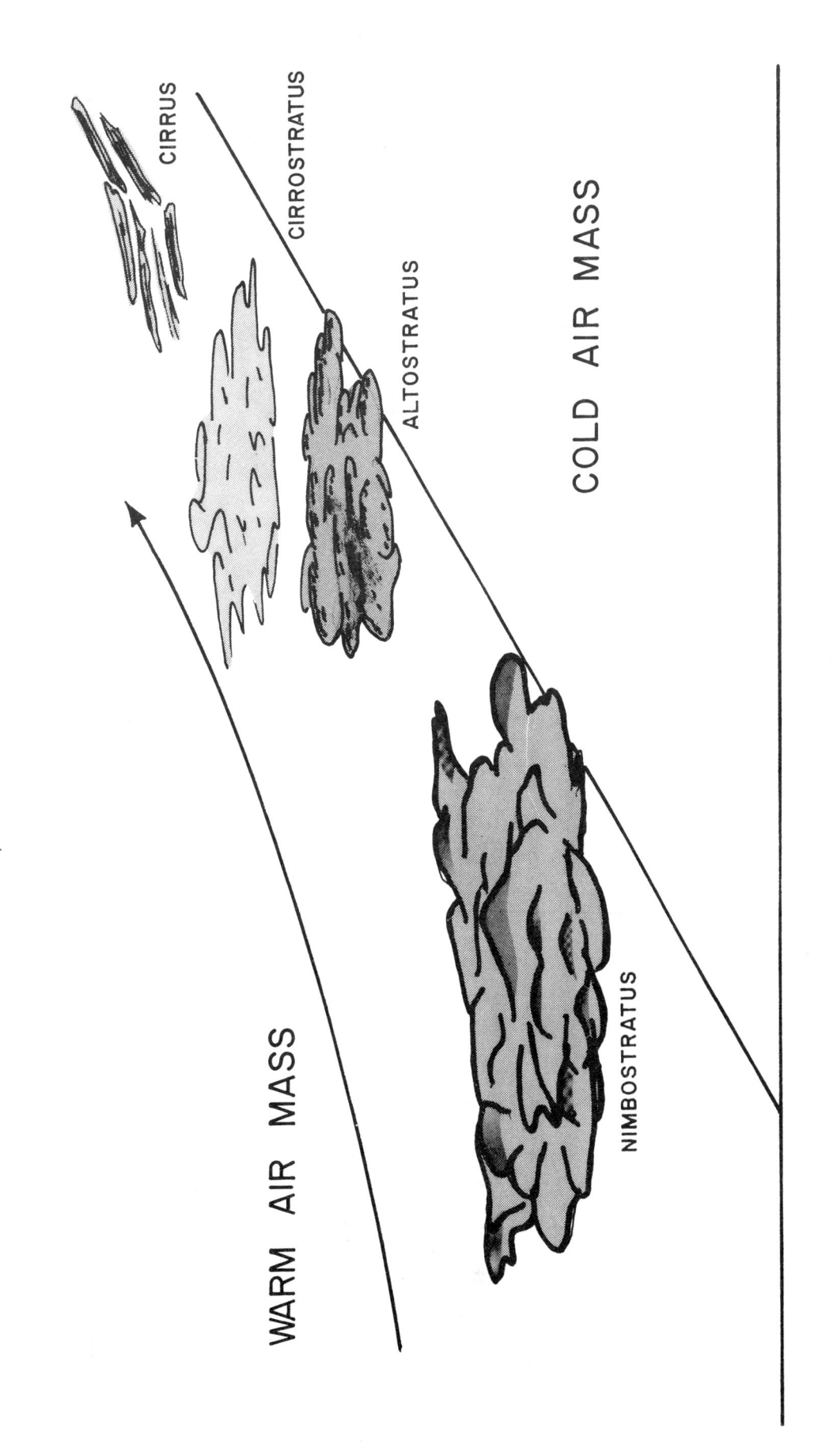

Fig. 11

Special Scientific Skills 233

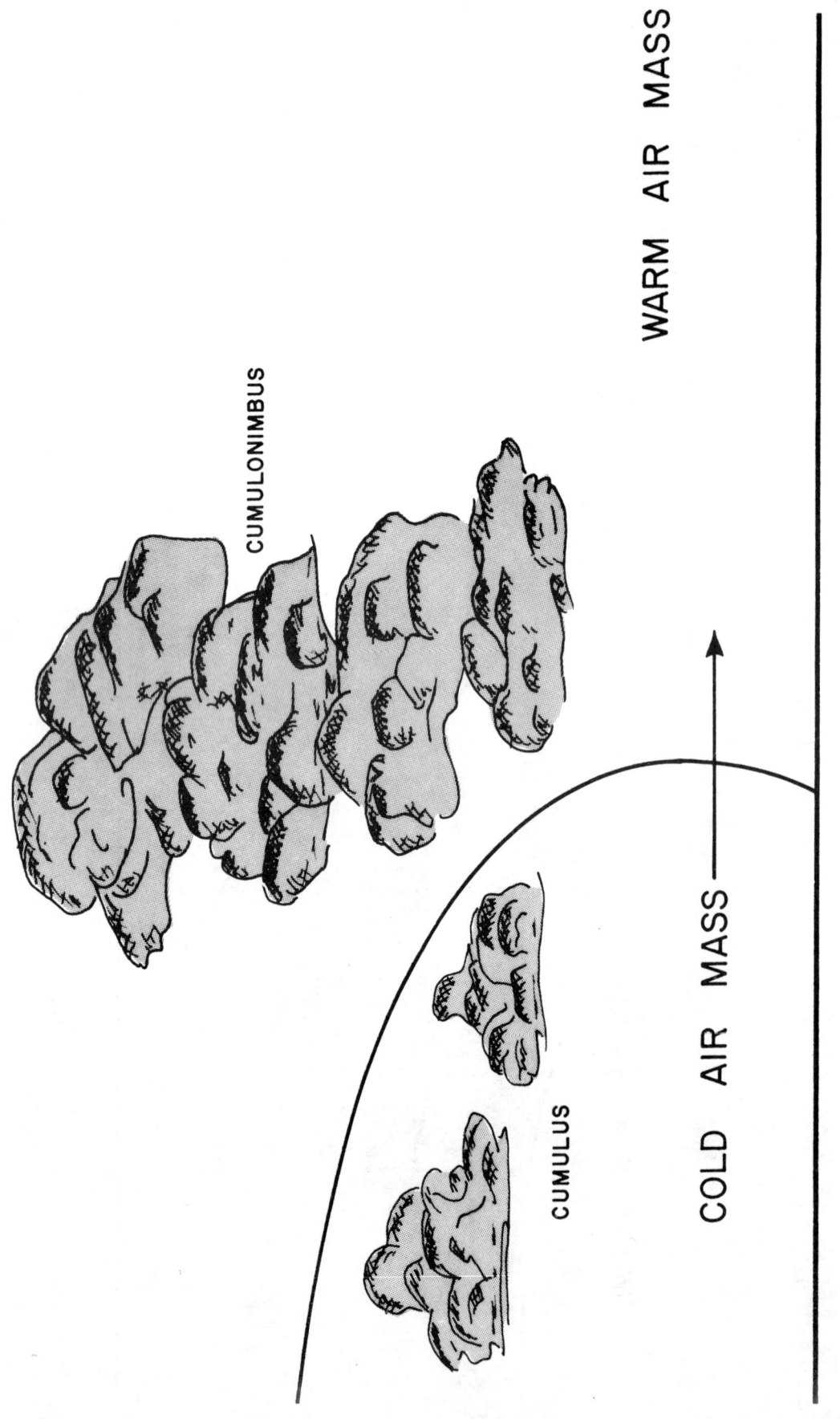

Fig. 12

234   *Section Nine*

Who would be interested in a weather forecast?	Why?
1. Owner of ski area	1. To know whether snow was expected
2. Your family	2. To know whether to plan a picnic
3.	3.
4.	4.
5.	5.
6.	6.

Weather information is collected at observational stations throughout the world. It is then sent to certain Analysis Centers where data from many stations are combined to produce a weather map. The symbols used in making a weather map are standard throughout the world. No matter where a map is constructed, any meteorologist in the world can read it and understand what it says. A typical weather map is shown in Figure 13 on page 236.

Every weather map contains information on a great many conditions: cloud cover, temperature, pressure, wind speed, type of clouds, and so on. There is a special code for each kind of cloud, each type of precipitation, every wind speed, and so on. There is not enough room to show all of those codes in this book. We have, however, reprinted in Figures 14-17 (pages 237-240) some of the ones you are more likely to run into when you look at a weather map. Further information about weather maps can be obtained from:

Director
Environmental Data Service
National Oceanic and Atmospheric Administration
Washington, D.C. 20235

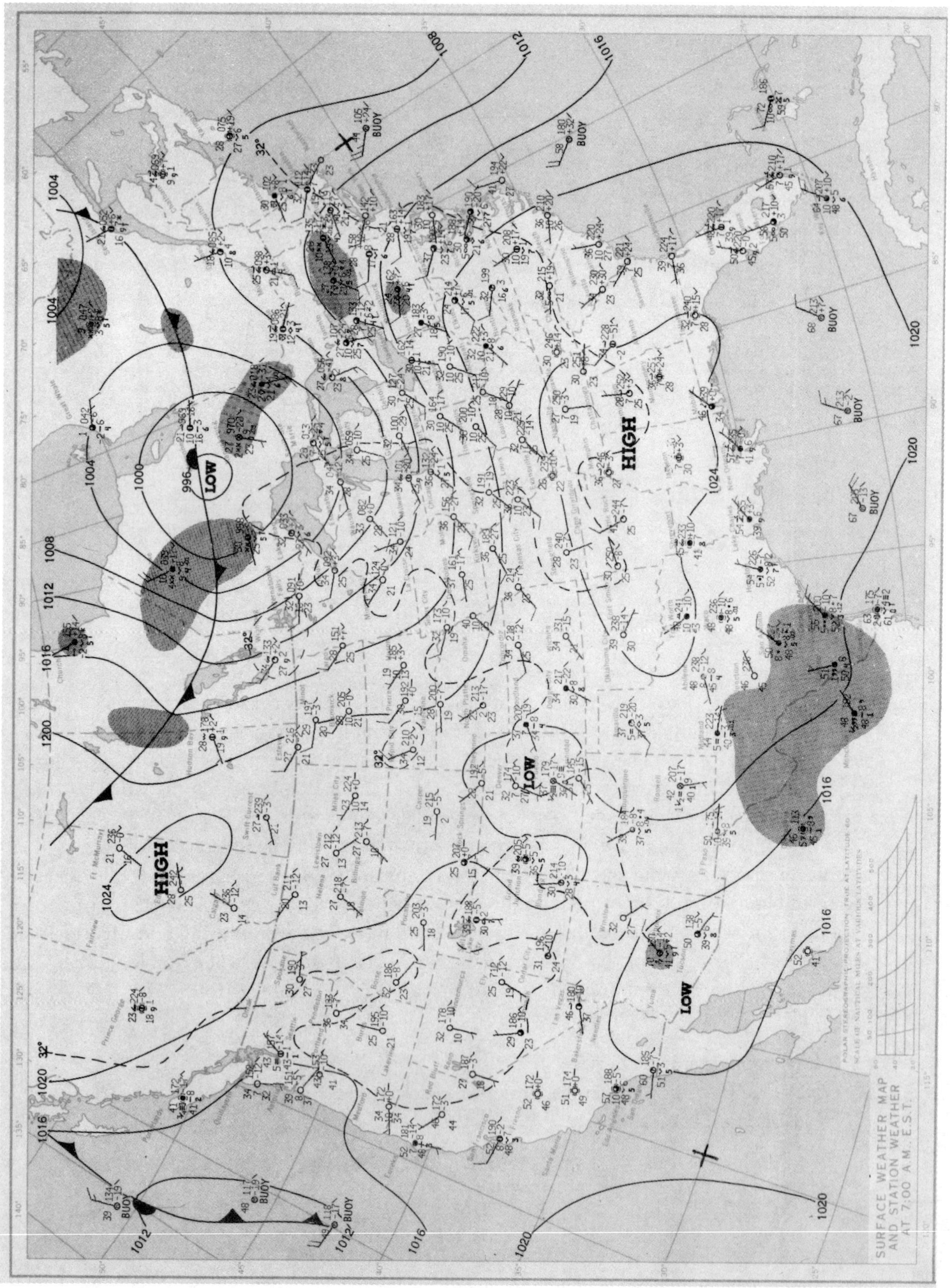

Fig. 13 Reprinted through the courtesy of the Environmental Data Service, National Oceanic and Atmospheric Administration.

236 Section Nine

Thin, solid lines, called isobars, connect points of equal barometric pressure. On the surface map, the isobars represent lines of equal sea level pressure, and are labeled in metric units called millibars. Where the isobars enclose an area, an H or the word HIGH identifies it as an area or center of high barometric pressure; an L or LOW is used to identify a center of low barometric pressure. Winds blow roughly parallel to the isobars. When the isobars are close together, wind speeds are large; when isobars are far apart, wind speeds are small. Winds blow clockwise around highs and counterclockwise around lows.

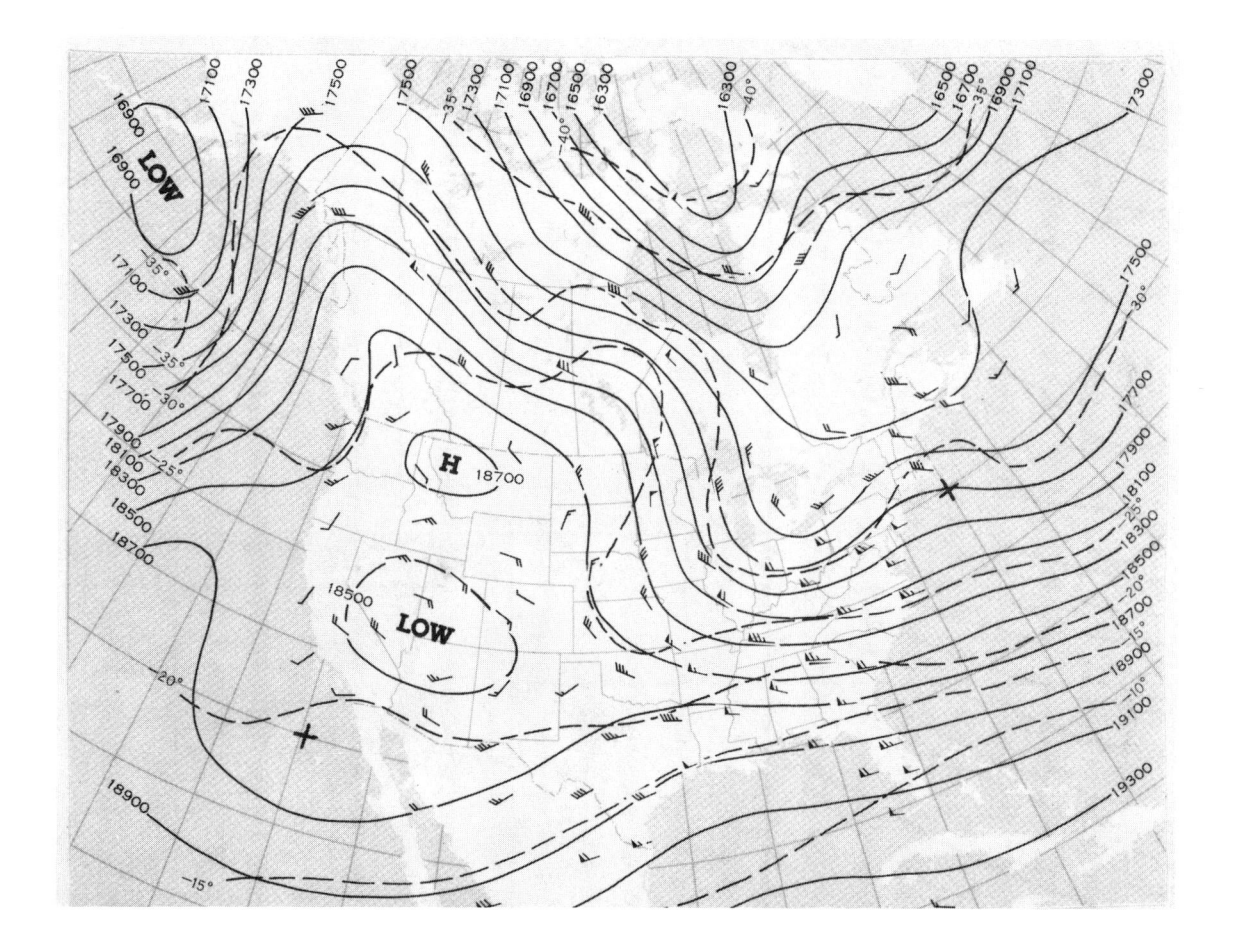

Fig. 14

Maps and charts on pages 236-240 are reprinted through the courtesy of the Environmental Data Service, National Oceanic and Atmospheric Administration.

SPECIMEN STATION MODEL

Cloud type (High cirrus.)
Cloud type (Middle altocumulus.)
Total amount of clouds. (Sky completely covered.)
Barometric pressure at sea level. Initial 9 or 10 omitted. (1014.7 millibars.)
Wind speed. (18–22 knots)
Amount of barometric change in past 3 hours. (In tenths of millibars.)
Direction of wind. (From the northwest.)
Barometric tendency in past 3 hours. (Rising.)
Temperature in degrees Fahrenheit.
Sign showing whether pressure is higher or lower than 3 hours ago.
Visibility. (¾ mile.)
Present weather. (Continuous slight snow in flakes.)
Time precipitation began or ended. (Began 3 to 4 hours ago.)
Dewpoint in degrees Fahrenheit.
Weather in past 6 hours. (Rain.)
Cloud type. (Low fractostratus and/or fractocumulus.)
Amount of precipitation in last 6 hours.
Part of sky covered by lowest cloud. (Seven or eight-tenths.)
Height of cloud base. (300 – 599 feet.)

Abridged from International Code

Fronts are shown on surface weather maps by the symbols below: (Arrows —not shown on maps—indicate direction of motion of front.)

→ ▲▲▲ Cold front (surface)   ▲▼▲▼ Stationary front (surface)
← ●●● Warm front (surface)   ▲▲▲ Warm front (aloft)
← ▲●▲● Occluded front (surface)   ▼▼▼ Cold front (aloft)

PRESSURE TENDENCY

Code No. a		
0	╱‾	Rising, then falling; same as or higher than 3 hours ago
1	╱⁻	Rising, then steady; or rising, then rising more slowly
2	╱	Rising steadily, or unsteadily
3	╱╱	Falling or steady, then rising; or rising, then rising more rapidly

Barometric pressure now higher than 3 hours ago

4	—	Steady; same as 3 hours ago
5	╲‾	Falling, then rising; same as or lower than 3 hours ago
6	╲⁻	Falling, then steady; or falling, then falling more slowly
7	╲	Falling steadily, or unsteadily
8	╲╲	Steady or rising, then falling; or falling, then falling more rapidly

Barometric pressure now lower than 3 hours ago

R_t TIME PRECIPITATION BEGAN OR ENDED

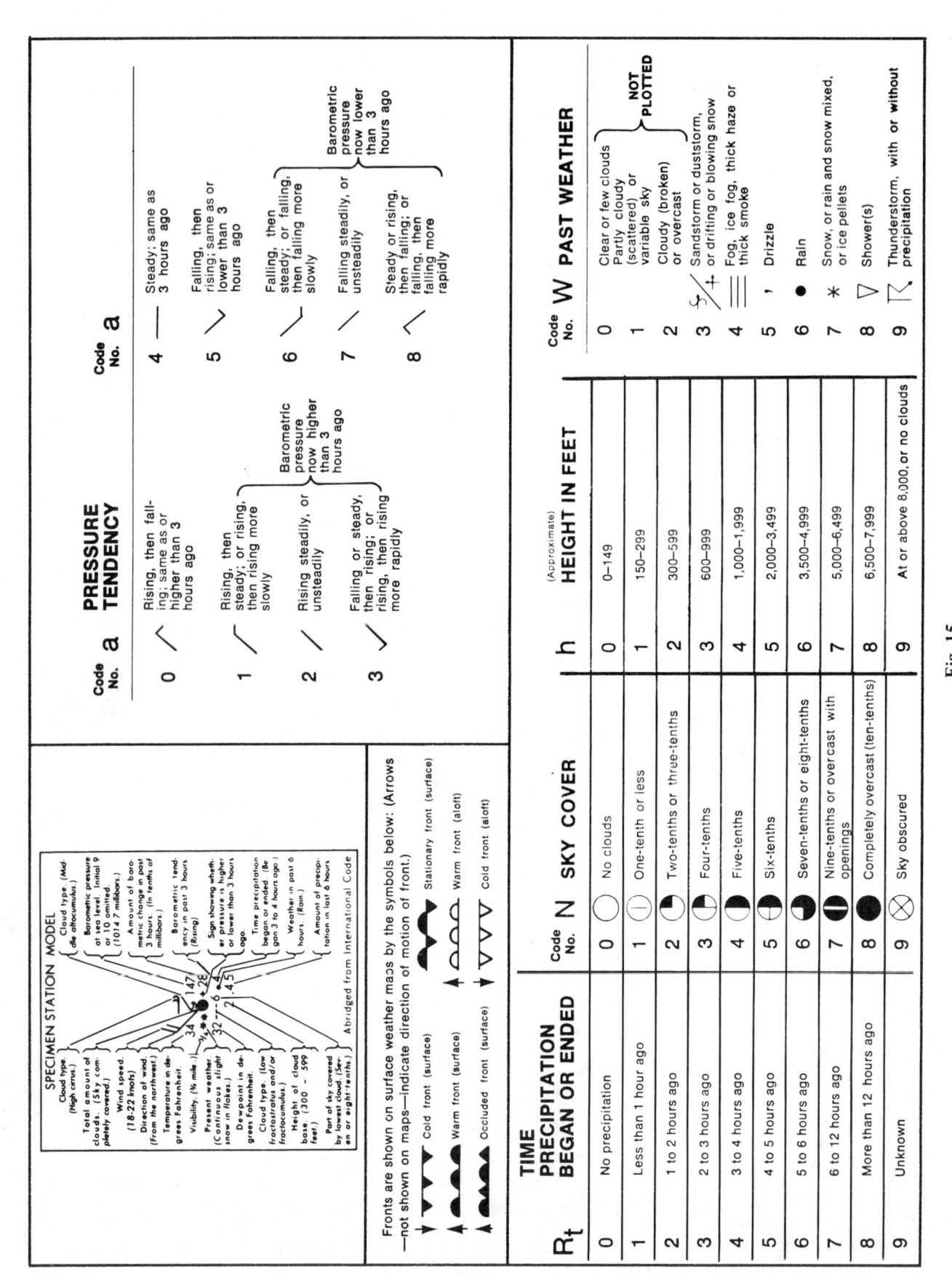

Code No.	
0	No precipitation
1	Less than 1 hour ago
2	1 to 2 hours ago
3	2 to 3 hours ago
4	3 to 4 hours ago
5	4 to 5 hours ago
6	5 to 6 hours ago
7	6 to 12 hours ago
8	More than 12 hours ago
9	Unknown

N SKY COVER

Code No.		
0	○	No clouds
1	◔	One-tenth or less
2		Two-tenths or three-tenths
3		Four-tenths
4	◑	Five-tenths
5		Six-tenths
6		Seven-tenths or eight-tenths
7		Nine-tenths or overcast with openings
8	●	Completely overcast (ten-tenths)
9	⊗	Sky obscured

h HEIGHT IN FEET (Approximate)

Code No.	
0	0–149
1	150–299
2	300–599
3	600–999
4	1,000–1,999
5	2,000–3,499
6	3,500–4,999
7	5,000–6,499
8	6,500–7,999
9	At or above 8,000, or no clouds

W PAST WEATHER

Code No.		
0		Clear or few clouds
1		Partly cloudy (scattered) or variable sky	NOT PLOTTED
2		Cloudy (broken) or overcast
3	⊖/+	Sandstorm or duststorm, or drifting or blowing snow
4	≡	Fog, ice fog, thick haze or thick smoke
5	,	Drizzle
6	●	Rain
7	✱	Snow, or rain and snow mixed, or ice pellets
8	▽	Shower(s)
9	⎰⎱	Thunderstorm, with or without precipitation

Fig. 15

Reprinted through the courtesy of the Environmental Data Service, National Oceanic and Atmospheric Administration.

238   Section Nine

Cloud Abbreviations
St—STRATUS
Fs—FRACTOSTRATUS
Sc—STRATOCUMULUS
Cu—CUMULUS
Fc—FRACTOCUMULUS
Cb—CUMULONIMBUS
Ac—ALTOCUMULUS
Ns—NIMBOSTRATUS
As—ALTOSTRATUS
Ci—CIRRUS
Cs—CIRROSTRATUS
Cc—CIRROCUMULUS

C_L Description (Abridged From International Code)

Code No.	Description
1	Cu of fair weather, little vertical development and seemingly flattened
2	Cu of considerable development, generally towering, with or without other Cu or Sc bases all at same level
3	Cb with tops lacking clear-cut outlines, but distinctly not cirriform or anvil-shaped; with or without Cu, Sc, or St
4	Sc formed by spreading out of Cu; Cu often present also
5	Sc not formed by spreading out of Cu
6	St or Fs or both, but no Fs of bad weather
7	Fs and/or Fc of bad weather (scud)
8	Cu and Sc (not formed by spreading out of Cu) with bases at different levels
9	Cb having a clearly fibrous (cirriform) top, often anvil-shaped, with or without Cu, Sc, St, or scud

C_M Description (Abridged From International Code)

Code No.	Description
1	Thin As (most of cloud layer semitransparent)
2	Thick As, greater part sufficiently dense to hide sun (or moon), or Ns
3	Thin Ac, mostly semitransparent; cloud elements not changing much and at a single level
4	Thin Ac in patches; cloud elements continually changing and/or occurring at more than one level
5	Thin Ac in bands or in a layer gradually spreading over sky and usually thickening as a whole
6	Ac formed by the spreading out of Cu or Cb
7	Double-layered Ac, or a thick layer of Ac, not increasing; or Ac with As and/or Ns
8	Ac in the form of Cu-shaped tufts or Ac with turrets
9	Ac of a chaotic sky, usually at different levels; patches of dense Ci are usually present also

C_H Description (Abridged From International Code)

Code No.	Description
1	Filaments of Ci, or "mares tails," scattered and not increasing
2	Dense Ci in patches or twisted sheaves, usually not increasing, sometimes like remains of Cb; or towers or tufts
3	Dense Ci, often anvil-shaped, derived from or associated with Cb
4	Ci, often hook-shaped, gradually spreading over the sky and usually thickening as a whole
5	Ci and Cs, often in converging bands, or Cs alone; generally overspreading and growing denser; the continuous layer not reaching 45° altitude
6	Ci and Cs, often in converging bands, or Cs alone; generally overspreading and growing denser; the continuous layer exceeding 45° altitude
7	Veil of Cs covering the entire sky
8	Cs not increasing and not covering entire sky
9	Cc alone or Cc with some Ci or Cs, but the Cc being the main cirriform cloud

ff WIND SPEED

	Knots	miles per hour
	Calm	Calm
	1-2	1-2
	3-7	3-8
	8-12	9-14
	13-17	15-20
	18-22	21-25
	23-27	26-31
	28-32	32-37
	33-37	38-43
	38-42	44-49
	43-47	50-54
	48-52	55-60
	53-57	61-66
	58-62	67-71
	63-67	72-77
	68-72	78-83
	73-77	84-89
	103-107	119-123

Fig. 16

Reprinted through the courtesy of the Environmental Data Service, National Oceanic and Atmospheric Administration.

WW PRESENT WEATHER (Descriptions abridged from International Code)*

	0	1	2	3	4
00	Cloud development NOT observed, or NOT observable during past hour	Clouds generally dissolving or becoming less developed during past hour	State of sky on the whole unchanged during past hour	Clouds generally forming or developing during past hour	Visibility reduced by smoke
10	Light fog	Patches of shallow fog at station, NOT deeper than 6 feet on land	More or less continuous shallow fog at station, NOT deeper than 6 feet on land	Lightning visible, no thunder heard	Precipitation within sight, but NOT reaching the ground
20	Drizzle (NOT freezing) or snow grains (NOT falling as showers) during past hour, but NOT at time of observation	Rain (NOT freezing and NOT falling as showers) during past hour, but NOT at time of observation	Snow (NOT falling as showers) during past hour, but NOT at time of observation	Rain and snow or ice pellets (NOT falling as showers) during past hour, but NOT at time of observation	Freezing drizzle or freezing rain (NOT falling as showers) during past hour, but NOT at time of observation
30	Slight or moderate dust storm or sandstorm, has decreased during past hour	Slight or moderate dust storm or sandstorm, no appreciable change during past hour	Slight or moderate dust storm or sandstorm, has begun or increased during past hour	Severe dust storm or sandstorm, has decreased during past hour	Severe dust storm or sandstorm, no appreciable change during past hour
40	Fog or ice fog at distance at time of observation, but NOT at station during past hour	Fog or ice fog in patches	Fog or ice fog, sky discernible, has become thinner during past hour	Fog or ice fog, sky NOT discernible, has become thinner during past hour	Fog or ice fog, sky discernible, no appreciable change during past hour
50	Intermittent drizzle (NOT freezing), slight at time of observation	Continuous drizzle (NOT freezing), slight at time of observation	Intermittent drizzle (NOT freezing), moderate at time of observation	Continuous drizzle (NOT freezing), moderate at time of observation	Intermittent drizzle (NOT freezing), heavy at time of observation
60	Intermittent rain (NOT freezing), slight at time of observation	Continuous rain (NOT freezing), slight at time of observation	Intermittent rain (NOT freezing), moderate at time of observation	Continuous rain (NOT freezing), moderate at time of observation	Intermittent rain (NOT freezing), heavy at time of observation
70	Intermittent fall of snowflakes, slight at time of observation	Continuous fall of snowflakes, slight at time of observation	Intermittent fall of snowflakes, moderate at time of observation.	Continuous fall of snowflakes, moderate at time of observation	Intermittent fall of snowflakes, heavy at time of observation
80	Slight rain shower(s)	Moderate or heavy rain shower(s)	Violent rain shower(s)	Slight shower(s) of rain and snow mixed	Moderate or heavy shower(s) of rain and snow mixed
90	Moderate or heavy shower(s) of hail, with or without rain, or rain and snow mixed, not associated with thunder	Slight rain at time of observation; thunderstorm during past hour, but NOT at time of observation	Moderate or heavy rain at time of observation; thunderstorm during past hour, but NOT at time of observation	Slight snow, or rain and snow mixed, or hail at time of observation; thunderstorm during past hour, but NOT at time of observation	Moderate or heavy snow, or rain and snow mixed, or hail at time of observation; thunderstorm during past hour, but NOT at time of observation

*This table incomplete. Horizontal categories continue to Class 9.

Fig. 17

Reprinted through the courtesy of the Environmental Data Service, National Oceanic and Atmospheric Administration.

240 Section Nine

The lines shown on a weather map are **isobars**. The word isobar means **equal** ("iso-") **pressure** ("-bar"). In other words, these lines connect places on the earth's surface where the atmospheric pressure is all the same. The isobar line that reads 1008, for example, connects all points that have reported an atmospheric pressure of 1008 millibars. (The millibar is a unit of pressure in the metric system.)

Isobars tend to mark off regions of **high pressure** ("highs") and **low pressure** ("lows"). Highs and lows tend to move across the country, from west to east, bringing certain characteristic kinds of weathers with them. They are called "highs" or "lows" because they are regions in which the barometric pressure is "higher" or "lower" than it is in regions around them. Find out what kinds of weather patterns are associated with highs and lows. List your findings in the space below.

Highs	**Lows**
1. cool temperatures	1. storms
2.	2.
3.	3.
4.	4.
5.	5.
6.	6.

Activity Page 51, pages 244-245, contains some exercises on weather prediction. Look carefully at the weather maps in Figures 18 and 19 (pages 242-243). Then answer the questions asked about those maps on the activity page.

Fig. 18

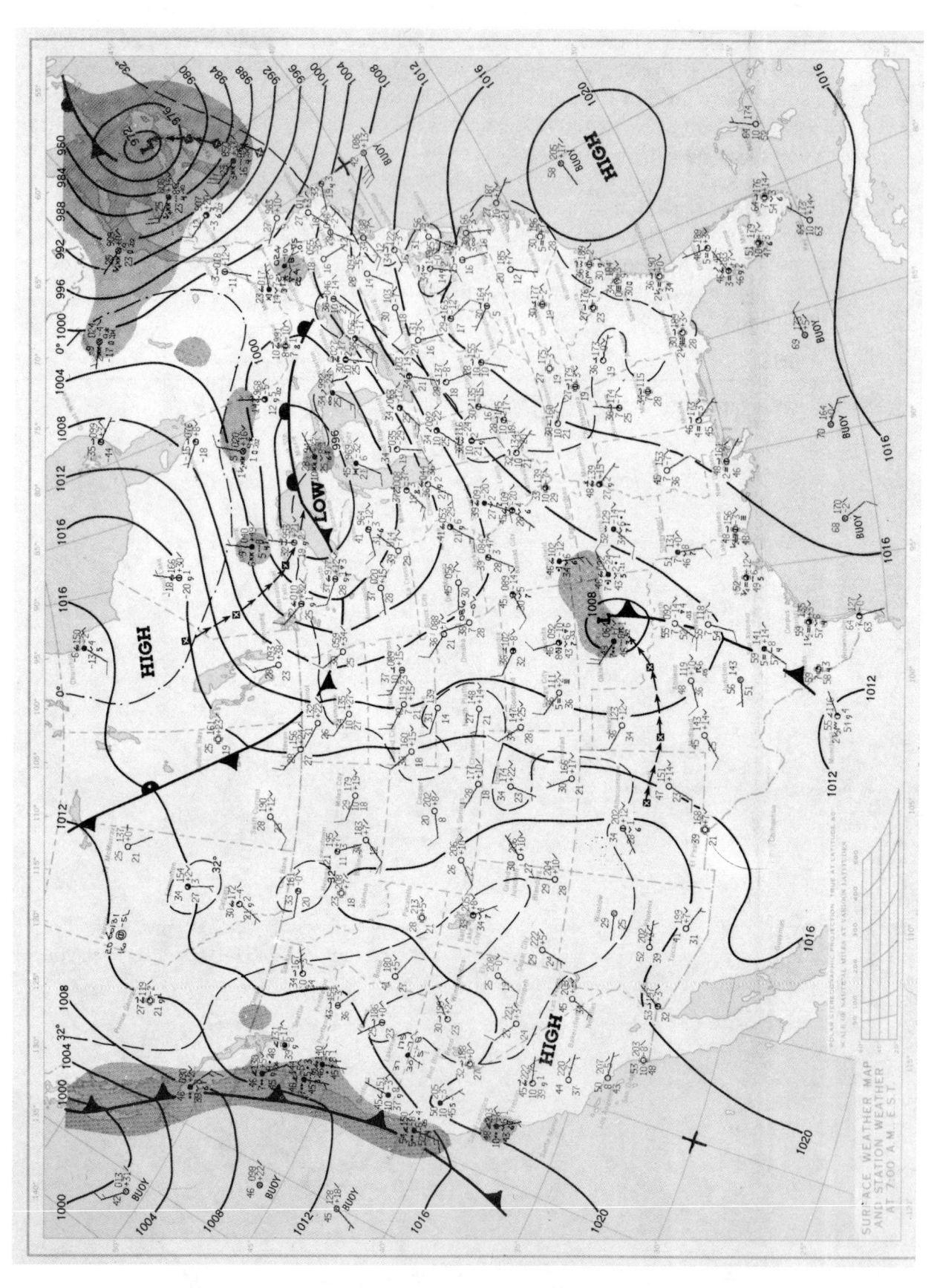

242 Section Nine

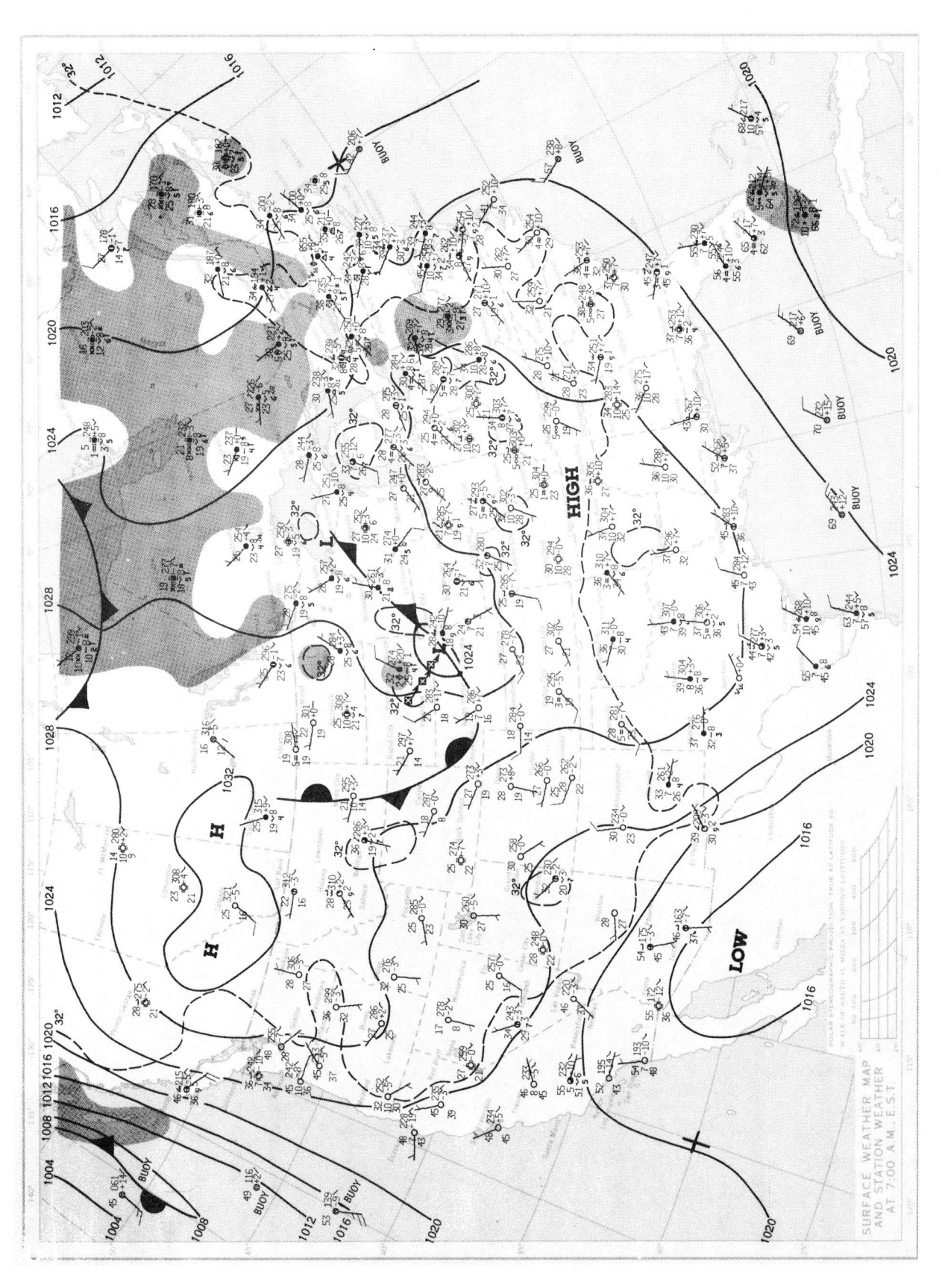

Maps on pages 242-243 are reprinted through the courtesy of the Environmental Data Service, National Oceanic and Atmospheric Administration.

Special Scientific Skills 243

ACTIVITY PAGE 51 UNDERSTANDING WEATHER MAPS

DIRECTIONS: Refer to the weather maps on pages 242-243 in order to answer the following questions. Refer to Figures 14-17 (pages 237-240) to help read the maps.

Map for March 15, 1981 (Figure 18, page 242)

1. How many highs are there on this map? Where are they located?

2. How many lows are there? Where are they located?

3. What areas were receiving precipitation on this day? What kind of precipitation was falling at each location?

4. Tell whether any of the following are shown on the map and, if so, where:

   a. warm front:

   b. cold front:

   c. stationary front:

   d. occluded front:

5. What temperature was reported on this day for:

   a. Phoenix, AZ

   b. Trout Lake, OR

   c. Jackson, MS

   d. Prince George, BC

   e. Casper, WY

   f. Lake Charles, LA

   g. Portland, ME

Map for March 9, 1981 (Figure 19, page 243)

1. What type of clouds were reported over each of the following cities:
   a. Atlanta, GA
   b. Fresno, CA
   c. International Falls, MN
   d. Tallahassee, FL
   e. Calgary, Alta.
   f. Roanoke, VA

2. What portion of the sky is covered with clouds at:
   a. Medford, OR
   b. Pittsburgh, PA
   c. Boston, MA
   d. San Antonio, TX
   e. Midland, TX
   f. Helena, MT
   g. Louisville, KY

3. What is the wind direction and velocity at:
   a. Boise, ID
   b. Huron, SD
   c. Concordia, KS
   d. Edmonton, Alta.
   e. Boston, MA
   f. Jacksonville, FL

4. What types of fronts are shown on this map and where are they located?

5. Describe the movement over the preceding 24 hours of the low now over Sioux City, IA:

6. What is the barometric pressure at:
   a. Calgary, Alta.
   b. Abilene, TX
   c. Milwaukee, WI
   d. The buoy directly west of Medford, OR
   e. The buoy directly east of Philadelphia, PA
   f. Casper, WY

7. Making Computer Flow Charts

Here is a skill that is fairly new in science. Twenty years ago, only a small number of scientists knew about or used computers very much. Today, the vast majority of scientists in almost every field have some contact with computers. By the time you are an adult, mastery of computer skills will probably be expected of every scientist . . . and perhaps of every citizen too! To remind you that computer skills are **not** just important in science, make a list of some ways in which computers are used in your life or that of your family.

Here are some ways computers are important in my life:

1.

2.

3.

4.

5.

6.

7.

8.

Computers help scientists in many ways. The one you may think of first is in doing mathematical work for them. As you know, a computer can add, subtract, multiply, divide, and carry out other mathematical calculations at an astonishing speed. Some calculations that would take a group of people many years to do can now be completed by a computer in a few seconds.

Computers help in other ways too. They can analyze information given to them, predict the results of experiments, draw graphs of data, compare alternative ways of doing things and decide which is best, and even examine a patient and diagnose possible illnesses! As brilliant as computers seem to be, they are, in some ways, really simple minded. The only mathematics they really know how to do, for example, is addition and subtraction. All the complicated things they can do have to be translated by some human into an "add and/or subtract" problem for them.

Computers are not really taking over from humans after all. They simply carry out instructions that humans give to them. In fact, in some ways computers are amazingly dumb. They do **exactly** what they are told to do, no more and no less. For this reason, a computer programmer must be very, very careful to say exactly what she or he means to say to the computer. A good deal of the programmer's time is spent in figuring out exactly what has to be said to the computer. The system used to work out this message is known as a flow chart.

A **flow chart** is a series of steps that must be followed by the computer if it is to handle the information it is given properly. For example, suppose we would like to have a computer solve all your math homework problems for you. You certainly don't want the teacher to know that the computer did your work for you, so you want to slip in one wrong answer. What would you tell the computer to do?

The following series of steps shows how you would solve this problem, taking care of each step one at a time. Suppose your homework assignment contains ten problems. The directions written are the statement or questions that you would give to the computer.

Step 1: Read problem.

Step 2: Solve problem.

Step 3: Have you solved ten problems?
If not, go back to step 1.
If so, go to step 4.

Step 4: Have you made any errors in solving a problem?
If so, go to step 5.
If not, go to step 6.

Step 5: You are finished. Print all answers.

Step 6: Select problem 5.
Add 1 to this answer.

Step 7: Go to step 5.

Notice that you have written different **kinds** of statements in this list. These include:

1. Commands to get information: Step 1

2. Commands to print results: Step 5

3. Commands to do mathematical calculations: Step 2 and Step 6

4. Commands to make a choice: Step 3 and Step 4.

In a flow chart, each kind of statement is contained in a special kind of box. The type used for each kind of statement is shown on page 248.

INPUT/OUTPUT

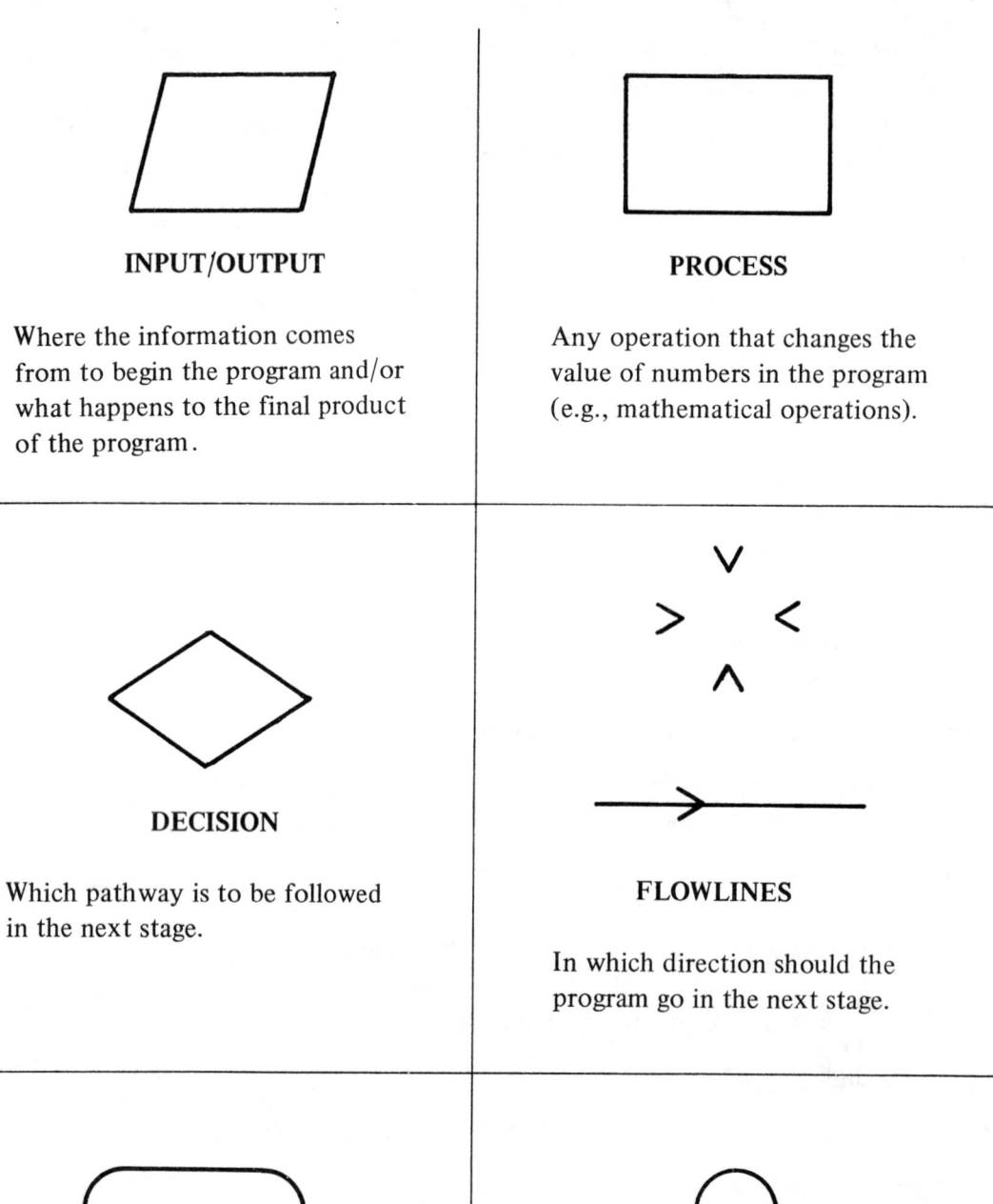

Where the information comes from to begin the program and/or what happens to the final product of the program.

PROCESS

Any operation that changes the value of numbers in the program (e.g., mathematical operations).

DECISION

Which pathway is to be followed in the next stage.

FLOWLINES

In which direction should the program go in the next stage.

TERMINAL/INTERRUPT

Start, stop, halt, delay or interrupt.

CONNECTOR

Exit to or enter from another part of the flow chart.

Flow Chart Key

Fig. 20

We can use symbols like these to make a flow chart for the "doing homework" problem described on page 247. It would look like this:

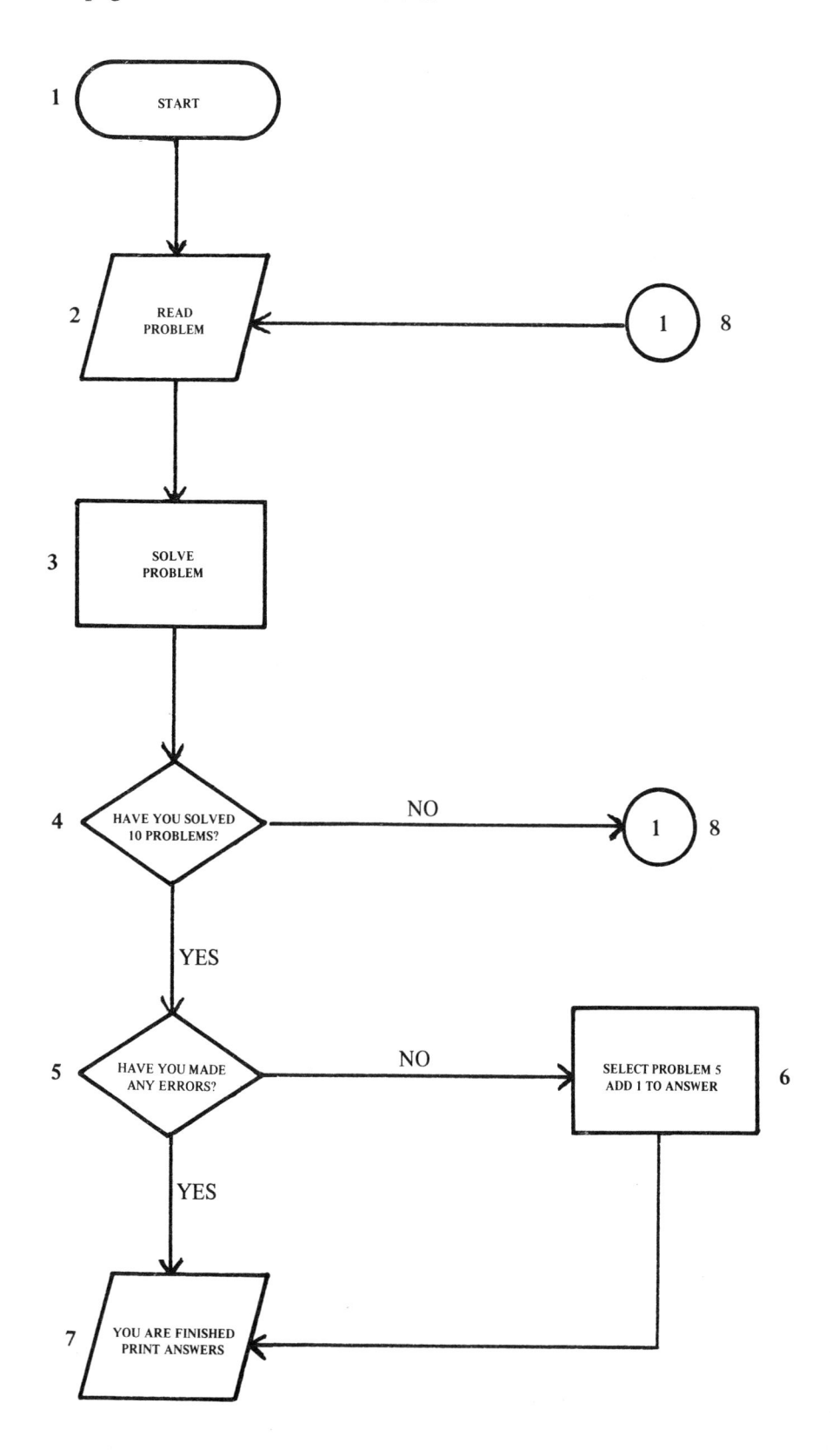

- 1: START
- 2: READ PROBLEM
- 3: SOLVE PROBLEM
- 4: HAVE YOU SOLVED 10 PROBLEMS? — NO → ① 8
- (YES ↓)
- 5: HAVE YOU MADE ANY ERRORS? — NO → 6: SELECT PROBLEM 5, ADD 1 TO ANSWER
- (YES ↓)
- 7: YOU ARE FINISHED, PRINT ANSWERS

Special Scientific Skills 249

Below you will find some practice examples for which you can write flow charts. You should begin by dividing up the problems into the smallest possible steps, as we did on page 247. After that, make a flow chart (like the one on page 249) for each of the problems. Show what kind of statement each one of your steps is. Use Activity Pages 52-54, pages 251-253, for the problem analysis and flow charts for these problems.

Problem 1: Your father has asked you to go to the grocery store. At the store you are to buy one pound of hamburger, four tomatoes, and a head of lettuce. If there is enough money left, you are also to buy a Sunday newspaper. You have $5.00 to spend.

Problem 2: You have to balance a checkbook. In order to do this, you must compare the amount of each check and deposit with the bank statement. Then, you must make sure the balance in your checkbook is the same as the one on the bank statement. Assume there are four checks in the amounts of **a,b,c,** and **d** and two deposits in the amounts of **e** and **f**. The bank statement entries corresponding to these are **p, q, r,** and **s**; and **t** and **u**. The beginning balance is **X**.

Problem 3: In order to get an A in science class, a student must have a test average of 94, or an average of 90 with one extra-credit project, or an average of 86 with three extra-credit projects. No student can get an A if he or she has been absent six times or more.

ACTIVITY PAGE **52** WRITING FLOW CHARTS–I

DIRECTIONS: In the space provided below, write a flow chart for Problem 1 on page 250.

Problem 1

ACTIVITY PAGE **53** WRITING FLOW CHARTS—II

DIRECTIONS: In the space provided below, write a flow chart for Problem 2 on page 250.

Problem 2

ACTIVITY PAGE 54 WRITING FLOW CHARTS—III

DIRECTIONS: In the space provided below, write a flow chart for Problem 3 on page 250.

Problem 3

8. Laboratory Skills

Much of the work done in science takes place in a laboratory. You can imagine how important it it to have good laboratory skills in order to be a successful scientist. We mean two things by "good laboratory skills." First, there are certain ways of working in a laboratory that are good and certain ways that are bad. The good techniques are those that increase the chances of your work turning out well and your getting good results. The bad techniques produce the opposite results.

The term "good laboratory skills" also refers to safety. It is **possible** for a laboratory to be a dangerous place to work. Flames, poisonous chemicals, and harmful biological materials may be present. Someone who doesn't work carefully in a laboratory has a good chance of harming himself or herself . . . as well as others in the lab.

An example of "good technique" is simply keeping the area in which you work clean and neat. If equipment and materials begin to pile up and make a messy work area, it's more difficult to pay close attention to the things happening in an experiment. An example of "safe procedure" is making sure that long hair is tied back in the laboratory so that it will not catch fire in a Bunsen burner.

This exercise is different from all others in the book. Rather than tell you what good techniques and safe working habits should be, we want you to think about these procedures. If you were assigned tomorrow to work in a chemistry, biology, earth science, or physics lab, what procedures **do you think would be needed**?

In order to answer that question, it will help for you to go into a laboratory and look around. There probably is a science laboratory in your own school or another school nearby. Arrange to have a teacher or older student show you through the laboratory. Keep your eyes open for possible sources of accidents. Try to think of ways in which your own work might go more smoothly if you worked in this lab. Do NOT let your guide answer this question for you.

After your tour, turn to Activity Page 55, page 255. In the spaces provided there, write down your ideas for effective laboratory techniques and safety rules. You may want to work with another student on this project. When you have completed that activity page, BUT NOT BEFORE, turn to page 256 and look at our list of rules. This is not the **only** set of laboratory rules that exists, and not even the **best** set. It is simply the rules that your author has used in a chemistry laboratory for many years. Perhaps you'll have some ideas of your own for improving or adding to these rules.

ACTIVITY PAGE **55** DEVELOPING SAFE LABORATORY PROCEDURES

DIRECTIONS: In the space provided below, list the safety precautions and good laboratory techniques you think should be used in this laboratory.

1. Safety precautions to be followed in this laboratory include:

2. Other good laboratory techniques to use in this laboratory include:

Special Scientific Skills 255

Safety Rules

1. Always wear safety glasses while working in the laboratory. Eye damage is probably the most serious hazard you face in the lab. Just don't take a chance! In some states, the law **requires** you to wear glasses in a lab, so think of yourself as a law-abiding citizen as well as a smart chemist.

2. Lab coats, aprons, or other protective covering are highly recommended. Better to replace a lab coat with an acid hole in it than spend $50 on a new sweater.

3. Know where safety and first aid equipment is kept in your lab. Your instructor will probably show you where each device is stored and how it works. Figuring out these things **after** an accident has happened is usually a lot more difficult. The equipment with which you should be familiar include: (1) safety shower, (2) fire blanket, (3) eye wash, and (4) fire extinguisher.

4. Cuts and burns (chemical and fire) are not uncommon, but they are almost never serious. Immediate treatment is to wash the wound with lots of cold water. Meanwhile, have someone else summon the instructor. He or she is the resident safety expert and will know what to do next. You are **never** the expert in such a case.

5. Experiments in which toxic, noxious, or objectional gases are produced must be performed in the fume hood.

6. NO SMOKING in the laboratory! Too many flammable liquids are around.

7. No eating or drinking in the laboratory! Too many toxic chemicals are around.

8. Clean up immediately after an accident. Spilled acids or bases should be neutralized with dilute sodium bicarbonate or a vinegar solution (respectively). These and other chemical spills should also be cleaned up with very wet paper towels. Broken glass should be swept up and disposed of properly.

9. Know how to dispose of wastes properly.

    a. Waste paper in a "Waste Paper" container.

    b. Waste chemicals and glass in a "Chemicals and Glass Only" container (usually a stone crock).

    c. Do NOT mix waste chemicals and waste paper. These can make a highly flammable combination. Exciting, but not very safe!

    d. Inorganic liquids ONLY down the drain, and then only with lots of water. No matches, sand, insoluble chemicals, or organic liquids down the drain EVER! PLEASE!

10. Think of sensible dress rules. Chemists are not very interested in having you look fashionable. Long hair, loose sleeves, and sandals are open invitations to unnecessary accidents. Don't invent new ways to get hurt!

11. Be neat and clean ALWAYS. Again, this is not a moral instruction, but a really good way of avoiding accidents to yourself and others who work around you. Keep your work space neat and orderly while you are doing an experiment. Then, leave it spotless at the end of the lab period. (That last "spot" could be a drop of concentrated sulfuric acid!)

Answer Section for Activity Pages

SECTION one VERBAL SKILLS

Activity Page 1

1. **baro-** = pressure; **-meter** = measure; **barometer** = a device for measuring pressure
2. **bio-** = life; **-graph-** = writing; **-er** = person who does something; **biographer** = a person who writes about someone's life
3. **circum-** = around; **-spect** = view; **circumspect** = cautious or watchful. (This is a good time for the teacher to explain how the meaning of words may evolve from a very literal meaning ["to look around"] to a more remote, but still related, meaning ["watchful" means "looking around" for something or someone].)
4. **cryo-** = cold; **-bio-** = life; **-logy** = study of; **cryobiology** = the study of life at very cold temperatures
5. **cyclo-** = round; **-oid** = resembling; **cycloid** = a figure that looks something like a circle (round object)
6. **encephalo-** = a combination of **in-** and **-cephalo-** ("within the head") = brain; **-itis** = inflammation; **encephalitis** = inflammation of the brain
7. **epi-** = outside; **-dermis** = skin; **epidermis** = the outer layer of the skin
8. **hemi-** = half; **-sphere** (not a root itself) = sphere; **hemisphere** = half a sphere
9. **hydro-** = water; **-cephal-** = head; **-ic** = having to do with; **hydrocephalic** = having to do with the condition of water on the brain
10. **iso-** = equal; **-bar** = pressure; **isobar** = a map line connecting places on the earth where there is equal pressure
11. **poly-** = many; **-chromat-** = color; **-ic** = having to do with; **polychromatic** = relating to something that displays a variety of colors
12. **trans-** = across; **-miss-** = to send; **-ion** = quality of; **transmission** = the sending of messages or objects across a distance

Activity Page 2

1. **heliocentric:** pertaining to a circular orbit of which the sun is the center
2. **microcosm:** a very tiny world
3. **bibliography:** a list of books on a subject
4. **isotherm:** a map line connecting places on the earth that all have the same temperature
5. **retrospect:** the act of looking back on something

Activity Page 2 (continued)

6. **metamorphic**: a type of rock that has been changed in shape
7. **hypodermic**: a needle inserted under the skin
8. **geomorphologists**: people who study the shape of the earth
9. **telephone**: a device for transmitting sounds over a distance
10. **ultramicroscope**: a device for examining very small objects
11. **hydrosphere**: the portion of the earth covered with water
    lithosphere: the portion of the earth covered with rock
12. **diameter**: a measure of the distance across a circle or sphere
13. **autograph**: a person's own signature
14. **astronomer**: a person who studies the stars
    planetoids: objects that are something like planets
15. **prescribed**: laid down in advance by someone

Activity Page 3

1.	c	5.	f	9.	e	13.	d
2.	g	6.	n	10.	i	14.	k
3.	m	7.	l	11.	a	15.	h
4.	j	8.	b	12.	o		

Activity Page 4

Selection A: first sentence
Selection B: fourth sentence
Selection C: first sentence
Selection D: second sentence

Activity Page 5

Selection A:
1. dental caries
2. exposure to fluorides and careful dental hygiene
3. 130 pounds per person per year
4. catsup, ice cream, flavored milk, breakfast cereals
5. See final paragraph of selection.

Selection B:
1. shield, explosive, composite
2. release of gas pressure that builds up within the earth
3. pahoehoe, aa, pillow
4. a loose pile of lapilli and scoria
5. materials blown out during an eruption (tephra, ash, lapilli, scoria)

Selection C:
1. the giving off of particles and rays from the nucleus of an atom
2. See Becquerel story in text.
3. See text description of alpha, beta, and gamma rays.
4. the time required for one half of a radioactive sample to decay
5. the elements polonium and radium

Activity Page 6

Selection D:
1. two spacecrafts, one orbiting the planet and the second sending probes to the planet's surface
2. elongation: the position of Venus east or west of the sun; inferior conjunction: closest approach of Venus to the earth; quadrature: positions of greatest elongation
3. The surface is covered with clouds. Probes are sent to the planet's surface.
4. It rotates at an unusually slow rate.
5. dry, rocky surface

Selection E:
1. Animals can control voluntary muscles by conscious actions, but they can't control involuntary muscles that way.
2. parts of the brain that control muscular movement
3. damage to the nervous system that prevents the voluntary control of muscular movement
4. See text for examples.
5. They increase in size.

Selection F:
1. helium, neon, argon, krypton, xenon, and radon
2. They generally do not react with other chemical elements.
3. research by Lord Rayleigh on nitrogen produced by chemical means and nitrogen obtained from the air
4. liquefaction and fractional distillation of air
5. lamps, lasers, lifting, diluent with oxygen for breathing systems

SECTION **two** LIBRARY SKILLS

Activity Pages 7-10

Individual student answers will vary.

SECTION **three** WRITING REPORTS

Activity Pages 11 and 12

Individual student answers will vary.

SECTION four MATH SKILLS WITH HAND CALCULATORS

Activity Page 13

1. 1005
2. 248
3. 1.309
4. 334.024
5. 0.468
6. 0.125
7. 0.258
8. 3.986
9. 0.433
10. 88.36
11. 1.175
12. 4.116
13. −0.275
14. 62.64

Activity Page 14

1. 23.316
2. −22.435
3. 757.827
4. 0.027
5. 0.257
6. 2.540
7. 259.938
8. 4.162
9. 264.506
10. 3.108
11. 13.3
12. 10.846
13. −10.287
14. 70.789

SECTION five MATH SKILLS WITH MEASUREMENT

Activity Pages 15-19

Student responses will vary according to measuring devices used and the objects chosen to be measured and weighed.

SECTION six MATH SKILLS WITH GRAPHS

Activity Page 20

Student histograms

Activity Page 21

Histogram 1:
1. forest land: 718 million acres (actual amount)
2. 382 million acres (actual amount)
3. 2264 million acres (actual amount)

Histogram 2:
1. 1966: 5,361 million dollars (actual amount)
2. 3,181 million dollars in both 1974 and 1975 (actual amounts)
3. 4,562 million dollars, 3,181 million dollars (actual amounts))
4. 27,545 million dollars (actual amount)

Histogram 3:
1. private automobiles: 1,234 billion passenger-miles (actual amount)
2. 176 billion passenger-miles, 10 billion passenger-miles (actual amounts)
3. 85.10% (actual percentage).

Activity Page 22

1. $s = n + 4$
2. $y = 3x$
3. $a = z^2$
4. $e = 2c + 1$
5. $s = 4t - 2$
6. $Q = r^2 - 3$
7. $B = 7.5a - 1.5$
8. $L = \dfrac{3e + 1}{2}$

Activity Page 23

Data tables are given top row first:

1. 1,2,3,4,5,6,7,8   4,5,6,7,8,9,10,11
2. 1,2,3,4,5,6,7,8   6,12,18,24,30,36,42,48
3. 1,2,3,4,5,6,7,8   7,9,11,13,15,17,19,21
4. 1,2,3,4,5,6,7,8   2,5,10,17,26,37,50,65
5. 1,2,3,4,5,6,7,8   -5,-2,1,4,7,10,13,16
6. 1,2,3,4,5,6,7,8   1,13,33,63,97,141,193,253
7. 1,2,3,4,5,6,7,8   0,7,26,63,124,215,342,511
8. 1,2,3,4,5,6   2,4,8,16,32,64

Activity Pages 24-26

These exercises require the plotting of points and drawing of graphs from given data.

Activity Page 27

Student responses will differ, depending upon the type of extrapolation they make for each graph. The important thing to check is that the numerical value they choose for each answer corresponds to the graphical extrapolation they have made.

SECTION seven EXPERIMENTING AND RELATED SKILLS

Activity Page 28

Students may be "suspicious" of drawings like these if they have had any experience with optical illusions. Through a process of "perverse logic" they may recognize that things that their eyes are telling them can't possibly be the case. For that reason, the column farthest to the right ("How might your senses be fooled?") is especially important. The examples used here illustrate the effect on a figure of other figures attached to or shown in conjunction with that figure (Figures 1-3, 6 and 7), the effects of perspective (Figures 4 and 5), and the problem of ambiguous figures (Figures 8 and 9). Use of some drawings by M. C. Escher would be especially appropriate at this point.

Activity Page 29

Figure 10
1. bottom
2. boiling chips
3. 95°C
4. 75 ml
5. clamped to ring stand and supported on wire gauze on ring
6. Bunsen burner
7. The bulb is near the outlet arm.
8. (student sketch)

Figure 11
1. six
2. basalt (or slate, if basalt is not called a stratum)
3. basalt (or slate)
4. more complex
5. shale
6. No fossils shown in basalt stratum.
7. toward the west
8. No minerals are shown anywhere in this section.

Activity Page 30

Student responses may differ. Some possible answers include the following:

1. air pollution
2. clear weather
3. soil erosion
4. erosion caused by rainstorms
5. trees killed by air pollutants or forest fires
6. collisions of meteors, or volcanic eruptions

Activity Page 31

Individual student answers will vary.

Activity Pages 32 and 33

The type of response given on these activity pages will vary for students of various levels. All should be able to write tables of data and express trends in sentences. Many should be able to draw graphs representing the data, and some may also be able to find a formula that represents the data. They probably should be able to say whether the relationships shown are inverse or direct, linear or square. In Part One of **Activity Page 32** the relationship is an inverse linear one, approximately corresponding to speed = 10 ÷ density, or $s = \frac{10}{d}$. In Part Two of **Activity Page 32** the relationship is approximately a direct square one, with number of germs killed = 2 x (dosage)^2, or $N = 2d^2$. In **Activity Page 33**, #1, the relationship is an inverse square, $r = \frac{64}{d^2}$, and in **Activity Page 33**, #2, the relationship is an inverse exponential, a mathematical relationship most students have not encountered in formula form at this level.

Activity Page 34

1. In theory, any one of the plants or reactions can be taken as control and others compared to it. The answers given here are merely the most probable ones to be expected from beginning students. For experiment A, if plant A is taken as the control, then plants B and C test for effects of various amounts of light, D and E for various amounts of water, and F, G, and H for various amounts of fertilizer. For experiment B, reaction 1 can be taken for the control. Then, reactions 2 and 3 measure the effects of temperature changes and 4-7 measure the effects of changes in concentration (amount) of chemicals A and B. Reaction 8 cannot be compared against reaction 1, as a control, since 8 differs from 1 by **two** factors. In this case, it would be possible to take #2 as the control, and compare 8 against 2 with concentration as the variable.

2. For this question, the following are acceptable answers:

	CONTROL	EXPERIMENTAL FACTOR
a.	bacterial growth at room temperature	growth at other temperatures
b.	weight of an object at the earth's surface	weight at various heights above the earth's surface
c.	erosion at some slow velocity of moving water	erosion at other, faster velocities
d.	boiling point of water with no salt present	boiling point with various concentrations of salt

Activity Pages 35 and 36

Student responses will vary.

SECTION eight — DECISION-MAKING SKILLS

Activity Pages 37-41

Student responses will vary.

SECTION nine — SPECIAL SCIENTIFIC SKILLS

Activity Page 42

1. KCl
2. NaOH
3. $CaBr_2$
4. $MgSO_4$
5. H_3PO_4
6. $AlCl_3$
7. LiI
8. $Fe(OH)_3$
9. K_2SO_4
10. Na_2O
11. H_2S
12. MgO
13. $AlPO_4$
14. $Fe_2(SO_4)_3$
15. $Ca_3(PO_4)_2$
16. Al_2S_3

Activity Page 43

1. $Pb + S \xrightarrow{\Delta} PbS$

2. $Ca + 2H_2O \xrightarrow{\Delta} Ca(OH)_2 + H_2\uparrow$

3. $2 NaCl \xrightarrow{\sim} 2 Na + Cl_2\uparrow$

4. $Na_2O + H_2O \rightarrow 2 NaOH$

5. $Cl_2\uparrow + CaBr_2 \rightarrow Br_2 + CaCl_2$

6. $MgCO_3 \xrightarrow{\Delta} MgO + CO_2\uparrow$

7. $KBr + LiI \rightarrow LiBr + KI$

8. $2 AgNO_3 + CaCl_2 \rightarrow Ca(NO_3)_2 + 2 AgCl\downarrow$

9. $K_2SO_4 + MgCl_2 \rightarrow MgSO_4\downarrow + 2 KCl$

10. $Fe(NO_3)_3 + 3 NaOH \rightarrow Fe(OH)_3\downarrow + 3 NaNO_3$

Activity Pages 44 and 45

Student responses will vary.

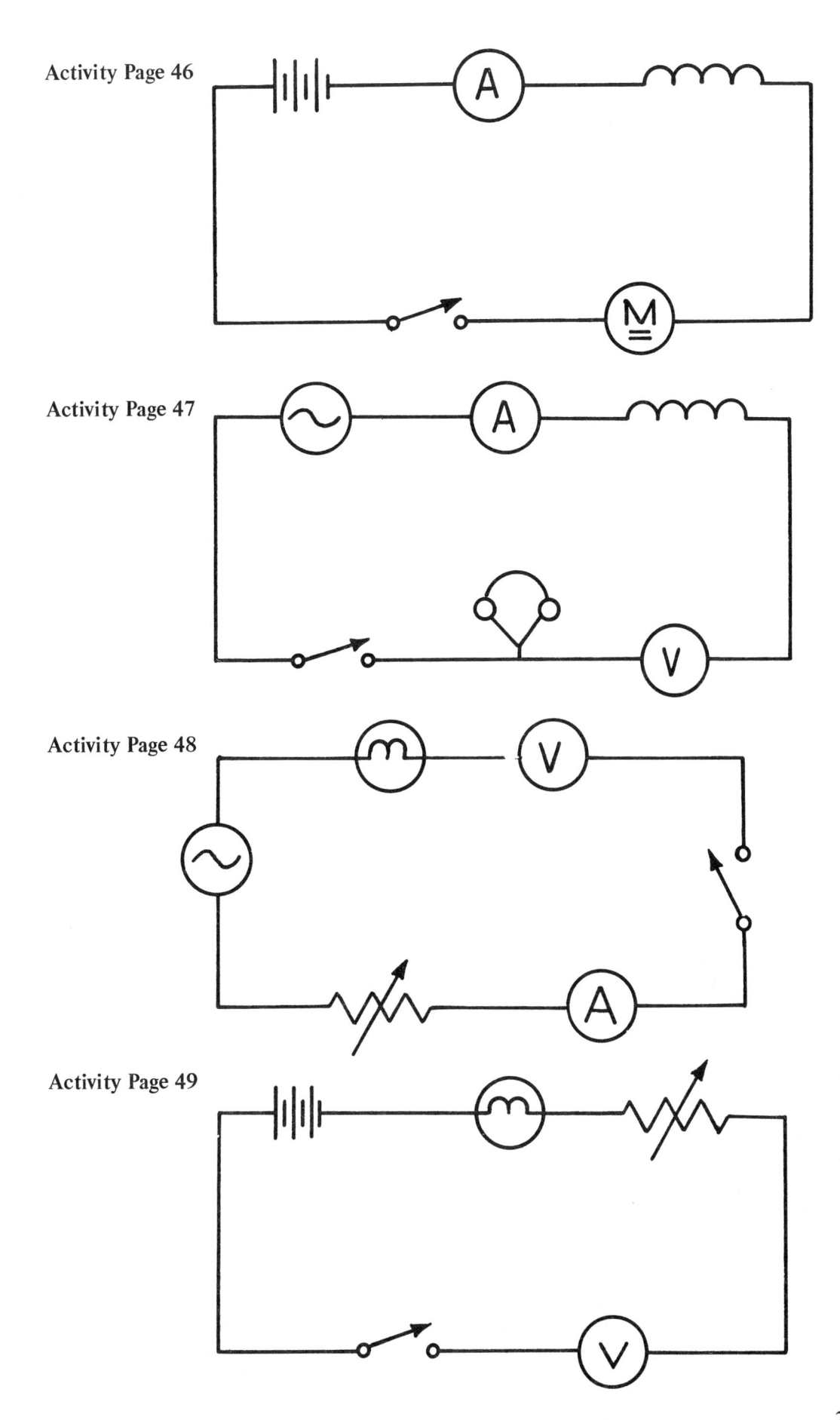

Activity Page 46

Activity Page 47

Activity Page 48

Activity Page 49

265

Activity Page 50

1. Students should look for a region in which the vertical distance drops sharply within a short distance, as, for example, between D and E and 4 and 6.
2. Uphill; height changes from about 600 m to between 700 and 800 m.
3. As the river flows from east to west, it drops from a height of about 650 m to a height of less than 500 m.
4. One possibility is the region around I6 to I7.
5. Neither term is strictly correct, although the town is surrounded by three regions of higher elevation, to the north, east, and south.
6. Probably little change in elevation, since both seem to lie between 700 and 800 m elevation lines.
7. Peak City lies between the 600 and 700 m elevation lines, while South Doris lies between the 700 and 800 m lines, indicating that Peak City is somewhat lower.
8. West, since the highest spot on the map has an elevation of more than 1300 m.

Activity Page 51

Figure 18:
1. three; one over the Atlantic east of Florida, one over central Canada, one over southern California
2. three, one northeast of Maine, one over the Great Lakes, one over Oklahoma
3. the shaded areas through eastern Canada are receiving a continuous fall of light snow, there is intermittent light snow on the Vermont-New Hampshire border, and there is continuous light rain up much of the Pacific coast
4. a. no warm fronts
   b. cold fronts: down the Pacific coast, and from Oklahoma to Mexico
   c. stationary front: from central Canada down over the Great Lakes
   d. occluded front: northeast corner of map
5. a. 52°F   c. 45°F   e. 20°F   g. 27°F
   b. −18°F   d. 27°F   f. 48°F

Figure 19:
1. a. no clouds   d. stratus
   b. no clouds   e. no clouds
   c. stratocumulus   f. stratocumulus
2. a. no clouds   e. completely overcast
   b. completely overcast   f. 2/10 or 3/10
   c. completely overcast   g. 9/10
   d. 7/10 or 8/10
3. a. S, 3-8 mph   d. calm
   b. NNE, 9-14 mph   e. ENE, 3-8 mph
   c. SW, 15-20 mph   f. W, 3-8 mph
4. stationary fronts in northwest corner of map and over the Dakotas, cold front over central Canada
5. it has moved southeast from central South Dakota
6. a. 1032.1   c. 1024.7   e. 1020.6
   b. 1030.4   d. 1013.9   f. 1028.7   (all in millibars)

Activity Pages 52-54

Students may find more than one correct way to set up a flow chart for each of the problems in **Activity Pages 52-54**. The ones suggested here are models that reflect the fact that students at this grade level will have no or very unsophisticated ideas of logic and/or of making flow charts. The teacher should emphasize the concepts of breaking down a problem into its basic units and then finding the relationship among these, rather than getting an exactly correct flow chart drawn.

Activity Page 52

Problem 1

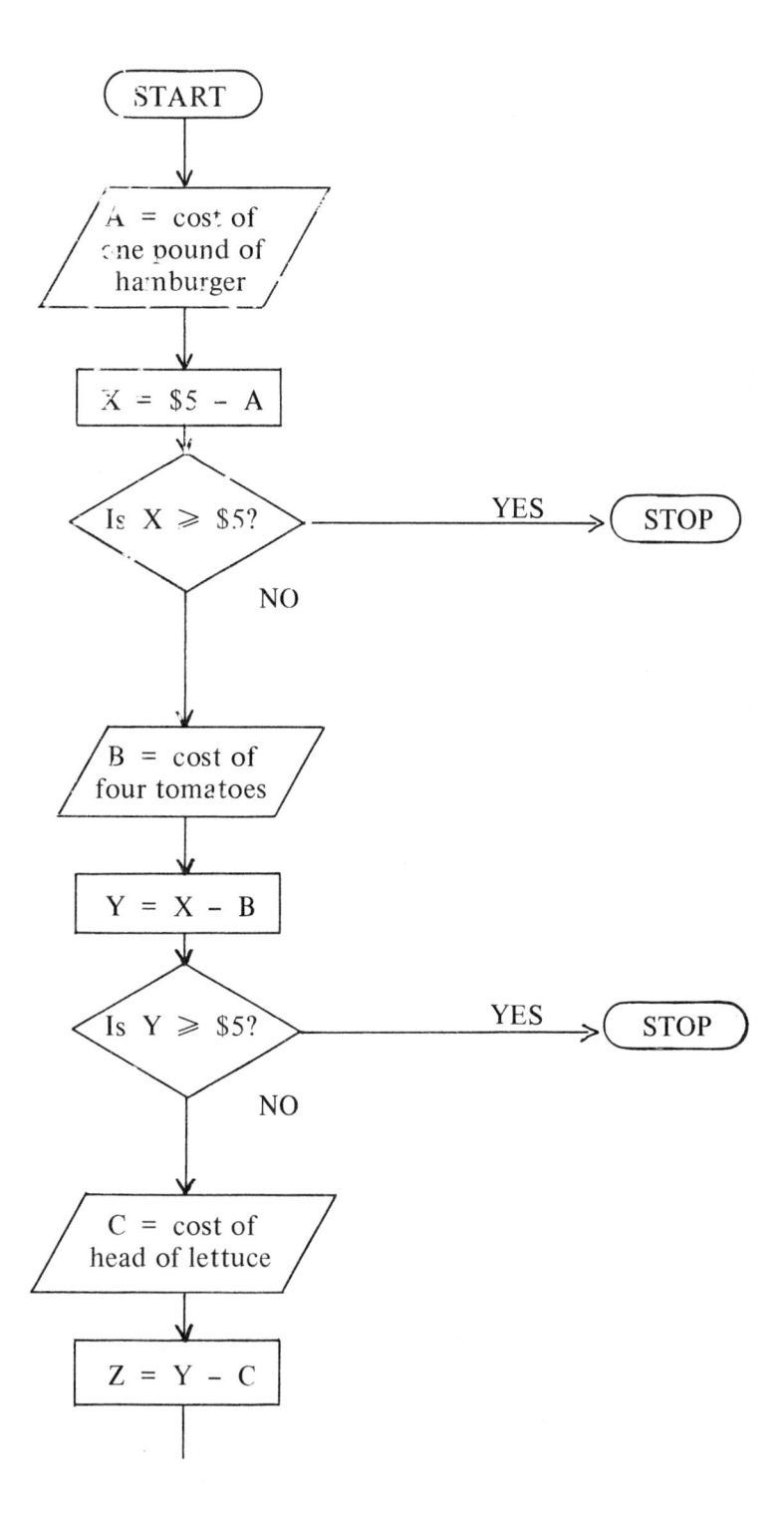

START

A = cost of one pound of hamburger

X = $5 - A

Is X ≥ $5? —YES→ STOP

NO

B = cost of four tomatoes

Y = X - B

Is Y ≥ $5? —YES→ STOP

NO

C = cost of head of lettuce

Z = Y - C

Activity Page 52 (continued)

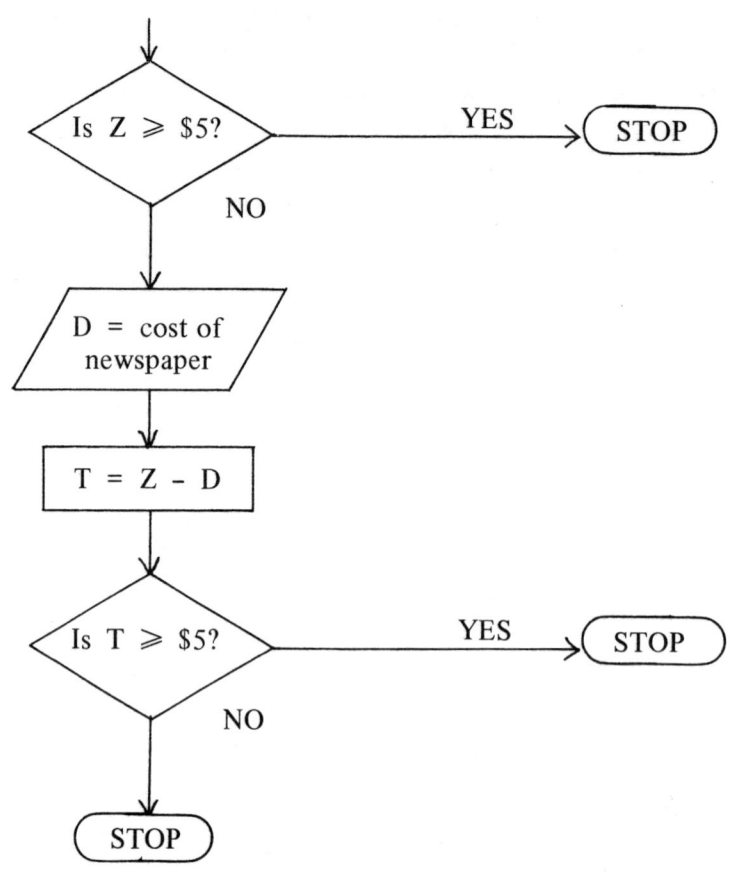

```
         ↓
    ╱Is Z ≥ $5?╲ ──YES──→ (STOP)
         ╲    ╱
          ╲  ╱
           NO
           ↓
    ╱D = cost of╲
    ╱ newspaper ╱
           ↓
    ┌─────────┐
    │ T = Z - D│
    └─────────┘
           ↓
    ╱Is T ≥ $5?╲ ──YES──→ (STOP)
           NO
           ↓
        (STOP)
```

Activity Page 53

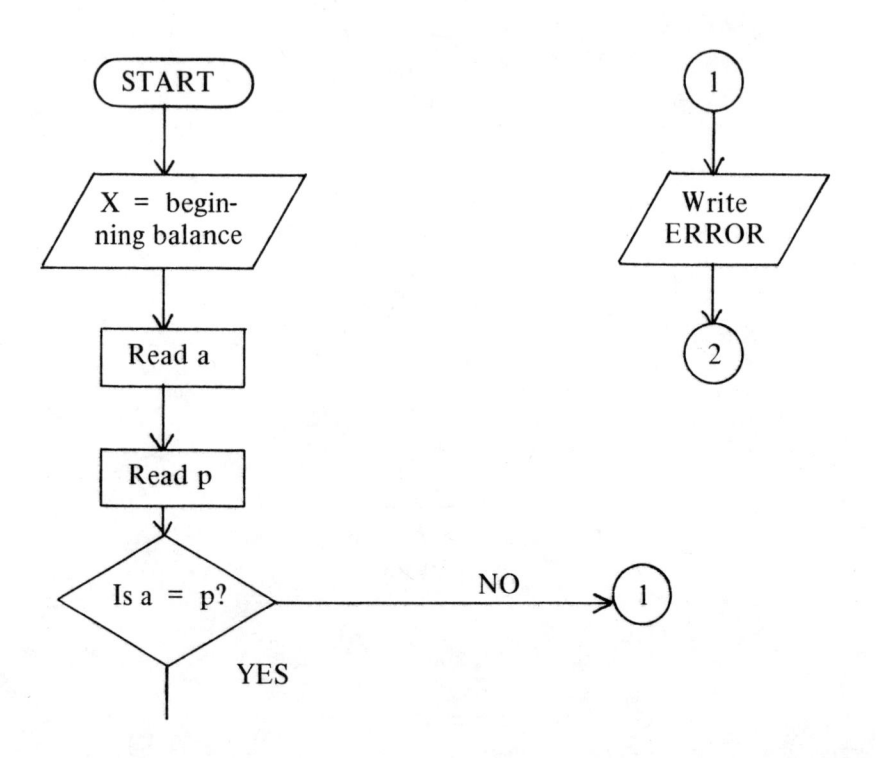

Problem 2

```
       (START)                          (1)
          ↓                              ↓
    ╱X = begin-╲                    ╱ Write ╱
    ╱ning balance╱                  ╱ ERROR ╱
          ↓                              ↓
      ┌──────┐                          (2)
      │Read a│
      └──────┘
          ↓
      ┌──────┐
      │Read p│
      └──────┘
          ↓
     ╱Is a = p?╲ ──NO──→ (1)
          YES
```

268

Activity Page 53 (continued)

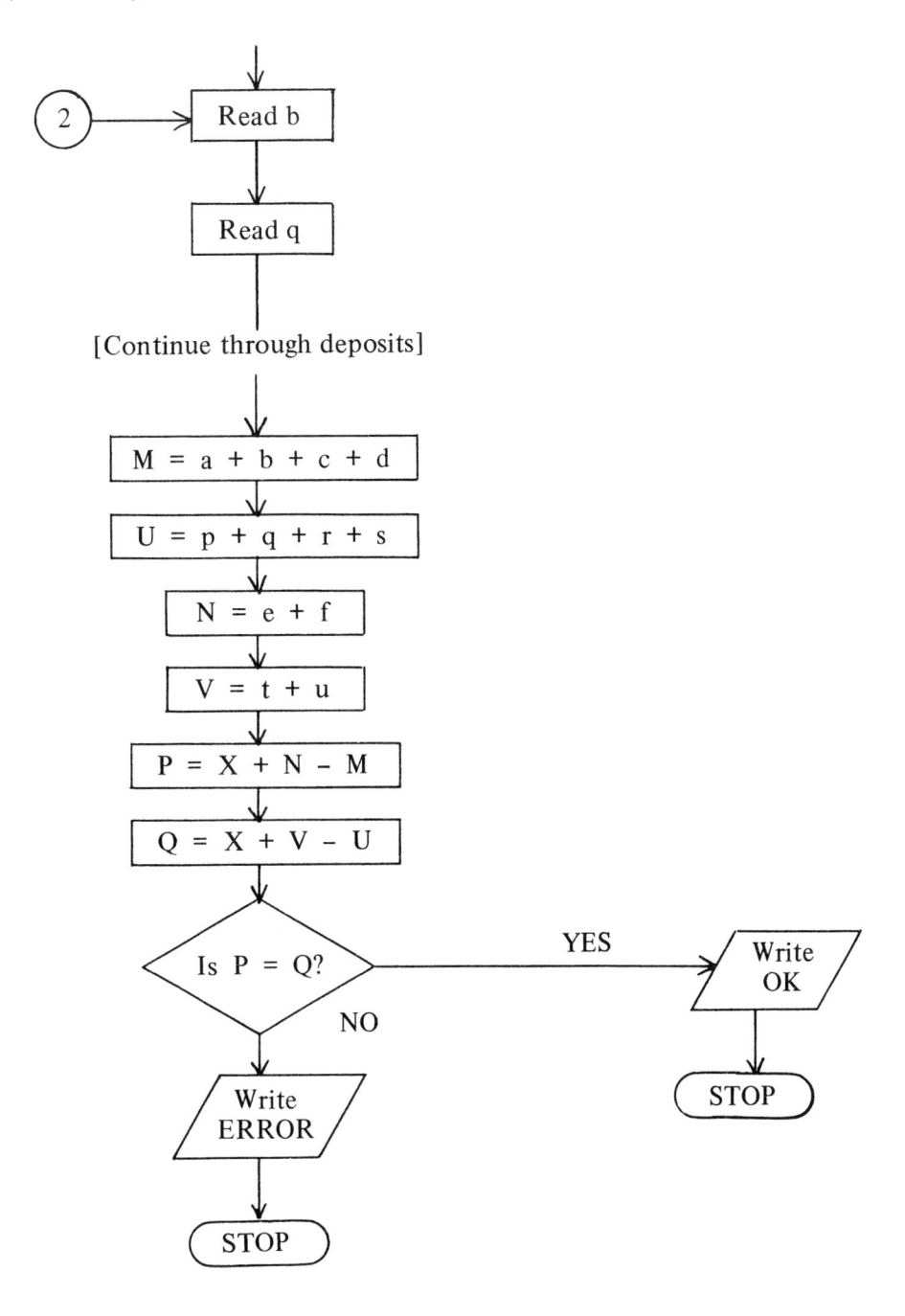

```
        ↓
(2) →  [Read b]
         ↓
       [Read q]
         ↓
  [Continue through deposits]
         ↓
   [M = a + b + c + d]
         ↓
   [U = p + q + r + s]
         ↓
      [N = e + f]
         ↓
      [V = t + u]
         ↓
    [P = X + N − M]
         ↓
    [Q = X + V − U]
         ↓
      < Is P = Q? > ──YES──→ [Write OK] → (STOP)
         │ NO
         ↓
     [Write ERROR]
         ↓
       (STOP)
```

Activity Page 54

Problem 3

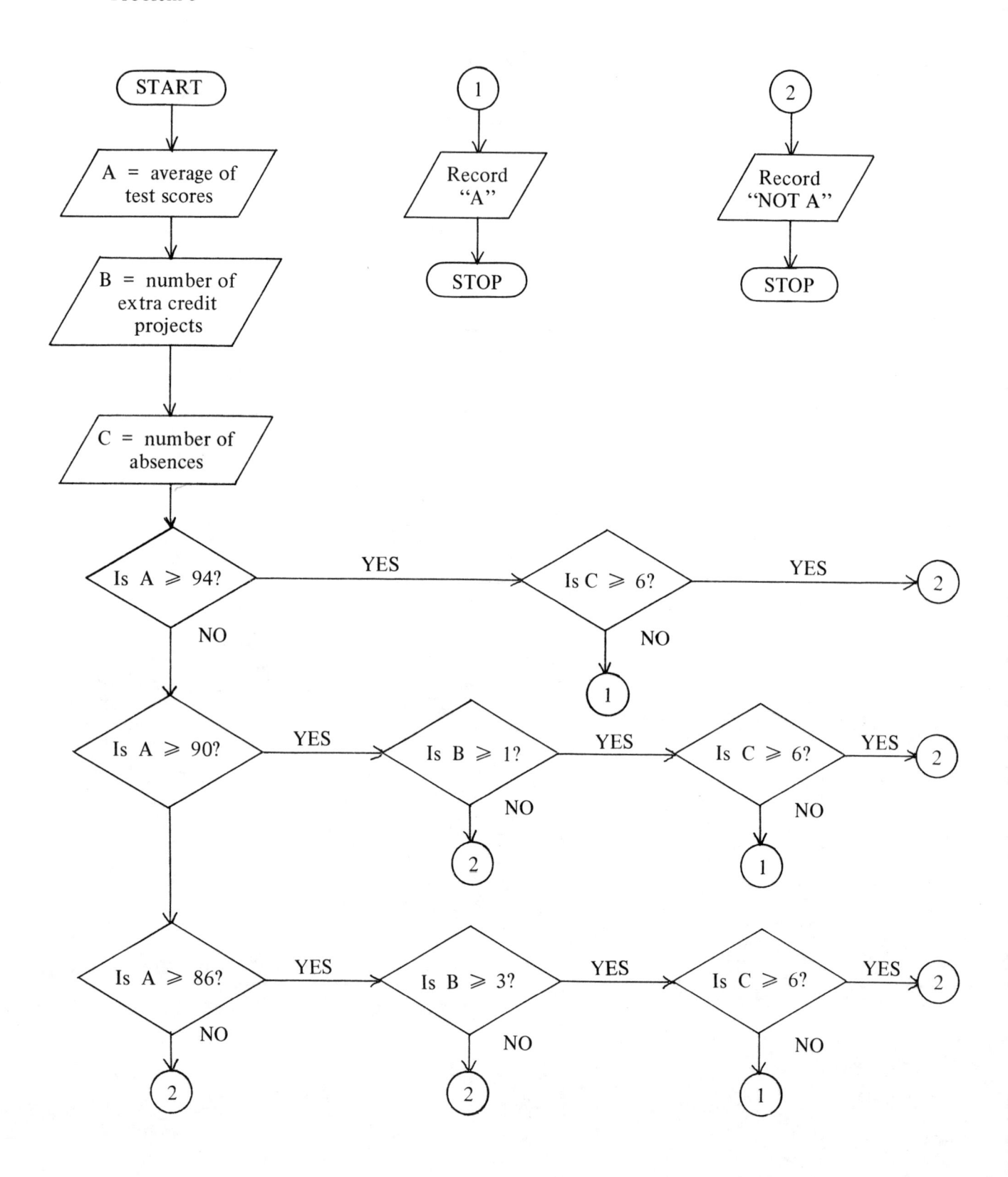

```
                    START
                      │
                      ▼
              A = average of
               test scores
                      │
                      ▼
              B = number of
              extra credit
                projects
                      │
                      ▼
              C = number of
                absences
                      │
                      ▼
              Is A ≥ 94?  ──YES──▶  Is C ≥ 6?  ──YES──▶ (2)
                 │                      │
                 NO                     NO
                 │                      │
                 ▼                      ▼
                                       (1)
              Is A ≥ 90?  ──YES──▶ Is B ≥ 1? ──YES──▶ Is C ≥ 6? ──YES──▶ (2)
                 │                      │                 │
                 NO                     NO                NO
                 │                      ▼                 ▼
                 ▼                     (2)               (1)
              Is A ≥ 86?  ──YES──▶ Is B ≥ 3? ──YES──▶ Is C ≥ 6? ──YES──▶ (2)
                 │                      │                 │
                 NO                     NO                NO
                 ▼                      ▼                 ▼
                (2)                    (2)               (1)


      (1)                    (2)
       │                      │
       ▼                      ▼
     Record                 Record
      "A"                   "NOT A"
       │                      │
       ▼                      ▼
     STOP                   STOP
```

270

Activity Page 55

Students will suggest a number of possible rules covering safety and general work conditions in the laboratory. An introductory chemistry laboratory manual usually lists rules and regulations of this kind. Some of the responses students might be expected to give include the following:

1. No eating, drinking or smoking in the laboratory.
2. Locate and know how to use safety equipment, such as fire extinguishers, safety shower, and eye bath.
3. Use safety glasses at all times in the laboratory.
4. Know how and where to dispose of broken glass and chemicals.
5. Know where supply chemicals are kept, how to obtain them, and how to use them.
6. Keep your work area neat and clean.
7. Be sure you understand the experiment to be performed. Read it through carefully before coming to class and ask any questions about the procedure before beginning work.
8. Always keep careful records of work performed in the laboratory.
9. Know how the fume hood is to be used and be sure you know which experiments should be performed there.
10. Learn the procedure for cleaning up acid, base, or chemical spills of any other kind.

Answer Section for Textual Questions

SECTION one VERBAL SKILLS

Page 11

The topic sentence in this paragraph is: "Today, mining in the Antarctic is a real possibility."

SECTION two LIBRARY SKILLS

Page 34

Books taller than about 25 cm often do not fit on normal bookshelves in a library.

Page 43

Under "Age," you are referred to "Geological time." Under "Temperature," you are told to look under "Earth temperature."

SECTION four MATH SKILLS WITH HAND CALCULATORS

Page 54

2.	287	6.	7.7091
3.	180.452	8.	121.41
4.	12.857	9.	45.9
5.	2097.64	10.	47.6
		11.	13.805

Page 55

12. 1.638
13. 58.5
14. 14.137

SECTION five MATH SKILLS WITH MEASUREMENT

Page 63

No matter how good a ruler is, there will always be an estimated digit. You will always have to guess whether the end of the line comes exactly to a marking on the ruler or extends a little way beyond it.

Your measurement should read 1.540 cm. That tells a reader that you think the line comes exactly to the "1.54" mark on the ruler.

It makes sense to estimate one digit, but not two. If you are uncertain about the first digit, you would have no idea at all about the second digit.

Page 70

- a. length, width, altitude
- b. radius (or diameter)
- c. length, width, altitude
- d. radius (or diameter), altitude

Page 73

- a. 44.361 cm^3
- b. 354.137 cm^3
- c. 59,185.186 cm^3
- d. 160.957 cm^3
- e. 160,782.71 cm^3
  (Formula: $V = \frac{1}{3} \pi r^2 h$)

A solid which dissolves in water could not be used in this method. You could use some other liquid, alcohol for example, for such a solid.

Page 77

To find the speed of an object, you need to know the *time* it takes to travel a certain *distance*.

SECTION six MATH SKILLS WITH GRAPHS

Page 94

The independent variables here are: 2, 3, 5, 7, 9. The dependent variables are: 1, 4, 6, 8, 10.

Page 101

Graph B: 0.5 cm; Graph C: 0.1 cm

SECTION seven EXPERIMENTING AND RELATED SKILLS

Page 143

Laws change because we find new facts that the laws cannot explain. One reason this happens is that scientific equipment is always getting better: we can observe things more accurately and get more precise information. What usually happens is that a new law builds on an old one, making it fit more cases and describe the world more accurately.

Page 150

The factors that might have made a difference are: the liquid used to do the dissolving (water or alcohol); the temperature difference (20°C vs. 40°C); or the pressure difference (1.0 atmosphere vs 2.0 atmospheres).

In this case, we can say that the carbon dioxide gas is more soluble in cold water than in warm water. Temperature is the only factor in which experiment 1 and experiment 2 differ from each other.

Page 151

There is no single answer to this question. Many factors need to be considered. If you are doing research on fruit flies and the experiment can be finished in a few days, then you could use thousands of subjects (fruit flies) and repeat the experiment many times. If you are testing a very rare, expensive mineral with a procedure that takes months, you can probably do the experiment only a few times.

Page 156

Many kinds of research in geology (on mountain-building, volcanoes, earthquakes, and the like), meteorology (patterns of weather and climate), and biology (studies of plants and animals and their interrelationships in the natural world) cannot be done in laboratories.

Page 157

magnifying glass: examine crystals in a mineral
acid: test rocks and minerals for the presence of certain chemicals (carbonates, sulfides, sulfites)
rock key: a systematic way of identifying rocks
rock hammer: used to split rocks and minerals to see if they break in certain ways; also to examine interior of certain rocks and minerals
measuring tape: needed to measure size of objects

SECTION nine SPECIAL SCIENTIFIC SKILLS

page 175

The symbol **K** represents one atom of potassium.
The symbol **Ca** represents one atom of calcium.
The formula **HCl** represents a molecule that contains one atom of hydrogen (H) and one atom of chlorine (Cl).
The formula **(CH$_4$)** represents a molecule that contains one atom of carbon (C), and four atoms of hydrogen (H).

Page 175 (continued)

The formula **H₃PO₄** represents a molecule that contains three atoms of hydrogen (H), one atom of phosphorus (P), and four atoms of oxygen (O).

The formula **NaNO₂** represents a molecule that contains one atom of sodium (Na), one atom of nitrogen (N), and two atoms of oxygen (O).

Page 177

Calcium: +2
Hydroxide: 2 x (−1) = − 2
Total positive = total negative

Page 180

iron (II): Fe^{+2}
sulfur (as sulfide): S^{-2}
Taking one of each atom will balance positive and negative valences: FeS

Page 181

In the formula H_3O:
3 H = 3 x (+1) = +3
1 O = 1 x (−2) = −2
positive and negative valences NOT BALANCED.

Page 208

Feldspar will scratch apatite, fluorite, calcite, gypsum, and talc. It will be scratched by diamond, corundum, topaz, and quartz.

Page 223

The first might be used by pleasure or business travelers, the second by geographers or geologists, and the third by people interested in business, industry, and economics.

Page 227

1. east
2. About 50 km ("as the crow flies") or about 60 km by I81.
3. One would have to go north to Peak City, and then change for S. Doris there.
4. One could travel on the Nichols River, by way of Emmasburg, from Durantsville to S. Doris.
5. Tennessee; Forks County
6. Interstate: I81; State highways: TN66 and TN22.